HANDBOOK

FOR MEMBERS AND VISITORS

MARCH 1998 TO FEBRUARY 1999

SPEKE HALL, LIVERPOOL

THE NATIONAL TRUST

Contents

Properties open to the public

For enquiries please write to:
The National Trust, PO Box 39, Bromley, Kent BR1 3XL
or telephone 0181 315 1111
Registered Charity No. 205846
Information about the National Trust and its work,
including places to visit, can be viewed on the Internet at
http://www.ukindex.co.uk/nationaltrust

ISBN 0 7078 0229 6
© 1998 The National Trust
Editor: James Parry
Editorial Assistants: Charlotte Stewart and Penny Clarke
Production: Lorna Simmonds
Managing Editor: Alex Youel
Designed by Pardoe Blacker Ltd, Lingfield, Surrey
Phototypeset in Monotype Photina Series 747
by Span Graphics Ltd, Crawley, West Sussex
Maps digitally produced by ESR Cartography, Byfleet, Surrey
Print managed by Centurion Press
Printed by Benham & Company Limited, Colchester

Illustrations by: Chris Beadle, F. N. Colwell, Brian Delf, Brin Edwards, Claude Page, David Peacock,
Neil Rutherford, Eric Thomas, Soun Vannithone

Front cover: Autumn view of door and window at Bateman's, East Sussex (NTPL/Rupert Truman)
Back cover: Martin Drury, Director-General (NTPL/David Levenson). Family enjoying the magnificent
scenery at Woolacombe, Devon (NTPL/Ian Shaw)

About the National Trust

The National Trust

- is a registered charity
- is independent of government
- was founded in 1895 to preserve places of historic interest or natural beauty permanently for the nation to enjoy
- relies on the generosity of its supporters, through membership subscriptions, gifts, legacies and the contribution of many thousands of volunteers
- now protects and opens to the public over 200 historic houses and gardens and 47 industrial monuments and mills
- owns more than 244,000 hectares (603,000 acres) of the most beautiful countryside and 565 miles of outstanding coast for people to enjoy
- looks after forests, woods, fens, farmland, downs, moorland, islands, archaeological remains, nature reserves, villages – for ever, for everyone
- has the unique statutory power to declare land inalienable – such land cannot be sold, mortgaged or compulsorily purchased against the Trust's wishes without special parliamentary procedure. This special power means that protection by the Trust is for ever
- spends all its income on the care and maintenance of the land and buildings in its protection, but cannot meet the cost of all its obligations – four in every five of its historic houses run at a loss – and is always in need of financial support.

How to use this Handbook

The Handbook gives details of how you can visit National Trust properties, including opening arrangements, admission charges and important information about visiting. Property entries are arranged by area (see map on page 25) and are ordered alphabetically within each area. Maps for each appear on pages 26 to 41, and these show properties with a charge for entry together with a selection of coast and countryside places mentioned in the introduction to each area. They also show main population centres.

To find properties within a particular county, please refer to the new additional index at the back of this Handbook. County names are also given in individual property entries.

A new feature this year is the inclusion of a simple grid reference in each property entry, after the ➔ symbol. These refer first to the appropriate map number then to the appropriate grid square eg 3:G6.

Property features are indicated by symbols alongside the property name. More detailed information about specific facilities is represented by symbols down the left-hand side of each entry. The key to the symbols is on page 23.

Please note the following points about this year's Handbook:

● it describes opening arrangements for the period from March 1998 to the end of February 1999

● areas are shown in hectares (1ha = 2.47 acres) with the acres equivalent in brackets. Heights and short distances are shown in metres (1m = 3.28 feet); longer distances continue to be measured in miles (ml)

● although opening times and arrangements do vary considerably from place to place, and from year to year, most houses are open from April to 1 November, usually on three or more afternoons per week between 1pm and 5pm (please note that last admission is usually 30 minutes before the stated closing time). However, always check the current Handbook for details and, if you are making a long or especially important journey, please telephone the property in advance for confirmation

● when telephoning, please remember that we can provide a better service if you call on a weekday morning, on days when the property is open to the public

● new properties, or properties featuring for the first time as separate entries in this year's Handbook: Blaise Hamlet (South West), Borrowdale (North West), Bradenham (South & South East), Buttermere and Ennerdale (North West), Coniston and Little Langdale (North West), 20 Forthlin Road, Liverpool (North West), Glastonbury Tor (South West), Grasmere and Great Langdale (North West), Hawkshead (North West), Langdon Cliffs

(South & South East), Ullswater (North West), Wasdale, Eskdale and Duddon (North West), Whipsnade Tree Cathedral (South & South East), Windermere and Troutbeck (North West), Woodchester Park (Central)

- whilst every care has been taken in compiling the Handbook to ensure complete accuracy, members and visitors are asked to recognise that arrangements can change, as can telephone numbers and other details. The Trust reserves the right to amend opening arrangements during the period covered by this Handbook, should this prove necessary

- please note that some telephone information lines, usually those with an 0891 prefix, are charged at a rate higher than the normal tariff. At the time of publication, this amounts to 49p per minute at peak rate, and 39p per minute at other times. Information provided on these lines will be kept as brief as possible, consistent with providing the necessary details.

How you can support the National Trust

JOIN AND ENJOY YOUR LOCAL MEMBERS' ASSOCIATIONS & CENTRES

Join your local Association and share your interest in the Trust with like-minded members from your area: more than 100,000 members already have.

A **National Trust Association or Centre** is a local club run by members for members. There are 194 all over England, Wales and Northern Ireland, and now one in Belgium: they offer coach outings, lectures, parties, rambles, tours and holidays in Britain and abroad – as well as **friendship**.

Last year they raised nearly £1 million for the National Trust, as well as providing practical help at Trust properties and offices.

To join please ask at any National Trust property for the free map leaflet 'Make the most of your membership'. This gives a contact name, address and telephone number for each Association. Alternatively, contact Tom Burr, Associations Liaison Secretary at **Eastleigh Court, Bishopstrow, Warminster, Wiltshire BA12 9HW, tel. 01985 843586,** or the Membership Department at **PO Box 39, Bromley, Kent BR1 3XL, tel. 0181 315 1111.**

Special Information for National Trust Members

- Membership of the National Trust allows you free entry to most properties open to the public during normal opening times and under normal opening arrangements, **providing you can present a valid membership card.**

- **Please check that you have your card with you before you set out on your journey. We very much regret that you cannot be admitted free of charge without it, nor can admission charges be refunded subsequently, due to the administrative costs of doing so.**

- Membership cards are **not transferable**.

- If your card is lost or stolen, please contact the Membership Department (address on p.20), tel. 0181 315 1111, Monday to Friday, 9am to 5.30pm.

- A replacement card can be sent to a temporary address if you are on holiday. Voluntary donations to cover the administrative costs of a replacement card are always welcome.

- Free entry is not guaranteed; additional charges may be made for the following:
  - When a special event is in progress at a property
  - When a property is opened specially for a National Gardens Scheme open day
  - Where the management of a property is not under the National Trust's direct control, eg Tatton Park, Cheshire
  - Where special attractions are not an integral part of the property, eg Steam Yacht *Gondola* in Cumbria

- The National Trust encourages educational use of its properties. Education Group Membership is open to all non-profit-making educational groups whose members are in full-time education. Subscription rates are banded according to the nature of the organisation and the number on roll.

- Life members of the National Trust who enrolled as such before 1968 have cards which admit one person only. Life members wishing to exchange these for 'admit two' cards, or those wishing to change from one category of life membership to another, should contact the Membership Department in Bromley for the scale of charges.

- Entry to properties owned by the Trust but maintained and administered by English Heritage or Cadw (Welsh Historic Monuments) is free to members of the Trust, English Heritage and Cadw.

- Members of the National Trust are also admitted free to properties of the National Trust for Scotland. The National Trust for Scotland *Guide to over*

100 Properties can be obtained by sending a self-addressed adhesive label and £2 to the National Trust for Scotland (see address on p.22).

● Reciprocal visiting arrangements also exist with certain overseas Trusts, including Australia, New Zealand, Barbados, Bermuda, Canada, Jersey, Guernsey and the Manx Museum and National Trust on the Isle of Man. For a full list please send a s.a.e. to the National Trust Membership Department.

● National Trust members visiting properties owned by the National Trust for Scotland or overseas Trusts are only eligible for free entry on presentation of a valid membership card.

How you can support the National Trust

BECOME A MEMBER TODAY

You will be helping the Trust protect and care for much-loved country-side and coastline as well as the many important historic houses and gardens listed in this Handbook. Your subscription goes directly to support this work.

Benefits of membership:

● free admission to most of the properties listed in this Handbook

● three mailings a year which include a free copy of this Handbook, three editions of the full colour *National Trust Magazine*, a gift catalogue and two editions of your regional newsletter

There is a wide range of different membership categories for you to choose from (see form opposite).

How to join:

For **immediate** membership, you can join at almost all National Trust properties or shops during your visit.

For **postal applications**, complete the form opposite and return it to the address given.

Or just **telephone** the National Trust Membership Department on **0181 315 1111**. Enquiries and credit card applications are welcome. The lines are open Monday to Friday 9am to 5.30pm. Please allow 21 days for receipt of your membership card and new member's pack.

Application for membership

TO: THE NATIONAL TRUST, FREEPOST MB1438, BROMLEY, KENT BR1 3BR

Twelve-month membership

☐ **Individual:** £28 and, for each additional member living at the same address, £20. One card for each member.

☐ **Family group:** £54 for two adults and their children under 18, living at the same address. Please give names and dates of birth for all children. **Two** cards cover the family.

☐ **Family one adult:** £42 for one adult and their children under 18, living at the same address. Please give names and dates of birth for all children. **One** card covers the family.

☐ **Child:** £14 Must be under 13 at time of joining. Please give date of birth.

☐ **Young person:** £14 Must be 13 to 25 at time of joining. Please give date of birth.

☐ **Education group membership:** See Special Information for National Trust Members, and tel. 0181 315 1111 for further details.

Life membership

☐ **Individual:** £675 (£450 if aged 60 or over and retired). One card admits the named member and a guest.

☐ **Joint:** £825 for lifetime partners (£525 if either partner is aged 60 or over and retired). Two cards, each admitting the named member.

☐ **Family joint:** £925 two cards, each admitting the named adult and their children under 18 living at the same address. Please give names and dates of birth for all children.

Rates valid until 28 February 1999.

SOURCE D73			DATE		
FULL ADDRESS					
			POSTCODE		
TITLE	INITIALS	SURNAME		DATE OF BIRTH	VALUE £

AMOUNT ATTACHED:
CHEQUE/POSTAL ORDER £
Delete as appropriate

Please allow 21 days for receipt of your membership card and pack

Credit/debit card payments can be made by telephoning 0181 315 1111 (office hours)

Immediate membership can be obtained by joining at a National Trust property, shop or countryside information point

How you can support the National Trust

YOUR WILL CAN PROTECT THE PLACES YOU LOVE

Whatever their size, legacies are vital to the National Trust. They are used to fund major restoration projects or to acquire and endow new properties around the country. Legacies are not spent on administration costs.

Including a legacy to the National Trust in your Will could prevent your estate paying inheritance tax, and would certainly help maintain Britain's heritage for future generations.

We appreciate the concern you take in our work. We have now written a free booklet for our members, giving you all the information you need about making your Will, or adding a codicil to an existing one. Help us protect the places you love – send for our Will booklet today.

Just telephone or write to: The Head of the Legacies Unit, 36 Queen Anne's Gate, London SW1H 9AS (tel: 0171 222 9251)

How you can support the National Trust in the USA

JOIN THE ROYAL OAK FOUNDATION

More than 30,000 Americans belong to the Royal Oak Foundation, the Trust's US membership affiliate. A not-for-profit organisation, the Royal Oak helps the National Trust through the generous tax-deductible support of members and friends by making grants towards its work. Member benefits include the National Trust Handbook, three editions of *The National Trust Magazine*, gift catalogue, the quarterly Royal Oak Newsletter, and free admission to properties of the National Trust and of the National Trust for Scotland.

Royal Oak also awards scholarships to US residents to study in Britain, and sponsors lectures, tours and events in both the US and the UK, designed to inform Americans of the Trust's work.

For further information please write, call, fax or email
The Royal Oak Foundation, 285 West Broadway, New York, NY 10013, USA. Tel. 00 1 212 966 6565, fax. 00 1 212 966 6619
email general@royal-oak.org
Internet http://www.royal-oak.org

Information and guidance for visitors

Please read these notes carefully as they apply to all National Trust properties. Visitors will recognise that the contents and fabric of many of the Trust's houses are fragile and valuable. After many years of thought and research into methods of improving preventive conservation and security, certain restrictive measures have been introduced. These constraints on visitors are essential to the safe-keeping of houses in the Trust's care – by respecting them you will be helping the Trust to ensure that its houses and contents are preserved for future generations to enjoy. Symbols indicating restrictions specific to that property are positioned to the right-hand side on the line following the property name. Restrictions on sharp-heeled shoes, bulky bags and photography apply at all Trust houses.

COAST AND COUNTRYSIDE

Whilst this Handbook deals primarily with those properties which are open at a charge, the National Trust also protects and manages very considerable areas of exceptionally beautiful coastline and countryside. Highlights of selected properties are mentioned briefly in the introduction to each area, but much more information is available in individual leaflets and in the Trust's Countryside Handbook (available at NT shops). The long-term care and management of our coast and countryside properties is a major continuing commitment for the National Trust, and we always welcome financial and practical support for this often pioneering work.

CONCESSIONS

As a registered charity, completely independent of government, the National Trust regrets it cannot afford to offer concessions on admission fees.

DOGS

Dogs (except guide dogs, hearing dogs for the deaf and dogs aiding the disabled) are not allowed inside Trust houses and restaurants, and seldom in gardens. The symbol showing a dog on a lead indicates properties which welcome leashed dogs in their grounds (not gardens). In these cases dogs must be kept on the lead at all times to minimise disturbance to deer and livestock.

Dogs are welcome at most countryside properties provided they are kept under close control. However, owners should take particular care in spring, which is a particularly sensitive time of year for ground-nesting birds in woodland, heath and moorland, and is also the period during which deer are calving. Lambing time is still beset by sheep-worrying incidents despite sustained publicity over many years.

On some beaches the Trust has found it increasingly necessary to introduce restrictions on dogs during the high season due to conflicts with other users, particularly families with children. Some of these conflicts have arisen due to the problem of dog fouling.

In 1996 the government passed new legislation on dog fouling, and in many areas of the country local authorities are now implementing it, including on Trust properties. Where the Act applies, if your dog fouls the land it will be an offence if you do not clear up the waste. Failure to do so could result in a fine of up to £1,000. Dog waste bins are now being installed at many of our heavily used sites. Where bins are not provided, please dispose of the waste thoughtfully. Where dogs have been restricted from areas, the Trust has attempted to find suitable alternative locations nearby.

Conscious of the dangers associated with leaving dogs in cars, we endeavour to provide a shady parking space in our car parks, water for drinking bowls, hitching posts where dogs may be safely left, and advice on suitable areas where dogs may be exercised. These facilities will vary from property to property, and according to how busy it may be on a particular day. The primary responsibility for the welfare of dogs remains, of course, with the owner.

FEEDBACK

We welcome feedback from our members and visitors on occasions when they have encountered especially good service, as well as when some element of a visit has proved less than satisfactory. Such feedback is most appropriately directed to the manager of the property concerned. Alternatively, please contact the relevant Regional Office or the Trust's London Head Office. Many properties provide their own suggestion forms and boxes which visitors are encouraged to use. All comments will be noted, and action taken where necessary, but it is not possible to answer every comment or suggestion individually.

The National Trust adheres to the English Tourist Board's Visitors' Charter for Visitor Attractions, and supports the 'Welcome Host' customer care training programme backed by the Wales, English and Northern Ireland Tourist Boards.

FOOTWEAR

Any heel which covers an area smaller than a postage stamp can cause irreparable damage to all floors, carpets and rush matting. We regret, therefore, that sharp-heeled shoes are not permitted. When necessary, plastic slippers are provided for visitors with unsuitable or muddy footwear. Alternative slippers are available for purchase.

We would also like to remind visitors that ridged soles trap grit and gravel, which scratch fine floors. Boot-scrapers and brushes are provided for visitors' use. Overshoes may be provided at properties with vulnerable floors.

Please remember to use appropriate footwear in the countryside and in gardens.

The Trust is committed to providing a welcoming, worthwhile and enjoyable visit for families with children. Family tickets are offered in every region, although not necessarily at every property. Many provide baby-feeding areas and baby-changing facilities (often combined in a purpose-designed parent and baby room). In restaurants there are high-chairs, together with children's menus, colouring sheets and, at some properties, play areas. There are children's guides, trails, or quiz sheets, and Trust shops stock a wide range of interesting and inexpensive items for children.

Trusty the Hedgehog, the new children's character, has been created specially for young members and visitors. As well as featuring on *Trust Tracks*, the newsletter for young members, Trusty also appears at many events at Trust properties across the country and is proving immensely popular in helping to develop children's interest in the Trust's vital conservation work. In June 1997 Trusty went hi-tech by launching his own interactive home pages, specifically for young visitors. Children can find out which properties Trusty will be visiting by clicking on the area where they live, view the special art gallery showing their own paintings, enter exciting competitions, email reports about their favourite places and discover more about hedgehogs. You can email Trusty at http:\\www.trusty.org

One note of caution on visiting historic houses: we ask parents to recognise the challenges which the Trust faces in preserving fragile interiors and delicate contents. Architecture, interior decoration and furnishings differ at every house, and therefore access arrangements for visitors vary too. Front slings for babies can be admitted but we regret that at the majority of historic houses (85), it is not possible to admit prams, pushchairs or baby back carriers, because of the considerable risk of accidents to babies and young children, damage to historic contents and inconvenience to other visitors on busy days. However, a few historic houses may admit back carriers on quiet days midweek, at the discretion of the staff on duty at the time.

The following houses are able to admit baby back carriers at all times: Aberconwy House; Ardress House; Canons Ashby; Castle Coole; Castle Drogo; Castle Ward; Charlecote Park; Clumber Chapel; Dunster Castle; Florence Court; Gibside Chapel; Hinton Ampner; Killerton; Knightshayes Court; Little Moreton Hall; Montacute House; Mount Stewart; Petworth House; Springhill; Tattershall Castle; Tatton Park; The Vyne.

For visitors with smaller babies, front slings are usually available on loan, and occasionally reins for toddlers. Prams can be stored at the entrance at the staff's discretion. We regret that the restriction on back carriers, prams and pushchairs can cause particular difficulties for parents with older and/or heavier babies. If you are unsure about restrictions, do please telephone a property in advance of your visit to check. Once at a property, please ask staff for help and advice, and do bear in mind that there is often plenty for children to see and do outdoors, whether on an estate with a garden and park, or at nearby countryside or coastal sites.

FREE ENTRY DAY

Each year the National Trust organises a day when all visitors are admitted free to many properties. It provides an opportunity to visit for those who would not normally be able to afford the admission charges. We are grateful to the many voluntary organisations who in 1997 provided transport and assistance to visitors on this day. Because Free Entry Day is generally very busy, National Trust members may prefer to plan their visits on other days. For the same reason we request groups planning to travel by coach to book their visits on Free Entry Day in advance with the property and to check beforehand for any restrictions.

The next Free Entry Day will be on **Wednesday, 16 September 1998**.

HEALTH AND SAFETY

We endeavour to provide a safe and healthy environment for visitors to our properties as far as is reasonably practicable, and to ensure that the activities of our staff, volunteers and contractors working on Trust properties do not in any way jeopardise the health and safety of visitors. You can help us by observing all notices and signs relating to this subject during your visit, by following any instructions given by Trust staff, by ensuring that children are properly supervised at all times and by wearing appropriate clothing and footwear at countryside properties and in gardens.

HEAVILY VISITED PROPERTIES

Many properties are extremely popular at Bank Holidays and summer weekends. At some houses and gardens timed tickets may be issued to smooth the flow of people entering the property (but not to limit the duration of a visit), and all visitors (including NT members) are required to use these tickets. This system is designed to create better viewing conditions for visitors and to minimise wear-and-tear on the historic interiors or gardens. On rare occasions entry to the property may not be possible on that day. If you are planning a long journey, you are encouraged to telephone the property in advance of your trip. At a few properties special considerations apply and pre-booking is essential, eg Chastleton, Mr. Straw's House.

HOW TO GET THERE

At the end of each property entry is a brief description of location together with a grid reference and OS Landranger series map number. Car-parking is usually available within 100m of the property.

Travelling on foot, by bike, boat, train or bus is environmentally friendly and enjoyable. Details of access by public transport are given throughout the

Handbook (correct as of October 1997). Regular updates are issued during the year; contact the Trust's London address (see p.20) and ask for 'Green Transport News'. Please note that no indication of frequency of transport services is given, so check the times of services before setting out. 'Passing ⊫' (NIR in N. Ireland) indicates the bus service passes the station entrance or approach road and 'Passing close ⊫' indicates that a walk is necessary. Unless otherwise stated, bus services pass the property (although there may be a walk from the bus-stop!), and the railway station name is followed by the distance from the property.

You can obtain train details from the national rail enquiry line 0345 484950 (at local rates) and Southern Vectis operates the train, bus and coach hotline on 0891 910910 (at premium rates – please mention this Handbook when calling). Many counties also provide a travel line for bus (and sometimes train) times.

Wheelchair users travelling by train should note that some stations are unstaffed. These are followed by a (U).

The National Trust is grateful to Barry Doe, a life member, for this travel information. If you experience difficulties following this information or have suggestions to make, he will be glad to reply to your comments. Please contact him at: Travadvice, 25 Newmorton Road, Moordown, Bournemouth, Dorset BH9 3NU (tel. 01202 528707).

LARGE OR BULKY BAGS

At some properties visitors will be asked to leave behind large items of hand luggage while they make their visit. This is to protect furniture and contents from accidental damage and to improve security. This restriction includes rucksacks, large handbags, carrier bags, bulky shoulder bags and camera/camcorder bags. These bags can be safely left at the entrance to any house where the restriction applies (principally historic houses with vulnerable contents, fragile decorative surfaces or narrow visitor routes). See 'For Families' section for additional information on back carriers and pushchairs.

LIGHT LEVELS

Light levels are regularly monitored and carefully controlled using blinds and sun-curtains to achieve the best balance between providing reasonable viewing conditions and preventing the deterioration of sensitive contents, especially textiles and watercolours. Visitors are recommended to allow time for their eyes to adapt to darker conditions inside houses, particularly in rooms where light levels are reduced to preserve light-sensitive material.

THE NATIONAL GARDENS SCHEME

Each year many of the National Trust's gardens are opened on extra days in support of the National Gardens Scheme. Money raised on these days is donated by NGS to support nurses' and gardeners' charities, including National Trust gardens (for upkeep and for training of young gardeners). The National Trust acknowledges with gratitude the generous and continuing support of the National Gardens Scheme Charitable Trust.

OPENING ARRANGEMENTS AND ADMISSION FEES

Members of the National Trust are admitted free to virtually all properties (see Special Information for National Trust Members, p.7). Each property entry shows the normal adult admission fee. This includes VAT and is liable to change if the VAT rate is altered.

Children: under 5s are free. Children aged 5–16 are half the adult price, unless stated. 17s and over pay the adult price. Children not accompanied by an adult are admitted at the Trust's discretion.

School parties: many properties offer educational facilities and programmes. Teachers are urged to make a free preliminary visit by prior arrangement with the property. Reductions are usually available for groups of 15 or more school-children aged under 19. Education Group Membership is recommended (see p.7 for more details).

Group visits: all groups are required to book in advance and confirm the booking in writing. Some properties have limited access for groups so early booking is recommended. A discount is usually available for groups of 15 or more at most properties. Full information on group visits to National Trust properties is available from the Travel Trade Office, tel. 0171 447 6700; fax. 0171 447 6701.

PHOTOGRAPHY

We welcome amateur photography out-of-doors at our properties. We regret, however, that such photography is not permitted indoors when houses are open to visitors.

However, special arrangements can be made for interested amateurs (as well as voluntary National Trust lecturers, research students and academics) to take interior photographs by appointment outside normal opening hours. **Applications must be made in writing to the property concerned, for a mutually convenient appointment. Please note that an admission charge may apply (including NT members) for this facility.**

All requests for commercial photography must be channelled through the Regional Public Affairs Manager at the appropriate regional office for permission.

PICNICS

Many properties welcome picnics; some make special provision, a few cannot accommodate them (this is usually indicated in the property entries). If you are planning a picnic at a Trust property for the first time, do please telephone in advance to check. Fires and barbecues are not allowed except where special provision is made.

SEATING

Seats for visitors' use are provided at various points in all the Trust's historic houses and gardens. Those visitors who wish to sit down – whether elderly, infirm, pregnant or simply tired – should feel free to use the seats available, or ask a room steward if seating is not immediately obvious.

SMOKING

Smoking is not permitted inside Trust houses, restaurants or shops. Smokers are also invited to exercise reasonable restraint in gardens, since the scent of flowers is such an important part of visitors' enjoyment of a garden.

VISITORS WITH DISABILITIES

We warmly welcome to our properties visitors with disabilities; also guide dogs for visually impaired and disabled people and hearing dogs for the deaf, so long as they are in harness. Most properties have a good degree of access, and provide manual wheelchairs. Self-drive and volunteer-driven powered buggies are available at some larger gardens and parks. (The Trust regrets that powered vehicles are rarely allowed in historic buildings; for exceptions please see individual entries.) The necessary companion of a disabled visitor is admitted free of charge on request, while the normal charge applies to the disabled visitor.

The paragraph signed with the wheelchair symbol indicates the facilities available for visitors with disabilities. The Sympathetic Hearing Scheme operates at many properties, and Braille guides are available at most. General information and a free 56-page booklet on access (also available in large print and tape), supported by Barclays Bank, are available from The National Trust's Membership Department, FREEPOST MB 1438, Bromley, Kent BR1 3BR. Please enclose stamped self-addressed adhesive label (31p in 1997)

The National Trust Magazine is available free on tape, as are several regional newsletters. Please contact Valerie Wenham, Adviser on Facilities for Disabled Visitors, at the Trust's Head Office – see p.20 for address – if you wish to receive these regularly.

National Trust Enterprises

The Trust's shops, restaurants, tea-rooms and holiday cottages are all managed by National Trust Enterprises. The profit they generate goes to support the work of the National Trust, and in 1996/7 contributed £7 million to funds.

SHOPS

Many Trust properties have shops offering a wide range of related merchandise – much of which is exclusive to the National Trust. These shops and their opening times are indicated in relevant property entries by the shop symbol. Many are also open for Christmas shopping and dates are given in the appropriate entries. In addition the Trust now operates a number of shops in towns and cities throughout the country, which are open during normal trading hours (see p.20 for full list).

RESTAURANTS AND TEA-ROOMS

The National Trust operates over 135 tea-rooms and restaurants. They are usually located in very special old buildings including castles, lighthouses, stables, and even hot-houses! The Trust aims to offer traditional home cooking, warm hospitality and value for money. As well as providing services for visitors, the Trust caters for groups and private parties, and many properties offer festive meals in the run-up to Christmas. For more information on functions and private parties in National Trust properties, tel. 0181 315 1111.

HOLIDAYS WITH THE NATIONAL TRUST

The Trust owns and manages over 240 holiday cottages, set in some of the most outstanding locations in England, Wales and Northern Ireland. From a converted 15th century stable block in Kent or a former brewhouse in Oxfordshire to a glorious manor house in Cornwall, they all feature in the full colour brochure. For a copy, please send a £2 contribution to cover the cost of production, postage and packing to The Holiday Booking Office, PO Box 536, Melksham, Wiltshire SN12 8SX. For booking enquiries please call 01225 791199.

For an overseas holiday visiting sites of historic or natural interest, The National Trust Travel Collection is available from tour operator Page & Moy. The Trust benefits financially from every holiday booked through this travel programme, which also features cruises and tours visiting Trust properties in this country. For a free brochure please call 0116 250 7676.

The National Trust for Scotland also offer holiday cottages. Please contact them direct for details (see p.22).

Many National Trust tenants offer bed-and-breakfast in their homes, which are often ideally situated for exploring Trust properties and countryside. Camping and caravans are also welcome at a number of attractive sites on Trust land. For details of b&b addresses or a list of camping and caravan sites, please send a s.a.e. (minimum size 11cm x 22cm) to our Membership Department (see p.20).

Publications

The National Trust produces a wide range of books. Most of these are available in Trust shops and good bookshops, but you can also order them from the Mail Order Department, PO Box 101, Melksham, Wiltshire SN12 8EA and through the Trust's Internet site (http://www.ukindex.co.uk/nationaltrust). Copies of guidebooks to Trust properties can be obtained from 36 Queen Anne's Gate, London SW1H 9AS. If you would like a Trust book catalogue, please write to this address, enclosing a stamped, self-addressed envelope.

Gardens of the National Trust by Stephen Lacey, £29.99. An authoritative guide with stunning colour photographs showing the wide range of Trust gardens, from great landscape parks like Studley Royal and Stowe to small gems like the town gardens of Mompesson House in Salisbury and Peckover House in Wisbech. (This publication is sponsored by Land Rover.)

The National Trust Guide by Lydia Greeves and Michael Trinick, £24.99. A revised edition of the Trust's illustrated 'bible' of information about all its properties.

The National Trust: The First Hundred Years by Merlin Waterson, £17.99 hardback, £10.99 paperback. A history of the National Trust, concentrating on the people behind the organisation – the donors, supporters and staff – brought to life with paintings and photographs.

Countryside (foreword by Richard Mabey) and *Coast* (foreword by Libby Purves), £14.99. Superbly illustrated books showing the places of natural beauty owned by the Trust through the images of three leading landscape photographers, Joe Cornish, David Noton and Paul Wakefield. Published April 1998.

The Polite Tourist: A History of Country House Visiting by Adrian Tinniswood, £24.99. Visitors to National Trust houses, using their Handbook for reference, are continuing a venerable tradition. Tudor sightseers, Georgians on the Grand Tour and Gothic fantasists are recalled with the help of paintings, drawings and photographs. Published September 1998.

National Trust Town Shops

Opening times vary, so please telephone to check if making a special journey

Barnstaple 5 High St
(tel. 01271 71551)

Bath Marshall Wade's House,
Abbey Churchyard
(tel. 01225 460249)

Cambridge 9 King's Parade
(tel. 01223 311894)

Canterbury 24 Burgate
(tel. 01227 457120)

Cardiff Castle
(tel. 01222 237997)

Chester 5 Northgate St
(tel. 01244 313465)

Cirencester Tourist Information Centre,
Cornhall, Market Place
(tel. 01285 654180)

Dartmouth 8 The Quay
(tel. 01803 833694)

Dorchester* 65 High West St
(tel. 01305 267535)

Exeter 18 Cathedral Yard
(tel. 01392 274102)

Grasmere Information Centre & Shop
Church Stile, Grasmere
(tel. 01539 435621)

Hexham
25/26 Market Place
(tel. 01434 607654)

London
Brentford Syon Park
(tel. 0181 569 7497)

Regent St
British Travel Centre
(tel. 0181 846 9000)

Victoria Blewcoat School,
23 Caxton St
(tel. 0171 222 2877)

Melksham* 5 Church St
(tel. 01225 706454)

Monmouth 5 Church St
(tel. 01600 713270)

St Alban's Tourist Information Centre,
Town Hall, Market Place
(tel. 01727 864511)

St David's
Captain's House, High St
(tel. 01437 720385)

Salisbury 41 High St
(tel. 01722 331884)

Sidmouth Old Fore St
(tel. 01395 577650)

Solva 21 Main St
(tel. 01437 720661)

Stamford Estate Office, Shop & Information Centre
18 Market St, Altrincham
(tel. 0161 928 0075)

Stratford-upon-Avon
45 Wood St
(tel. 01789 262197)

Tewkesbury
39 Church St
(tel. 01684 292919)

Totnes Waterside,
The Plains
(tel. 01803 863475)

Truro 9 River St
(tel. 01872 241464)

Wells 16 Market Place
(tel. 01749 677735)

Windsor 14 High St
(tel. 01753 850433)

York – Shop & Tea-room
32 Goodramgate
(tel. 01904 659050)

* clearance shop only

Who to contact in the National Trust

We are very willing to answer questions and receive comments from our members and visitors. For queries about a particular place, please telephone the property (see property entry for address and tel. number). If your query relates to several properties in a region, or is about other regional matters, please telephone the appropriate regional office (see details below)

1. **National Trust Membership Department**, PO Box 39, Bromley, Kent BR1 3XL (tel. 0181 315 1111; fax. 0181 466 6824) for all straightforward queries, including membership and requests for literature

2. **London Head Office**, 36 Queen Anne's Gate, London SW1H 9AS (tel. 0171 222 9251; fax. 0171 222 5097) for queries of a national nature. National Trust guidebooks can be purchased from the reception desk

3. Regional Offices

Cornwall: Lanhydrock, Bodmin PL30 4DE
(tel. 01208 74281; fax. 01208 77887)

Devon: Killerton House, Broadclyst, Exeter EX5 3LE
(tel. 01392 881691; fax. 01392 881954)

East Anglia: Blickling, Norwich NR11 6NF
(tel. 01263 733471; fax. 01263 734924)

East Midlands: Clumber Park Stableyard, Worksop, Notts S80 3BE
(tel. 01909 486411; fax. 01909 486377)

Kent & East Sussex: The Estate Office, Scotney Castle, Lamberhurst,
Tunbridge Wells, Kent TN3 8JN (tel. 01892 890651; fax. 01892 890110)

Mercia: Attingham Park, Shrewsbury, Shropshire SY4 4TP
(tel. 01743 709343; fax. 01743 709352)

North West: The Hollens, Grasmere, Ambleside, Cumbria LA22 9QZ
(tel. 01539 435599; fax. 01539 435353)

Northumbria: Scots' Gap, Morpeth, Northumberland NE61 4EG
(tel. 01670 774691; fax. 01670 774317)

Severn: Mythe End House, Tewkesbury, Glos GL20 6EB
(tel. 01684 850051; fax. 01684 850090)

Southern: Polesden Lacey, Dorking, Surrey RH5 6BD
(tel. 01372 453401; fax. 01372 452023)

Thames & Chilterns: Hughenden Manor, High Wycombe, Bucks HP14 4LA
(tel. 01494 528051; fax. 01494 463310)

Wessex: Eastleigh Court, Bishopstrow, Warminster, Wiltshire BA12 9HW
(tel. 01985 843600; fax. 01985 843624)

Yorkshire: Goddards, 27 Tadcaster Road, Dringhouses, York YO2 2QG
(tel. 01904 702021; fax. 01904 707982)

Wales: Trinity Square, Llandudno, Gwynedd LL30 2DE
(tel. 01492 860123; fax. 01492 860233)

Northern Ireland: Rowallane House, Saintfield, Ballynahinch,
Co. Down BT24 7LH (tel. 01238 510721; fax. 01238 511242)

4. The National Trust London Information Centre, Blewcoat School,
23 Caxton Street, Westminster, SW1H OPY (tel. 0171 222 2877) for
queries about visiting properties in Greater London

5. Volunteers' Office, 33 Sheep St, Cirencester, Glos GL7 1RQ
(tel. 01285 651818), or contact the Regional Volunteers Coordinator in
each region (see list of regional addresses above) for offers of volunteer help

6. **National Trust Enterprises**, The Stable Block, Heywood House, Westbury, Wilts BA13 4NA (tel. 01373 858787) for matters relating to shops, restaurants, holidays and the catalogue. For **Mail Order**, write to PO Box 101, Melksham, Wiltshire SN12 8EA (tel. 01225 790800); for **Holiday Cottage** information, tel. 01225 791199

7. **National Trust Estates Dept**, 33 Sheep Street, Cirencester, Glos GL7 1RQ (tel. 01285 651818)

8. **National Trust for Scotland**, 5 Charlotte Square, Edinburgh EH2 4DU (tel. 0131 226 5922)

9. **Young National Trust Theatre (YNTT)**, The National Trust, Sutton House, 2 & 4 Homerton High Street, Hackney, London E9 6JQ (tel. 0181 986 0242)

How you can support the National Trust

WORKING AS A VOLUNTEER

The National Trust welcomes the practical involvement of members through its developing volunteer programme. Some 35,000 volunteers, members and non-members of all ages and backgrounds, support the Trust's permanent staff as active partners. In over 140 different ways, they work on tasks ranging from the highly skilled to those requiring only a gift of time and enthusiasm.

To learn more about the opportunities open to volunteers, including our regional and property-based volunteer groups and more than 400 environmental working holidays, please send a large s.a.e. to the **National Trust Membership Department**, PO Box 39, Bromley, Kent BR1 3XL.

Key to Symbols

Castle

Historic house

Other buildings

Mill

Church, chapel etc

Garden

Park

Countryside

Coast

Prehistoric/Roman site

Industrial archaeology

Farm/farm animals

Nature reserve

Country walk

Opening arrangements

Guided tours

Admission details

Wheelchair access

For visually
handicapped visitors

Parent & child facilities

Education

Information for dog-owners

Refreshments

How to find the property

Railway station

Shop

Events

Map symbols:

▲ Buildings & gardens

■ Coast & countryside

Abbreviations

AONB	Area of Outstanding Natural Beauty
BH	Bank Holiday
ha	hectares
m	metres
ml	miles
SSSI	Site of Special Scientific Interest

Area Maps

The key map opposite shows how England, Wales and Northern Ireland are divided into nine areas for the purposes of this Handbook. Following the key map are individual maps for each area, showing those properties which have individual entries as well as those which are mentioned briefly in the area introduction. Please note that the map for London is incorporated within that covering the South & South East.

In order to help with general orientation, the maps show main roads and population centres. However, the plotting of each site serves only as a guide to its location. Those properties marked ▲ are buildings and/or gardens, whilst ■ denotes a coast or countryside property. Please note that some countryside properties, eg. those in the Lake District, cover many thousands of hectares. In such cases the appropriate symbol is placed centrally as an indication of general location.

LINDISFARNE CASTLE,
NORTHUMBERLAND

24

1. South West
2. South & South East
3. London
4. East
5. Central
6. North West
7. North East
8. Wales
9. Northern Ireland

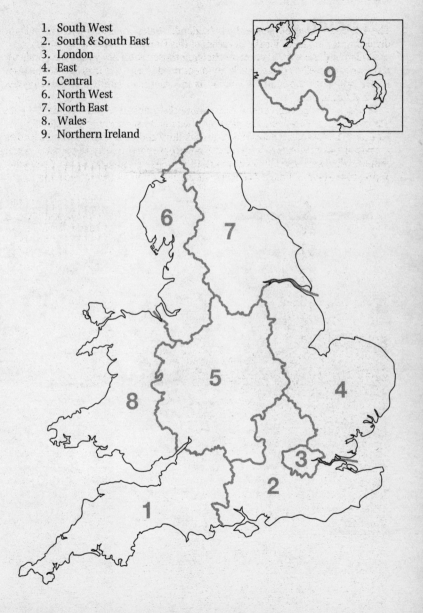

2 & 3 South & South East, London

Royston
A10
507
Ware
A120
Bishop's Stortford
Hatfield Forest
Hertford
A414
Cheshunt
Bar
Waltham Abbey
A25
A10
A406
nton House
Sutton House
illow Road
George Inn
Roman Bath
Eastbury Manor House
Rainham Hall
A12
Chislehurst Common, Hawkwood & Petts Wood
A226
Sheerness
ewcoat School
indsey House
Morden Hall Park
St John's Jerusalem
Owletts
Coldrum Long Barrow
Tudor Yeoman's House
Chatham
Herne Bay
Margate
Broadstairs
Ramsgate
Watermeads
Selsdon Wood
Whitstable
A299
A28
Faversham
A2
A299
Quebec House
Knole
Old Soar Manor
Ightham Mote
Maidstone
A249
M2
Canterbury
A2
A257
A258
Deal
Emmetts Garden
Stoneacre
A252
A28
Chartwell
Sprivers Garden
Sissinghurst Castle Garden
Ashford
M20
South Foreland Lighthouse
Langdon Cliffs
Toys Hill
A264
Tunbridge Wells
Dover
den
Chiddingstone
Scotney Castle Garden
Tenterden
M20
A259
Hythe
Folkestone
Wakehurst Place
Hawkhurst
Smallhythe Place
Royal Military Canal
Hymans Garden
Sheffield Park Garden
A265
Bodiam Castle
Lamb House
Lydd
A272
A26
Bateman's
Battle
A28
A259
Rye
vil's Dyke
Lewes
Hailsham
A271
A21
A259
Hastings
Bexhill
Monk's House
A271
Alfriston Clergy House
righton
Newhaven
Eastbourne
Frog Firle Farm
Birling Gap
Crowlink

Bedfordshire   Isle of Wight
Berkshire   Kent
Buckinghamshire   London
Hampshire   Surrey
Hertfordshire   Sussex

0   5   10   15 Miles
0   5   10   15   20   25 Km

G   H   J   K   L   M

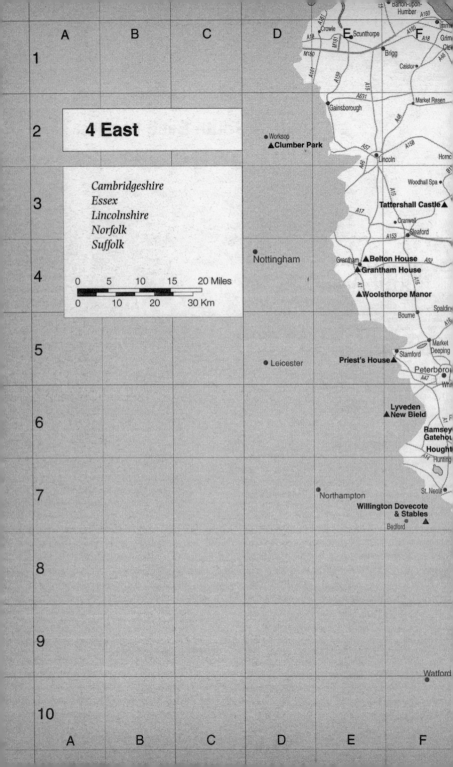

4 East

Cambridgeshire
Essex
Lincolnshire
Norfolk
Suffolk

0	5	10	15	20 Miles
0	10	20	30 Km	

Barton-upon-Humber
A160
Immi
A18
Crowle
Scunthorpe
A150
Grim
M181
Clee
A18
M160
Brigg
Caistor
A159
A15
A631
Market Rasen
Gainsborough
A46
Worksop
▲Clumber Park
A57
A158
Horn
Lincoln
A46
Woodhall Spa
Bri
A15
Tattershall Castle ▲
A17
Cranwell
A153
Sleaford
Nottingham
Grantham ▲Belton House
A52
▲Grantham House
A1
▲Woolsthorpe Manor
Spaldin
Bourne
A16
Market
Deeping
Leicester
Priest's House▲
Stamford
Peterboro
A47
Whit
Lyveden
▲New Bield
A1
Ramsey
Gateho
Hought
Hunting
St. Neots
Northampton
Willington Dovecote
& Stables
▲
Bedford
Watford

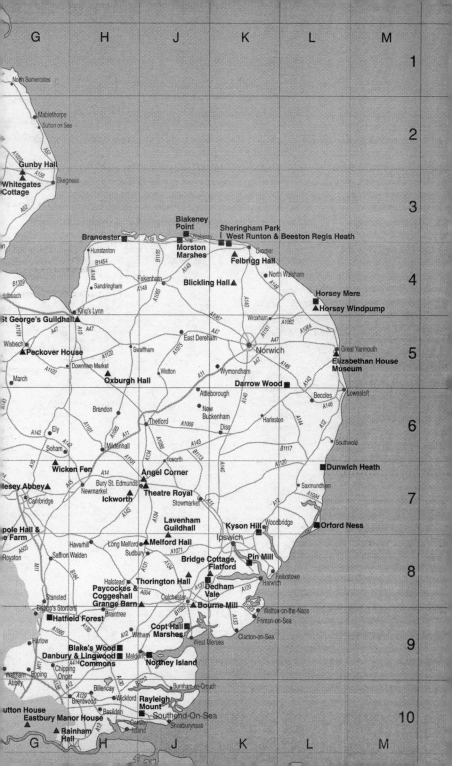

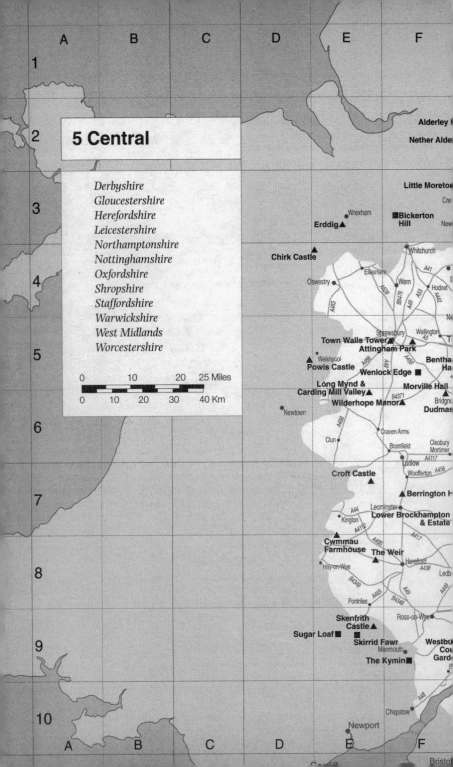

5 Central

Derbyshire
Gloucestershire
Herefordshire
Leicestershire
Northamptonshire
Nottinghamshire
Oxfordshire
Shropshire
Staffordshire
Warwickshire
West Midlands
Worcestershire

0		10		20	25 Miles
0	10	20	30	40 Km	

Alderley
Nether Alde

Little Moreto
Cre
Wrexham
Erddig▲ ■Bickerton
Hill New
Whitchurch
Chirk Castle▲ A41
Ellesmere Wem Hodnet A442
Oswestry A528 A53
A483 B5476 A49
Ne
Shrewsbury Wellington
Town Walls Tower▲ A5 T
Attingham Park
Welshpool A458 A49 A458 Bentha
Powis Castle▲ Ha
Wenlock Edge ■
Long Mynd & B4371 Morville Hall
Carding Mill Valley▲ Bridgno
Wilderhope Manor▲ Dudmas
Newtown A488
Craven Arms
Clun Bromfield Cleobury
Ludlow Mortimer
Woofferton A4117
Croft Castle A456
▲ ▲ Berrington H
Leominster
A44 Lower Brockhampton
Kington A4112 & Estate
A417
Cwmmau A4103
Farmhouse ▲ The Weir
Hay-on-Wye Hereford
A438
B4349 Ledb
A465 A49
Pontrilas B4348
Ross-on-Wye
Skenfrith
Castle▲ Westbu
Sugar Loaf■ Cou
Skirrid Fawr■ Gard
Monmouth
The Kymin■
A48
Chepstow
Newport
Bristol

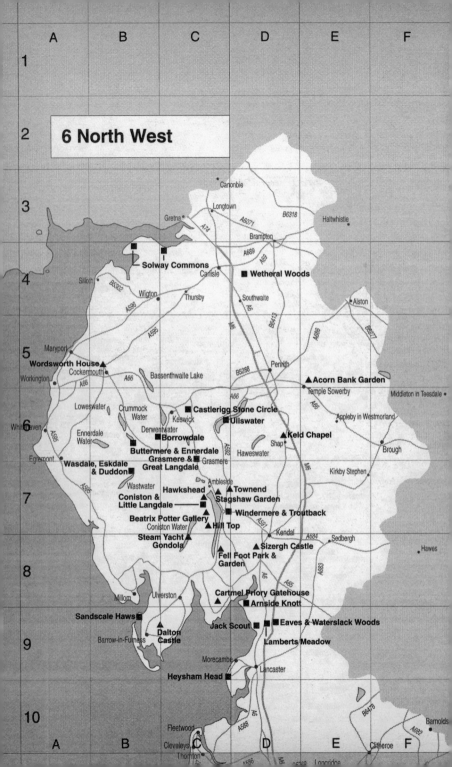

6 North West

- Canonbie
- Longtown
- A6071
- B6318
- Gretna
- A74
- Brampton
- Haltwhistle
- A689
- A69
- **Solway Commons**
- Carlisle
- **Wetheral Woods**
- Silloth
- B5302
- Wigton
- Thursby
- Southwaite
- Alston
- A596
- A595
- A6
- B6413
- A686
- B6277
- Maryport
- B5288
- Penrith
- **Wordsworth House** ▲
- Cockermouth
- Bassenthwaite Lake
- **Acorn Bank Garden** ▲
- Workington
- A66
- Temple Sowerby
- Middleton in Teesdale
- Whitehaven
- Loweswater
- Crummock Water
- Keswick
- **Castlerigg Stone Circle**
- A66
- Appleby in Westmorland
- A595
- Ennerdale Water
- Derwentwater
- **Borrowdale**
- **Ullswater**
- **Keld Chapel**
- Brough
- Egremont
- **Buttermere & Ennerdale**
- **Grasmere &**
- **Great Langdale**
- Grasmere
- Shap
- Haweswater
- A592
- A6
- Kirkby Stephen
- A595
- Wastwater
- **Wasdale, Eskdale & Duddon**
- **Hawkshead**
- Ambleside
- **Townend** ▲
- **Coniston & Little Langdale** ▲
- **Stagshaw Garden**
- **Windermere & Troutback**
- **Beatrix Potter Gallery**
- Coniston Water
- **Hill Top** ▲
- Kendal
- A684
- Sedbergh
- Hawes
- **Steam Yacht Gondola** ▲
- **Sizergh Castle** ▲
- A591
- **Fell Foot Park & Garden** ▲
- A6
- A683
- Millom
- Ulverston
- **Cartmel Priory Gatehouse** ▲
- **Sandscale Haws**
- **Arnside Knott**
- **Dalton Castle**
- **Jack Scout**
- **Eaves & Waterslack Woods**
- Barrow-in-Furness
- **Lamberts Meadow**
- Morecambe
- **Heysham Head**
- Lancaster
- B6478
- Barnolds
- A6
- Fleetwood
- A5688
- Cleveleys
- Clitheroe
- A682
- Thornton
- A586
- Longridge

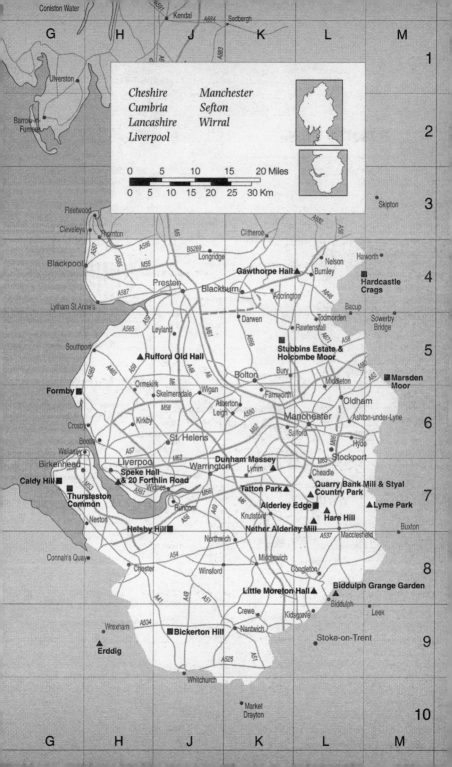

7 North East

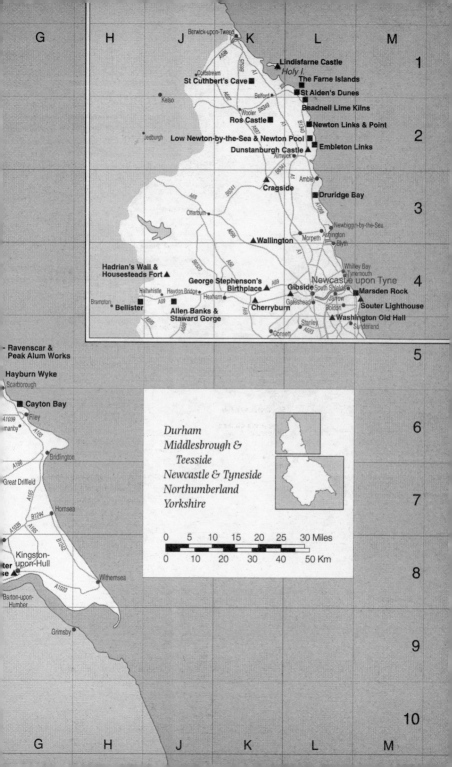

G H J K L M

Berwick-upon-Tweed

1

Lindisfarne Castle
Coldstream
Holy I.
St Cuthbert's Cave
The Farne Islands
Kelso
Belford
St Aiden's Dunes
Wooler
Beadnell Lime Kilns
Ros Castle
Newton Links & Point
Jedburgh
Low Newton-by-the-Sea & Newton Pool
Embleton Links
Dunstanburgh Castle
Alnwick

2

Amble
Cragside
Druridge Bay

3

Otterburn
Newbiggin-by-the-Sea
Wallington
Ashington
Morpeth
Blyth

Whitley Bay
Tynemouth
Hadrian's Wall &
Housesteads Fort
Newcastle upon Tyne
George Stephenson's
Birthplace
Gibside South Shields **Marsden Rock**
Haltwhistle Haydon Bridge
Hexham Gateshead Jarrow **Souter Lighthouse**
Brampton
Bellister
Cherryburn Boldon
Allen Banks & **Washington Old Hall**
Staward Gorge Stanley
Sunderland
Consett

4

- **Ravenscar &**
Peak Alum Works

5

Hayburn Wyke
Scarborough

Cayton Bay
Filey

6

Bridlington

Great Driffield

7

Hornsea

Kingston-
upon-Hull

8

Withernsea

Barton-upon-
Humber

Grimsby

9

10

Durham
Middlesbrough &
Teesside
Newcastle & Tyneside
Northumberland
Yorkshire

0   5   10   15   20   25   30 Miles

0   10   20   30   40   50 Km

G H J K L M

8 Wales

Con
Suspensi
Brid

Amlwch

Moelfre

Holyhead
Valley

Holy I.

Rhosneigr

A5

Aberconwy House

Beaumaris

Llangefni

Bangor

Penrhyn
Castle

Plas Newydd

Glan Faenol

Carneddau

Caernarfon

Segontium

Tŷ Mawr Wybrnant

Ysb

Aberglaslyn

Llwelyn
Cottage

Blaenau
Ffestiniog

Ffes

Porthdinllaen

Nefyn

Criccieth

Porthmadog

A487

Penrhyndeudrae

Llŷn

Pwllheli

Harlech

Porthor

Plas-yn-Rhiw

Dolmelynllyn

Braich Y Pwll

Abersoch

Penarfynydd

Dinas Oleu

Mynydd Bychestyn

Barmouth

Dolge

Bardsey I.

Cwrt

Llwyngwril

Cregennan

Tywyn

Aberdyfi

Mach

Aberystwyth

A44

Ponter

A4120

30 Miles

40 Km

Aberaeron

New Quay

Llanerchaeron

Trega

Lampeter

Mwnt

Penbryn

Cardigan

Dolaucothi
Gold Mines

Newport

Cilgerran
Castle

Fishguard

Llanwrda

St David's

Llandeilo

Solva

Carmarthen

A40

Dinefwr P

Haverfordwest

St Clears

Paxton's Tower

Narberth

Ammanford

St Martin's Haven

Colby
Woodland
Garden

Deer Park

Penrice

Pontardulais

Milford
Haven

Kidwelly

Llanelli

Pontardawe

Pembroke

Tenby

Burry Port

Tudor Merchant's
House

Rhossili

Swansea

Lydstep
Headland

Stackpole
Estate

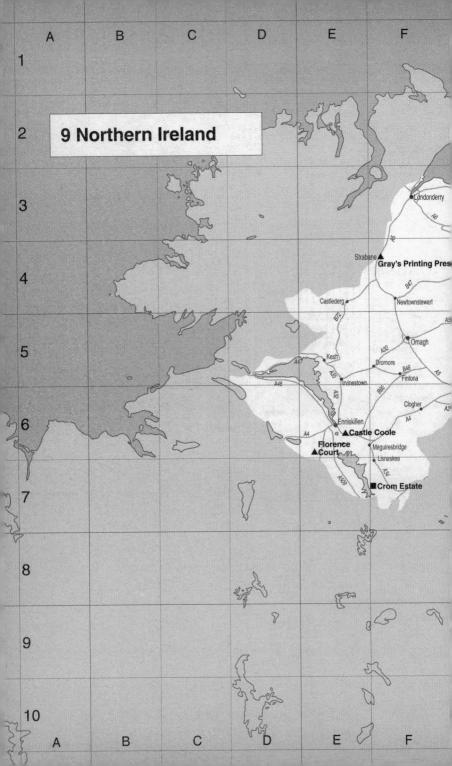

9 Northern Ireland

Londonderry

Strabane ▲
Gray's Printing Pres

Castlederg ●   Newtownstewart

B72

● Omagh

Kesh   Dromore

A32   B46
●Fintona

Irvinestown

Clogher

Enniskillen
○ ▲Castle Coole

Florence
▲Court   ● Maguiresbridge

● Lisnaskea

■ **Crom Estate**

1

2

3

4

5

6

7

8

9

10

G   H   J   K   L   M

North Antrim Cliff Path
Whitepark Bay
Larrybane
Rathlin Island

Giant's Causeway
Portstewart
Strand
Carrick-A-Rede
Fair Head
Downhill
Bar Mouth
Murlough Bay
Hezlett House
Portrush
Coleraine

Cushendun

A2
Limavady
A37
A54
A26

Ballymoney

A29
Kilrea
A43
A2

Dungiven
B40
A42
A5

Maghera
Ballymena
M2
A36
Larne

Magherafelt
A54
Randalstown
Ballyclare
A8
A2

Moneymore
M22
Antrim
Whitehead

Cookstown
Patterson's Spade
Mill
Carrickfergus
Lighthouse
Island

Springhill
A52
Newtownabbey
Ballymacormick Point

Wellbrook
Beetling Mill
A29
Belfast
Bangor

Coalisland
Crown Liquor
Saloon
Holywood
A2

Dundonald
Newtownards
Mount Stewart

Dungannon
A26
Lisburn
Comber

The Argory
M1
A3
M1
A49
Strangford
Lough

Ardress House
Lurgan
Rowallane Garden
Saintfield

Aughnacloy
Craigavon
Portadown
Dromore
Ballynahinch
Killyleagh

Armagh
N51
A3
Banbridge
B7
Castle Ward
Kearney

Markethill
A50
Tandragee
A27
Downpatrick

Keady
A28
A1
Rathfriland
B7
A50
Castlewellan

Newtownhamilton
A25
Bessbrook
Newcastle
Murlough Nature
Reserve

Derrymore House
Newry
Slieve Donard
A2

B25
Warrenpoint
Mourne
Coastal Path

Crossmaglen
A1

Kilkeel
Blockhouse &
Green Islands

0   10   20   30 Miles

0   10   20   30   40 Km

G   H   J   K   L   M

Introduction to the South West

In the far west of the area, the Trust's holdings in Cornwall amount to almost 9000ha (22,000 acres), including 110 miles of one of Europe's most spectacular coastlines. This ownership includes magnificent country houses such as **Lanhydrock**, **Cotehele** and **Antony**, the renowned gardens of **Trelissick**, **Glendurgan** and **Trengwainton**, as well as fascinating reminders of Cornwall's industrial past, such as the **Cornish Engines** near Redruth. There are magnificent walks throughout the county, many with breathtaking views. Details of the Trust's extensive coast and countryside properties here, and of the recreational opportunities they provide, are given in a series of leaflets (*see* Further Information).

In neighbouring Devon, the Trust owns 86 miles of coast, including **Foreland Point**, **Countisbury Hill**, the wooded valleys of **Watersmeet** and the beautiful stretch between **Woody Bay** and Coombe Martin on the Exmoor coast. The Trust also protects much of the coastal land running from Ilfracombe to **Woolacombe**, where there is a superb beach, and including **Morte Point** and **Damage Cliffs**. At Bideford Bay, there are fine walks on the remote coastline between **Abbotsham** and **Bucks Mills**, and also further west at **South Hole**, near Hartland.

South Devon has an equally interesting coastline, and the Trust has recently acquired an area of spectacular coastal landscape at **Scobbiscombe**. From **Bolt Tail** to **Overbecks** near Salcombe run 6 miles of rugged Trust-owned cliffland, crossed by the coastal footpath, which dips to give access to safe bathing at **Soar Mill Cove** and **Starehole Bay**. The area between **Portlemouth Down** and **Prawle Point** offers low cliffs with walks, views and sandy coves. The cliffs become more impressive again towards **Gammon Head** to the east.

The River Dart is a famous beauty spot, and the Trust protects several woods along the estuary, as well as coast on either side of the mouth at **Little Dartmouth** and between **Kingswear** and Southdown Cliff, near Brixham. To the east the Trust owns 3 miles of coastline between **Salcombe Hill**, Sidmouth and **Branscombe**.

The Trust also owns extensive areas within the Dartmoor National Park, including fine walking country in the woodland of the dramatic Teign Gorge, between **Whiddon Deer Park** and **Fingle Bridge**, opposite the impressive **Castle Drogo**. Downstream are the spectacular hanging oakwoods at **Steps Bridge**. Further west is **Hentor**, **Willings Walls** and **Trowlesworthy Warren**, on which there are many archaelogical sites. Near Plymouth lie the **Plym Bridge Woods**, interesting for their industrial archaeology, and on the fringes of the National Park is the beautiful **Parke Estate**, with delightful walks along the River Bovey.

The Dorset coast offers equally splendid walking opportunities, and at **Golden Cap** the Trust owns the highest cliff in Southern England. From here there are breathtaking views along the coast towards **Ringstead Bay**, with its famous Burning Cliff, and **Cogden Beach**, where the dramatic Chesil Bank starts. At **Spyway Farm** in Purbeck there are information panels about the area, and access to the sea at Dancing Ledge. To the north lies **Studland**, noted for its rare birds, unspoilt heathland and glorious beach. In total the Trust protects over 15 miles of Dorset coastline.

Inland Dorset boasts some of England's classic landscapes, with rolling chalk downland and hidden valleys. This is an area rich in archaeological remains, such as those at **Hod Hill** and **Turnworth Down**, near Blandford, as well as the famous ancient figure of the **Cerne Giant**, cut into the chalk near Cerne Abbas. The Fontmell Down Estate includes **Melbury Beacon** and botanically rich **Melbury Down**, from where there are magnificent views across the Blackmore Vale. To the north lies evocative Cranborne Chase and **Win Green Hill**, its highest point.

The prehistoric heritage of Wiltshire is celebrated worldwide. Apart from **Stonehenge Down** and **Avebury**, the Trust also owns the Iron Age hillfort of **Figsbury Ring**, which gives fine views over Salisbury, as does **Pepperbox Hill**, a 17th-century folly to the south east. Near Warminster is the Iron Age hill-fort of **Cley Hill**.

In the north of the area at Kewstoke near Weston-super-Mare there are fine coastal walks at **Sand Point** and **Middle Hope**. To the west is **Brean Down**, once the site of a Roman temple and now a bird sanctuary. Nearby are **Crook Peak**, **Wavering Down** and **Shute Shelve Hill**, a limestone landscape with heath, scrub and woodland rich in wildlife. Inland, the Trust owns some dramatic parts of the Quantocks, including **Beacon and Bicknoller Hills**, east of Williton, and further east are **Glastonbury Tor** and **Walton and Collard Hills**, overlooking the remote expanse of the Somerset Levels.

Highlights for Disabled Visitors
The recently opened and sloping path at **Snapes Point** near Salcombe allows wheelchair users to enjoy spectacular views, both out to sea and upstream of the beautiful Kingsbridge estuary with its interesting birdlife; in Dorset, there is easy access from the car park down a gentle slope to the shingle beach at **Burton Bradstock**; **Stonebarrow Hill** at Golden Cap has an adapted WC and marvellous views, and nearby **Langdon Hill Wood** has good level access to a circular forest route suitable for powered vehicles (please tel. Warden in advance on 01297 489628).

... and for Families
Heddon Valley in north Devon is especially recommended for children, with bridges and stepping stones along the river, meadows full of flowers and easy walks which start from the NT shop and information centre; **Pilsdon Pen, Coney's Castle and Lamberts Castle**, all in Dorset, provide fine viewpoints, with much of archaeological interest and marked footpaths; **Leigh Woods**, on the Avon Gorge near Bristol, offers wonderful nature walks with varied trees, flowers and fungi.

Further Information
NT Regional Offices:

- **Cornwall** (tel. 01208 74281)
- **Devon** (tel. 01392 881691)
- **Wessex** (tel. 01985 843600) – for properties in Bristol/Bath area, Dorset, Somerset and Wiltshire.

Please contact any of the above offices for a free copy of the NT Countryside Guide to the South West, sponsored by Barclays, which gives full details of a range of countryside properties in Cornwall, Devon, Dorset and Somerset.

A series of detailed leaflets (with maps), covering the Trust's Cornish coastal properties, is available for sale from NT shops in the county or from the Regional Office (please enclose donation to cover postage).

A set of leaflets covering the Trust's coast and countryside properties in Devon is currently in production: please tel. the Devon office for details. Four leaflets – West Exmoor Coast, Watersmeet & Countisbury, Arlington and Killerton – are already available.

The Wessex office offers a number of detailed walks leaflets, including 'Bath Skyline' and 'Cheddar Gorge and Crook Peak' (both 70p).

A LA RONDE 🏠
Devon

Summer Lane, Exmouth EX8 5BD Tel: 01395 265514

A unique 16-sided house built on the instructions of two spinster cousins, Jane and Mary Parminter, on their return from a grand tour of Europe. Completed c.1796, the house contains many 18th-century contents and collections brought back by the Parminters. The fascinating interior decoration includes a feather frieze and shell-encrusted gallery which, due to its fragility, can only be viewed on closed circuit television

O 1 April to 1 Nov: daily except Fri & Sat 11–5.30. Last admission 30min before closing. Timed tickets may be in operation during busy periods

£ £3.20, children £1.60. No party reduction; unsuitable for coaches or large groups except by prior arrangement with the Custodian

🛍 Same days as house: 10.30–5.45

🍽 Same days as house: 10.30–5.30. Morning coffees, lunches and afternoon teas

➔ (1: G7) 2ml N of Exmouth on A376 [192: SY004834] *Bus:* Stagecoach Devon 57 Exeter–Exmouth to within ¼ml (tel. 01392 427711) *Station:* Lympstone Village (U) 1¼ml; Exmouth 2ml

ANTONY 🏠 🏠 ✝ ❀ 🌳 ⛰
Cornwall

Torpoint, Plymouth PL11 2QA Tel: 01752 812191

One of Cornwall's finest early 18th-century houses, faced in lustrous silvery-grey Pentewan stone, offset by colonnaded wings of red brick and set within grounds landscaped by Repton. These include the formal garden with the National Collection of Day Lilies and fine summer borders, and the superb woodland garden with its outstanding displays of rhododendrons, azaleas, camellias and magnolias. Also of note is the 18th-century dovecote and the 1789 Bath Pond House. Antony has been the home of the Carew family for almost 600 years

O 1 April to 29 Oct: Tues, Wed, Thur & BH Mon (also Sun in June, July & Aug) 1.30–5.30, car park opens 12.30. Last admission 4.45. Bath Pond House can be seen by prior written application to Custodian and only when house is open. Woodland Garden (not NT – Carew Pole Garden Trust) open 1 March to 31 October, daily 11–5.30

£ £4. Pre-arranged parties £3. £2.50 for access to Woodland Garden (NT members free on days when house open). Combined gardens-only ticket for Antony garden and adjoining woodland garden £3. Pre-arranged parties £2.40 per person

🕴 Available at less busy times. Last tour 4.45

🛍 Shop open as house

♿ House not suitable for wheelchair users. Garden largely accessible; recommended circular route. Shop, tea-room & family history exhibition accessible. WC

👁 Braille guide

🍽 Tea-room, lunches available from 12.30 on open days

🐕 No dogs allowed

➡️ **(1: F8)** 5ml W of Plymouth via Torpoint car ferry, 2ml NW of Torpoint, N of A374, 16ml SE of Liskeard, 15ml E of Looe [201: SX418564] *Bus:* Western National 80/1, from Plymouth (passing close ⊠ Plymouth), alight Great Park Estate, ½ml, (tel. 01752 222666) *Station:* Plymouth 6ml via vehicle ferry *Ferry:* Torpoint 2ml

---

ARLINGTON COURT 🏠 ❀ ♠ 🛶 🐴 🚶 🎭 *Devon*

Arlington, nr Barnstaple EX31 4LP Tel: 01271 850296 Fax: 01271 850711

The plain exterior of this house, built in neo-classical style in 1822, does little to prepare the visitor for the astonishing rooms inside. Full of collections for every taste, many of them amassed by the eccentric and widely travelled Miss Rosalie Chichester, they include displays of model ships, costume, pewter, shells and other fascinating objects. The Trust's large collection of horse-drawn carriages is housed in the stables and there are carriage rides in the grounds, starting at the house. Walks lead through attractive gardens into extensive parkland grazed by Shetland ponies and Jacob sheep

What's new in 1998: Extracts from Miss Chichester's extensive library of diaries, journals and photograph albums are now displayed in the Music Room

🅾️ **House, Victorian garden & park:** 1 April to 1 Nov: daily except Sat but open Sat of BH weekends 11–5.30. Last admissions 5. **Park:** footpaths across parkland open during daylight hours Nov to March. **Events:** 18 April, 10km run; 15 Aug, Folk Festival; regular carriage driving tuition. Please tel. 01271 850296 for details

💷 £5.10; family ticket £12.80. Garden only £2.80. Pre-arranged parties of 15 or more paying visitors £4.30 per person. Parking 300m

🛍️ Same days as house 11–5.30 (tel. 01271 850348)

♿ Garden (gravel paths), grounds & shop accessible. Ramps at rear of house, help available; then ground floor accessible. Limited access to carriage collection. Close parking arrangements; disabled visitors may be driven to house by arrangement with Property Manager. WC. Batricar and wheelchairs available; ask at visitor reception

👁 Braille guides for house and carriage collection; audiotapes for house; some carriages and horses may be touched

🍽 Licensed restaurant open 12–5.30 (tel. 01271 850629). Restaurant opening during Oct may vary from that printed, although light refreshments will always be available during opening hours. Tea-room open as house. If in doubt, please telephone the property when you are planning a visit

👶 Parent and baby facilities; children's quiz; children's menu; babies in back carriers admitted to all areas; children's play carriage at stables

🏛 Schools' room available; book with Property Manager. Children's study book

🐕 Welcome, on short leads please

➔ **(1: F5)** 7ml NE of Barnstaple on A39 [180: SS611405] *Bus:* Red Bus 13, 295 Barnstaple–Lynton (passing close ≋ Barnstaple) (tel. 01271 45444) *Station:* Barnstaple 8ml

---

AVEBURY 🐕 🏛 👶 Wiltshire

nr Marlborough SN8 1RF Tel: 01672 539250

One of the most important megalithic monuments in Europe and spread over a vast area, much of which is under Trust protection. The great stone circle, encompassing part of the village of Avebury, is enclosed by a ditch and external bank and approached by an avenue of stones. Many of the stones were re-erected in the 1930s by the archaeologist Alexander Keiller. West of Avebury, the Iron Age earthwork of Oldbury Castle crowns Cherhill Down, along with the conspicuous Landsdown Monument. With the spectacular folds of Calstone Coombes, this area of open downland provides wonderful walking opportunities

What's new in 1998: The guide 'Walking Around Avebury' features six local walks, including sites not previously open to the public. Priced at £2, it is available from the property, or the NT Wessex Regional Office (please add 50p towards p&p)

🅾 Stone Circle: open daily. **Alexander Keiller Museum:** 1 April to 31 Oct, daily 10–6 (or dusk if earlier); 1 Nov to 31 March 1999: daily 10–4 (closed 24 to 26 Dec, 1 Jan)

£ Alexander Keiller Museum: Adult £1.60; children 80p. English Heritage Members free (tel. 01672 539250)

🏪 Open 1 April to 1 Nov: daily 11–5 (minimum opening hours); 2 Nov to 13 Dec: Sat & Sun only 11.30–4 (tel. 01672 539384)

♿ Access to museum, barn and parts of circle (access for disabled drivers to barn area). WCs at Great Barn and off village High St

👁 Some objects in museum may be touched

🍽 Lunches & teas at licensed Stones Restaurant and Red Lion Inn (not NT)

🏛 Study centre available

🐕 On leads in stone circle

➔ (1: L4) 6ml W of Marlborough, 1ml N of the Bath road (A4) on A4361 and B4003 [173: SU102699] *Bus:* Thamesdown 49A Swindon–Devizes/Marlborough (passing close ⊟ Swindon); Wilts & Dorset 5, 6 Salisbury–Swindon (tel. 0345 090899) *Station:* Pewsey, no practical Sun service, 10ml; Swindon 11ml

---

AVEBURY MANOR AND GARDEN 🏠 ✤   *Wiltshire*

nr Marlborough SN8 1RF Tel: 01672 539250

A much-altered house of monastic origin, the present buildings dating from the early 16th century, with notable Queen Anne alterations and Edwardian renovation by Colonel Jenner. The topiary and flower gardens contain medieval walls, ancient box and numerous 'rooms'

🅾 **Garden**: 1 April to 1 Nov: daily except Mon & Thur (open BH Mon) 11–5.30. Last admission 5 or dusk if earlier. **House**: 1 April to 28 Oct: Tues, Wed, Sun & BH Mon 2–5.30. Last admission as garden

£ House and garden: £3, children £1.50. Parties £2.95, children £1.25; garden only: £2.25, children £1. Parties £2, children 75p

🛍 See Avebury

♿ Garden mostly level and accessible

🐕 No dogs

➔ (1: L4) As Avebury *Bus:* As Avebury

BARRINGTON COURT 🏠 🏠 ✤ 🎭   *Somerset*

Barrington, nr Ilminster TA19 0NQ Tel: 01460 241938

An enchanting formal garden, influenced by Gertrude Jekyll and laid out in a series of walled rooms, including the White Garden, the Rose and Iris Garden and the Lily Garden. The working kitchen garden has espaliered apple, pear and plum trees trained along high stone walls. The Tudor manor house was restored in the 1920s by the Lyle family. It is let to Stuart Interiors and is also open to NT visitors

🅾 1 April to 31 Oct: daily except Fri 11–5.30. Last admission 5. Coach parties by appointment only (tel. 01460 241938). **Events**: 12 April, Easter Egg Hunt; for details tel. 01985 843601

£ £4.20, children £2.10. Parties £3.70, children £1.90

🛍 Shop open as house; tel. 01460 242112

♿ Garden & restaurant accessible, ideal for wheelchairs. Powered self-drive buggy available. WC

👁 Braille guide and restaurant menu; scented plants and flowers

🍴 Licensed restaurant facilities, open as house & garden and offering fresh produce from kitchen garden; morning coffees, lunches & cream teas. Also available for functions and meetings (tel. 01460 241244)

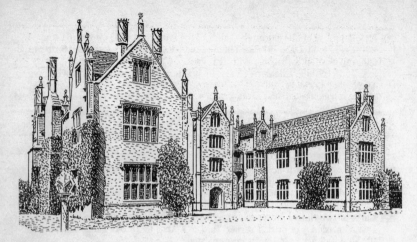

 Guide dogs only

→ (1: J6) In Barrington village, 5ml NE of Ilminster, on B3168. Visitors approaching from A303 follow signs for Ilminster town centre *Bus:* Southern National 32/3 Martock–Ilminster with connections from Taunton on Southern National 31 (passing close ⊞ Taunton) (tel. 01823 272033) *Station:* Crewkerne 7ml

BATH ASSEMBLY ROOMS 🏛 🛡 *Bath & NE Somerset*

Bennett Street, Bath BA1 2QH Tel: 01225 477789 Fax: 01225 428184

Designed by John Wood the Younger in 1769, at a time when Bath was becoming fashionable among polite society, the Rooms were both a meeting place and venue for public functions. Bombed in 1942, they were subsequently restored and are now let to Bath & North East Somerset Council, whose Museum of Costume is in the basement

🅾 The Rooms are open to the public all year daily (Mon to Sat 10–5, Sun 11–5; closed 25 & 26 Dec), when not in use for pre-booked functions. Access is guaranteed during Aug, but otherwise visitors are advised to check in advance. **Events:** available for wedding functions; please tel. for details

£ No admission charge to Rooms; admission charge to Museum of Costume (incl. NT members)

🎭 Hourly, when Rooms not in use for pre-booked functions

🎁 Open daily

♿ Street parking not always available; disabled visitors may be set down at door. Level access; WC

🍴 No refreshments available

🐕 Guide dogs only

→ (1: K4) N of Milsom Street, E of the Circus [156: ST749653] *Bus:* From ⊞ Bath Spa and surrounding areas (tel. 01225 464446) *Station:* Bath Spa ¼ml

BLAISE HAMLET 🏠 *Bristol*

Henbury, near Bristol   Tel: (Regional Office) 01985 843600

A hamlet of nine different picturesque cottages, designed by John Nash in 1809 for John Harford, to accommodate Blaise Estate pensioners

O All year

£ Free. Access to green only; cottages not open

& Wheelchair access to green

🐕 No dogs allowed

➜ (1: J3) 4ml N of central Bristol, W of Henbury village and just N of B4057 [172:ST559789] *Bus:* Cityline 1 from ☒ Bristol/Temple Meads; also 40/3 from city centre (tel. 0117 955 3231) *Station:* Sea Mills 3ml; Filton Wood 3½ml

BRADLEY 🏠 ✝ 🏞 *Devon*

Newton Abbot TQ12 6BN Tel: 01626 54513

A small medieval manor house, set in woodland and meadows

Note: The property is occupied and managed by Mrs A.H. Woolner and family

O 1 April to 30 Sept: Wed 2–5; also Thur 2 & 9 April, 17 & 24 Sept. Last admission 4.30

£ £2.60. No party reduction; organised parties by appointment with Secretary. Lodge gates are too narrow for coaches. No refreshments. No WC

➜ (1: G8) Drive gate (with small lodge) is on outskirts of town, on Totnes road (A381) [202: SX848709]; ¼ml walk to house from lodge *Bus:* Western National 89, 184, Stagecoach Devon 75 Newton Abbot–Totnes (passing close ☒ Newton Abbot) (tel. 01392 382800) *Station:* Newton Abbot 1½ml

BRANSCOMBE: THE OLD BAKERY, MANOR MILL & FORGE
🏠 🏞 🏭 🚶 *Devon*

Branscombe, Seaton EX12 3DB
Tel: (Old Bakery) 01297 680333; (Manor Mill enquiries) 01392 881691;
(Forge) 01297 680481

The Old Bakery is a stone-built and partially-rendered building beneath thatch, which until 1987 was the last traditional working bakery in Devon. The old baking equipment has been preserved in the baking room and the rest of the building now serves as a tea-room. Manor Mill, still in working order and recently restored, is a water-powered mill which probably supplied the flour for the bakery. The forge is open on an occasional basis and the blacksmith sells the ironwork he produces

Old Bakery: daily Easter to Oct and weekends in winter 11–5. **Manor Mill:** 1 April to 1 Nov: Sun 2–5; also Wed 2–5 from 15 July to 2 Sept. **Forge:** open on occasional basis, please tel. to check

£1, Manor Mill only. Car park adjacent to village hall on opposite side of road, donations in well

WC (in Old Bakery)

Morning coffee, light lunches and teas available at Old Bakery

Admitted to garden and information room of Old Bakery only

(1: H7) In the village of Branscombe off A3052 [192: SY198887] *Bus:* Axe Valley 899 Sidmouth–Lyme Regis (connections from ⇌ Axminster or Honiton) (tel. 01392 382800) *Station:* Honiton 8ml

---

BROWNSEA ISLAND 🏖 🏞 🚹 👤 🎭 *Dorset*

Poole Harbour BH13 1EE Tel: 01202 707744 Fax: 01202 701635

A wonderfully atmospheric island of heath and woodland, privately owned until acquired by the Trust in 1962, and now haven for a rich variety of wildlife, including red squirrels and many species of bird. Part of the island is leased as a nature reserve to the Dorset Wildlife Trust. There are many fine walks and spectacular views of Poole Harbour

Note: Boats run from Poole Quay, Swanage, Bournemouth and Sandbanks. Visitors may land from own boats at Pottery Pier at west end of island, accessible at all stages of the tide. Please note that the island's paths are uneven in places

1 April to 4 Oct: daily 10–5 (6 in July & Aug). **Events:** open-air theatre, and other events in summer; for details tel. 01985 843601

Landing fee: £2.40, children £1.20; family ticket £6 (2 adults & 2 children). Parties £2.10, children 95p, by written arrangement with Property Manager

Guided tours of nature reserve; please contact Dorset Wildlife Trust Warden (tel. 01202 709445)

Shop open 1 April to 4 Oct: daily 10.30–4.45 (closes 5.45 in July & Aug); (tel. 01202 700852)

Island paths hilly and rough, but area around quay accessible; two self-drive powered vehicles, and two manual wheelchairs available; mainland car-parking near Poole Quay; all boats will accept and help manual wheelchair users; WC near island quay. Access to cafeteria and shop from quay; enquire at reception desk

Braille guide and menu

Coffee, snacks and teas in the café near landing quay. Open daily 1 April to 4 Oct from 10.15; closes 30min before last boat departs (tel. 01202 700244). Tuck shop open daily

Nursing room, baby-changing facilities

Portman Study Centre. School groups welcome (tel. 01202 707744)

No dogs allowed on to the island

→ (1: L7) In Poole Harbour [195: SZ032878] *Bus:* Wilts & Dorset 150
Bournemouth–Swanage, alight Sandbanks; 152 Poole Quay–Sandbanks
(tel. 01202 673555). Yellow Buses 30 Poole Quay–Boscombe (passes ⊠ Poole),
also 12 Christchurch Quay–Sandbanks, June–Sept only (tel. 01202 557272);
also from surrounding areas to Poole bridge, few mins walk (tel. 01202 673555)
Station: Poole ½ml to quay; Branksome or Parkstone, both 3½ml to Sandbanks

BUCKLAND ABBEY 🏠 🖼 ✝ ❀ ⓘ ⛨ *Devon*

Yelverton PL20 6EY Tel: 01822 853607 Fax: 01822 855448

*Tucked away in its own secluded valley above the River Tavy, Buckland was originally a small
but influential Cistercian monastery. The house, which incorporates the ruins of the 13th-
century abbey church, has rich associations with Sir Francis Drake and his rival, Sir Richard
Grenville, and contains many interesting memorabilia from their time. There are also
exhibitions on seven centuries of history at Buckland, as well as a magnificent monastic barn,
craft workshops, herb garden and delightful estate walks*

Note: Buckland Abbey is jointly managed by the National Trust and Plymouth City
Council

What's new in 1998: Estate information room; thyme garden. During the first half of
1998 a new decorated plasterwork ceiling is being created in the fire-damaged Drake
Chamber and a sundial window installed in the top gallery

◎ 1 April to 1 Nov: daily except Thur 10.30–5.30; also 7 Nov to end March 1999:
Sat & Sun 2-5 (weekdays for pre-arranged parties only). Last admission 45min
before closing. Closed 4–22 Jan 1999. *Note:* Some rooms in the Abbey may be
closed or access restricted during the early part of the year for refurbishment -
please ring to check. **Events:** 27/28 June, Summer Craft Fair; 10/11 Oct, Tudor
Experience; first three weekends in Dec, Christmas decorations. Please ask for
events leaflet

£ £4.30; family ticket £10.70. Grounds only £2.20. Pre-arranged parties of 15 or more £3.50. Winter admission (2 Nov to March): reduced price for house; grounds and workshops only at no charge. NB: Additional charge (incl. NT members) on 27/28 June Craft Fair days. Car park 150m, occasional charge of £1 refundable on admission

🏠 Shop (tel. 01822 853706) open as house, but 7 Nov to end March 1999 Sat & Sun 12.30–5. Additional opening 2 Nov to 21 Dec, Mon & Fri 12–3. Independent craft workshops throughout year, variable opening (not Thur). Please check with individual workshops: basket-maker (tel. 01822 841187), potter (tel. 01822 841220), wood-turners (tel. 01364 631485/631585)

♿ Car park area for disabled drivers near reception/shop. After admission at main reception, disabled passengers may be set down at the Abbey. Access via gravel paths from car parks. Steep site. Motorised volunteer-driven buggy may be operating; please ask in car park or at reception. Wheelchairs available, also wheelchair stairclimber for access to upper levels of Abbey. Restaurant accessible via path with short steep slope. WC. Information leaflet on request

🌿 Scented herbs and plants. Braille and audio guides. Advice leaflet on request

☕ Licensed restaurant/tea-room open as shop. Restricted menu Nov to March 1999. Last servings 30min before closing. Also open for pre-booked Christmas lunches and candlelit dinners in Dec (tel. 01822 855024). Picnics in car park only

👶 Children's guide, parent and baby room, baby slings available, special children's menu, children's activities and events, including Fun Day (21 Aug). Leaflet available

📖 Sandford Award for Education 1996. Fully equipped school base and handling collection; book with Property Manager. Resource book available

🐕 In car park only, on leads. Dog posts in shade

➡ (1: F8) 6ml S of Tavistock, 11ml N of Plymouth: turn off A386 ¼ml S of Yelverton [201: SX487667] *Bus:* Plymouth Citybus 55 from Yelverton (not Sun) (with connections from ⭑ Plymouth), not Sun (tel. 01392 382800)
Station: Bere Alston (U), not Sun (except June to Sept), 4½ml

---

CASTLE DROGO 📖✝✿♠♿👶 *Devon*

Drewsteignton, nr Exeter EX6 6PB Tel: 01647 433306 Fax: 01647 433186

This granite castle, built between 1910 and 1930 for the self-made millionaire Julius Drewe, is one of the most remarkable works of Sir Edwin Lutyens. Perched on a moorland spur above the River Teign, it commands spectacular views of Dartmoor. The interior is designed for comfortable and elegant living, with an interesting kitchen and scullery, and elaborately appointed bathrooms. There is a delightful formal garden with roses and herbaceous borders, spring flowers, and many fine walks in the estate

What's new in 1998: Childrens' playground with replica Bunty House and Castle adjacent to picnic site

🅾 **Castle:** 1 April to 1 Nov: daily except Fri 11–5.30 (open Good Fri).
Garden: 1 April to 1 Nov: daily 10.30–5.30. Last admission 5

£ Castle, garden & grounds £5.20; family ticket £13. Garden & grounds only £2.40. Pre-arranged parties £4.30 per person. Car park 400m. The croquet lawn is normally open; equipment for hire. Please book through visitor reception

🚶 Occasional guided walks on estate

🏠 Shop and plant centre by car park, open daily 1 April to 1 Nov 10.30–5.30. Also 4 Nov to 20 Dec Wed to Sun 11–4.30 (tel. 01647 433563)

♿ Limited access to part of castle. Lift available (via two steps) to lower floor, dining and kitchen area; too small for most wheelchairs, but seat in lift. Garden accessible. Close parking and access by arrangement at visitor reception. Restaurant and shop accessible. WC near shop. Wheelchairs available

🌼 Scented plants. Braille guide; audio guide to castle

🍴 Licensed restaurant at castle, open 1 April to 4 Oct, same days as castle: 12–5.30. Tea-room in grounds, open daily 1 April to 1 Nov: 10.30–5.30; also limited refreshments available in Nov & Dec. Restaurant open for pre-booked Christmas lunches and suppers in Nov & Dec (tel. (01647) 432629)

🧒 Children's guide, children's menu, baby-changing facilities, babies in back carriers admitted to all areas. Children's playground adjacent to picnic site

🐕 On leads in car park and surrounding public footpaths only

➡ (1: G7) 5ml S of A30 Exeter–Okehampton road via Crockernwell or A382 Moretonhampstead–Whiddon Down road; coaches must use the latter and turn off at Sandy Park [191: SX721900] *Bus:* DevonBus 359 from Exeter (passing ⊠ Exeter Central), Carmel 174 from Okehampton (from ⊠ Okehampton) (tel. 01392 382800) *Station:* Yeoford (U) 8ml

THE CHURCH HOUSE 🏠   *Devon*

Widecombe in the Moor, Newton Abbot TQ13 7TA Tel: 01364 621321

Originally a brewhouse dating back to 1537, this former village school is now leased as a village hall. The adjacent Sexton's Cottage is a NT and Dartmoor National Park Information Centre and gift shop

🕐 During normal shop opening hours and by arrangement

£ Church House free (donation box)

🏠 Information centre and shop in Sexton's Cottage, open daily: mid Feb to 4 April 10–4.30; 5 April to end Sept 10–6; Oct to 24 Dec 10–5; closed Jan 1999

♿ Ground floor only

🍴 In village (not NT)

🐕 Not admitted

➡ (1: F7) In centre of Dartmoor, N of Ashburton, W of Bovey Tracey [191: SX718768] *Bus:* Western National 170/1 Newton Abbot–Tavistock (tel. 01392 382800)

CLEVEDON COURT 🏛 ✤   *North Somerset*

Tickenham Road, Clevedon BS21 6QU Tel: 01275 872257

An outstanding 14th-century manor house, virtually unaltered since then and incorporating a massive 12th-century tower and 13th-century great hall. Home to the Elton family, the house contains many striking Eltonware pots and vases and a fine collection of Nailsea glass. There is also a beautiful 18th-century terraced garden to enjoy

O 1 April to 30 Sept: Wed, Thur, Sun & BH Mon 2–5. Last admission 4.30

£ £4, children £2. Parties of 20 or more by prior arrangement; no reduction. Coaches by appointment. Unsuitable for trailer caravans or motor caravans

👤 Evening and afternoon tours by prior arrangement

♿ Access to ground floor via 4 steps. No wheelchair available

◉ Tea-room in Old Great Hall 2–4.45 (not NT)

👶 Children's trail

▦ School parties in the mornings by prior arrangement

➜ (1: J4) 1½ml E of Clevedon, on Bristol road (B3130), signposted from M5 exit 20 [172: ST423716] *Bus:* Badgerline X7, X25/6, 360–3, Swiftlink 662/3 from Bristol; X23/4, 823 from Weston-super-Mare; 360, 660, 823 from Yatton (pass close ⊞ Yatton). On all alight Clevedon Triangle ¾ml (tel. 0117 955 3231). For information on Waverley Paddle Steamer trips tel. 01446 720656 *Station:* Yatton 3ml

CLOUDS HILL 🏠   *Dorset*

Wareham, Dorset BH20 7NQ Tel: 01929 405616

A tiny isolated brick and tile cottage, bought in 1925 by T. E. Lawrence ('Lawrence of Arabia') as a retreat. The austere rooms inside are much as he left them and reflect his complex personality and close links with the Middle East

O 5 April to 1 Nov: Wed, Thur, Fri, Sun & BH Mon 12–5 or dusk if earlier; no electric light. Party viewing outside these times by prior arrangement with the Custodian (tel. 01929 405616)

£ £2.30. No reduction for parties or children. Unsuitable for coaches or trailer caravans. No WC

🗂 T. E. Lawrence books on sale

✋ Braille guide

➜ (1: K7) 9ml E of Dorchester, 1½ml E of Waddock crossroads (B3390), 4ml S of A35 Poole–Dorchester road, 1ml N of Bovington Camp [194: SY824909] *Bus:* Southern National 67, Dorchester Coachways from ⊞ Wool, alight Bovington, 1ml (tel. 01305 783645) *Station:* Wool 3½ml; Moreton (U) 3½ml

COLERIDGE COTTAGE 🏠 *Somerset*

35 Lime Street, Nether Stowey, Bridgwater TA5 1NQ Tel: 01278 732662

The home of Samuel Taylor Coleridge for three years from 1797, with mementoes of the poet on display. It was here that he wrote The Rime of the Ancient Mariner, *part of* Christabel *and* Frost at Midnight

🅾 Parlour and reading room only shown: 1 April to 1 Oct: Tues to Thur & Sun 2–5. In winter by written application to the Custodian. Parties please book

💷 £1.70, children 80p. No reduction for parties which must book

🅿 In village (not NT)

➡ (1: H5) At W end of Nether Stowey, on S side of A39, 8ml W of Bridgwater [181: ST191399] *Bus:* Southern National 15 Bridgwater–Minehead (passing close ⊠ Bridgwater) (tel. 01823 272033) *Station:* Bridgwater 8ml

COLETON FISHACRE GARDEN 🌼 📷 🧍 🎭 *Devon*

Coleton, Kingswear, Dartmouth TQ6 0EQ Tel: 01803 752466

Spectacularly set on a beautiful stretch of NT-owned coast, this delightful garden was created by Rupert and Lady Dorothy D'Oyly Carte between 1925 and 1948. Nestling in a stream-fed valley, it features a variety of rare and exotic trees and shrubs and boasts particularly dramatic autumn colours

What's new in 1998: The largely unfurnished house is open periodically. Please refer to regional events leaflet or tel. 01803 752466 or 01392 881691

🅾 March: Sun only 2–5; also 1 April to 1 Nov: Wed, Thur, Fri, Sun & BH Mon 10.30–5.30 or dusk if earlier. Last admissions 30min before closing. **Events:** for details please send s.a.e or telephone the property

💷 £3.50. Pre-booked parties £2.80

🚶 Occasional guided walks by arrangement or as advertised under special events

🛍 Small selection of garden gifts, postcards and unusual plants for sale at reception

♿ Limited access to parts of garden, steep slopes (strong companions essential). Wheelchair available; can be pre-booked. Tea-garden has wheelchair-accessible tables

🦯 Braille guide. Scented herbs and plants

☕ Tea-garden open as garden for morning coffee, light lunches and afternoon teas, weather permitting. Picnics in car park area only

🚼 Baby-changing facilities in women's WC; children's trail leaflet

🐕 In car park only

➜ (1: G8) 3ml from Kingswear; take Lower Ferry road, turn off at toll house [202: SX910508] *Bus:* Stagecoach Devon 200 Torquay–Kingswear (passing ⊞ Paignton); otherwise Stagecoach Devon 22 Brixham–Kingswear (with connections from ⊞ Paignton). On both, alight ¾ml SW of Hillhead, 1½ml walk to garden (tel. 01803 613226) *Station:* Paignton 8ml; Kingswear (Paignton & Dartmouth Rly) 2¼ml by footpath, 2¾ml by road

---

COMPTON CASTLE 🏰 ✝ ✾   *Devon*

Marldon, Paignton TQ3 1TA Tel: 01803 872112

A magical fortified manor house, built between the 14th and 16th centuries and home to the Gilbert family for most of the last six hundred years. Sir Humphrey Gilbert (1539–1583) was coloniser of Newfoundland and half-brother to Sir Walter Raleigh. The dramatic towers and battlements shelter a stone courtyard, medieval great hall, spiral staircase and minstrels' gallery

Note: Compton Castle is occupied and administered by Mr & Mrs G. E. Gilbert

🅾 1 April to 29 Oct: Mon, Wed & Thur 10–12.15 and 2–5, when the courtyard, restored Great Hall, solar, chapel, rose garden and old kitchen are shown. Last admission 30min before closing

£ £2.80. Pre-booked parties £2.20; organisers should notify Secretary. Additional parking and refreshments at Castle Barton opposite entrance

🛍 Guidebooks, postcards and slides available

♿ Limited access for wheelchair users

☕ Morning coffee, lunches and teas at Castle Barton (not NT) from 10 (tel. 01803 873314)

🚼 Children's guidebook available

🐕 On leads in car park only

➜ (1: G8) At Compton, 3ml W of Torquay, 1ml N of Marldon; from the Newton Abbot–Totnes road (A381) turn left at Ipplepen crossroads and W off Torbay ring road via Marldon [202: SX865648] *Bus:* Stagecoach Devon 7 ⊞ Paignton–Marldon, thence 1½ml (tel. 01803 613226) *Station:* Torquay 3ml

CORFE CASTLE ■ E ▼ *Dorset*

Corfe Castle, Wareham BH20 5EZ Tel/fax: 01929 481294

One of Britain's most majestic ruins, the castle controlled the gateway to the Isle of Purbeck and had been an important stronghold since the time of William the Conqueror. Defended during the Civil War by the redoubtable Lady Bankes, the castle fell to treachery from within, and was heavily slighted afterwards by the Parliamentarians. Many fine Norman and early English features remain. Nearby are Corfe Common, rich in wildlife and archaeology, and Creech Grange Arch, a folly with spectacular views

What's new in 1998: Family Exhibition at Castle View visitor centre; new walks leaflet for Corfe Common which offers exciting views of the castle and surrounding countryside, available for 50p from local NT shops, NT Wessex Regional Office (please add 50p for p&p)

🅾 1 March to 1 Nov: daily 10–5.30 (4.30 in early March/late Oct); 3 Nov to 1 March 1999: daily 11–3.30 (closed 25/26 Dec and for 2 days at end Jan for training). **Events:** medieval and civil war events, archaeology days, evening opening and tours; please tel. for details

💷 £3.80, children £2; family tickets £9.60/£5.80. Parties £3.50, children £1.80. Car- & coach-parking available at Castle View off A351; also at Norden park & ride and West St (not NT)

🧍 Guided tours are often available during normal opening hours. Private groups by arrangement; please contact the castle for details

🏛 Shop open 1 April to 30 Sept: daily 10–6; 1 to 31 Oct: daily 10–5; 1 Nov to 1 March 1999: daily 10–4 (closed 1 week at end Jan for stock-taking); 2 to 31 March 1999: daily 10–5 (tel. 01929 480921)

♿ WC at ticket office (RADAR lock). Wheelchair access to ruins very difficult; not recommended beyond Outer Bailey. Shop, tea-rooms and Castle View visitor centre accessible (RADAR WC)

👁 Braille guide and menu. Many items and surfaces can be enjoyed by touch

☕ Tea-room (at castle entrance) serves coffee, lunches and cream teas, open 1 April to 1 Nov: daily 10–5.30 (opens 12 on Fri); 2 Nov to 1 March: daily except Thur & Fri 10–4.30 (closed end Jan/early Feb for redecoration; tel. for dates)

📖 Children's guidebook; baby-changing facilities at castle and visitor centre; baby carriers, highchairs and children's menu in tea-room. Children must be accompanied by an adult within the castle

📖 Education pack, schools' room with hands-on materials and guided tours available; for details tel. 01929 481294

🐕 On leads only

➡ (1: L7) On A351 Wareham–Swanage road [195: SY959824] *Bus:* Wilts & Dorset 142/3/4 Poole–Swanage (passing ⇄ Wareham) (tel. 01202 673555) *Station:* Wareham 4½ml; Corfe Castle (Swanage Railway) a few mins walk (park-and-ride from Norden Station)

CORNISH ENGINES 🔧🚹

Cornwall

Pool, nr Redruth

Tel: 01209 216657

Cornwall's engine houses are dramatic reminders of the time when the county was a powerhouse of tin, copper and china clay mining. These two great beam engines were used for pumping water (from a depth of over 550m) and for winding men and ore. The engines were originally powered by high-pressure steam, patented by the local engineer Richard Trevithick in 1802, but today are rotated by electricity. Nearby is the Geological Museum of the Camborne School of Mines, where the Trust's Norris collection of minerals can be seen

Note: The property is managed by the Trevithick Trust on behalf of the National Trust. Trevithick's Cottage is nearby at Penponds and is open every Wed 2–5, free of charge (donations welcome)

What's new in 1998: The Taylor's Centre at East Pool (tel. 01209 315027) is now a major Visitor Information Point, providing an overview of the industrial heritage of Cornwall

🅾 1 April to 31 Oct: daily 11–5 (Geological Museum Mon to Fri, 9–5, free entry). For group visits outside these times, please contact Trevithick Trust (tel./fax 01209 612142)

💷 £3, pre-arranged parties £2.70; concessions £2.50; students £1.50; family ticket £8

🚹 Available

🏠 Shop open as above

♿ Engines unsuitable for disabled visitors at present, many flights of stairs. Taylor's Centre accessible, plus WC

👁 Braille guide for Mitchell's Whim Engine (Braille and tape guides planned for Taylor's Shaft in 1999)

🍽 Refreshments available nearby

📖 Mining diagrams and working models in both properties

➡ (1: C9) At Pool, 2ml W of Redruth on either side of A3047 [203: SW672415] *Bus:* From surrounding areas (some passing ⇄ Redruth) (tel. 01209 719988) *Station:* Redruth 2ml; Camborne 2ml

COTEHELE 🏠 🏚 🎿 ✝ ☘ 🎭 🛗 🧍 🛡 *Cornwall*

St Dominick, nr Saltash, PL12 6TA Tel: 01579 351346

Nestling into the hillside high above the Tamar, the house was mainly built 1485–1627 and was a home of the Edgcumbe family for centuries. The mainly granite and slatestone walls contain intimate chambers adorned with sumptuous tapestries, original furniture and armour. Outside, the formal gardens overlook the richly planted valley garden below, with medieval dovecote, stewpond and Victorian summerhouse, and 18th-century tower above. Cotehele Mill has been restored to working condition, and at the Quay there are interesting old buildings housing an art and craft gallery and an outstation of the National Maritime Museum. The restored Tamar sailing barge Shamrock *is moored alongside*

Note: The number of visitors in this small and fragile house has to be limited to no more than 80 at any one time. Please arrive in good time and be prepared to wait to gain entry. There is no electric light in the rooms, so visitors should avoid dull days early and late in the season

What's new in 1998: Temporary exhibitions at certain times in the East Wing, tel. for details; re-presentation of the Mill in 1998

House: 1 April to 1 Nov: daily except Fri (open Good Fri) 11–5 (11–4.30 in Oct). Last admission 30min before closing or dusk if earlier (tel. 01579 350434) **Mill:** 1 April to 1 Nov: daily except Fri (open Good Fri and Fri in July & Aug) 1.30–5.30 (1.30–6 in July & Aug, 1.30–4.30 in Oct). Last admission 30min before closing or dusk if earlier (tel. 01579 350606). **Garden:** open daily 11 to dusk (tel. 01579 350909). **Events:** Please contact the Property Manager for details (tel. 01579 351346)

£ House, garden & mill £5.60; family ticket £14. Garden & mill only £2.80; family ticket £7. Pre-arranged parties £4.50 by prior written arrangement only with the Property Manager. Coach party organisers must book and obtain a copy of the route from the Property Manager. No parties Sun or BH weekends

▣ Shop open 1 April to 1 Nov: daily 11–5. Also limited opening Nov to Christmas (tel. 01579 350072). Cotehele Quay Art & Craft Gallery: open daily 12–5; limited opening Nov to Christmas (tel. 01579 351494)

♿ Hall and kitchen only accessible to wheelchairs. Ramps available at house, restaurant and shop (please enquire); most of garden unsuitable as very steep; loose gravel. Close parking by prior arrangement. WC. Tea-room on Quay & some woodland walks accessible. Wheelchairs available from reception

♨ Braille guides for house, garden & mill; some items in house may be touched on request and piano may be played by musicians; tactile route guide available. Scented plants in garden

🍽 Coffee, lunches and teas in the Barn (closed Fri) and on Cotehele Quay (open daily) during season, and limited opening Nov to Christmas (tel. 01579 350652)

🚼 Parent & baby room

🏛 Schools' resource pack available. Environmental education facilities available. National Maritime Museum Outstation on Quay. The Loft education room available on Quay. General school enquiries please tel. 01579 351346; for pre-booked guided tours of the House for schools, please tel. 01579 350434

🐕 Dogs under control welcome on woodland walks

→ (1: F8) On W bank of the Tamar, 1ml W of Calstock by footpath (6ml by road), 8ml SW of Tavistock, 14ml from Plymouth via Saltash Bridge; 2ml E of St Dominick, 4ml from Gunnislake (turn at St Ann's Chapel); Calstock can be reached from Plymouth by water (contact Plymouth Boat Cruises Ltd, tel. 01752 822797) [201: SX422685] *Bus:* Western National 79, Callington–Tavistock (passing ⊠ Gunnislake), tel. 01752 222666) *Station:* Calstock (U), not Sun (except June to Sept), 1½ml (signposted from station)

THE COURTS GARDEN � *Wiltshire*

Holt, nr Trowbridge BA14 6RR Tel: 01225 782340

A small 20th-century garden in the Hidcote tradition, full of charm and variety and set within an arboretum containing fine specimen trees. There are many interesting plants and an imaginative use of colour, with surrounding topiary, water features and garden ornaments

○ **Garden only:** 1 April to 1 Nov: daily except Sat 1.30–5.30. Out of season by appointment

£ £3, children £1.50. Parties by arrangement in advance with the Head Gardener. No WC. NT shop in Melksham, 4ml (tel. 01225 706454)

♿ Much of the garden is accessible

🐕 No dogs

→ (1: L4) 3ml SW of Melksham, 3ml N of Trowbridge, 2½ml E of Bradford-on-Avon, on S side of B3107 [173: ST861618] *Bus:* Badgerline 237 Melksham–Trowbridge (passing close ⊠ Trowbridge) (tel. 01225 464446) *Station:* Bradford-on-Avon 2½ml; Trowbridge 3ml

DUNSTER CASTLE 🏰 ❋ 🍃 🎭 *Somerset*

Dunster, nr Minehead TA24 6SL Tel: 01643 821314; 24hr Infoline: 01643 823004; Shop: 01643 821626; Fax: 01643 823000

Dramatically sited atop a wooded hill, there has been a castle here since at least Norman times. The 13th-century gatehouse survives, but the present building was remodelled in 1868–72 by Antony Salvin for the Luttrell family, who have lived here for 600 years. The fine oak staircase and plasterwork of the 17th-century house he adapted can still be seen. There is a sheltered terrace to the south, on which tender plants and shrubs grow, and beautiful parkland in which to walk

🅾 **Castle**: 30 March to 30 Sept: daily except Thur & Fri (closed Good Fri) 11–5; also 3 Oct to 1 Nov: daily except Thur & Fri 11–4. **Garden and park**: Jan to March, Oct to Dec: daily 11–4 (closed 25 Dec); April to Sept 10–5 (open Good Fri). Last admission in all cases 30min before closing. **Events**: outdoor theatre and family activity days; ghost tours and Christmas activities; for full events programme tel. 01985 843601

💷 Castle, garden & park: £5.20, children (under 16) £2.70; family ticket £13.40 (2 adults & up to 3 children). Pre-booked parties £4.60. Garden & park only £2.80, children (under 16) £1.30; family ticket £6.70. A 10min steep climb to castle from car park, but electrically powered vehicle available to give lifts when necessary. Car park in grounds

🎟 Contact Visitor Services for details of out of hours guided tours of house and/or attics & basements

🛍 Shop open daily 30 March to 27 Sept 10–5; 28 Sept to 24 Dec 11–4; Jan weekends only and 2 Feb to end March 1999 11–4, weather permitting

♿ Castle & garden are situated on a steep hill. Volunteer-driven multi-seater and self-drive vehicle available from car park. Castle accessible to manual wheelchairs via stairclimber, but no access for heavy powered chairs; shop accessible, but cobbled floor. WC. Property plan shows wheelchair-friendly routes. Sympathetic Hearing Scheme. Members of staff have British Sign Language Stage I

👁 Braille and large-print guides. Audiotapes. Guided tours can be booked. Scented plants & flowers in conservatory and garden

☕ In Dunster water-mill and village (not NT). Picnic area in park, near car park

⚐ Children's guidebook. Activity trails and colouring sheets available. Baby-changing facilities. Buggy park; back carriers, slings and reins available at front porch. Activity days; tel. for details

▦ Study centre. Teachers' resource book (£3.50). For assistance and bookings, contact Education Coordinator

⚐ Guide dogs only in garden, but all dogs welcome in park on leads

➔ (1: G5) In Dunster, 3ml SE of Minehead. NT car park approached direct from A39 [181: ST995435] *Bus:* Southern National 39 from Minehead; otherwise 28, 300 Taunton–Minehead (passing ⊠ Taunton), alight Dunster Steep, ½ml (tel. 01823 272033) *Station:* Dunster (W Somerset Steam Rly) 1ml

---

DUNSTER WORKING WATER-MILL ⊠ ⛨   *Somerset*

Mill Lane, Dunster, nr Minehead TA24 6SW Tel: 01643 821759

Built on the site of a mill mentioned in the Domesday Survey of 1086, the present mill dates from the 18th century and was restored to working order in 1979

🅾 1 April to end June: daily except Sat (open Easter Sat) 10.30–5. July & Aug: daily 10.30–5. Sept & Oct: daily except Sat 10.30–5. **Events:** 10 May, National Mills Day; mill in operation. Opportunity to taste samples of products baked with mill flour. Normal admission charges apply

£ £1.80; family tickets available; party rates by prior arrangement. The mill is run and maintained by private funding; NT members must pay normal admission charge. Parking, ¾ml

⚐ For groups by arrangement

⚐ Selling mill flour, muesli & mill souvenirs

⚐ Ground floor only at no charge

⚐ Tea-room and tea-garden (not NT)

▦ School parties welcome, but please book in advance

➔ (1: G5) On River Avill, beneath Castle Tor; approach via Mill Lane or Castle Gardens on foot; from car park in Dunster village or in old park [181: ST995435] *Bus:* As Dunster Castle

---

DYRHAM PARK ⌂ ✿ ♣ ⛨   *South Gloucestershire*

nr Chippenham SN14 8ER
Tel: Property Office 0117 937 2501; Warden's Office 01225 891364

Crowned with a balustrade and with fine views over its ancient deer park, Dyrham was built between 1691 and 1710 for William Blathwayt, William III's Secretary at War and Secretary of State. The rooms have changed little since they were furnished by Blathwayt and their contents are recorded in his housekeeper's inventory. There are many fine textiles and paintings, as well as items of beautiful blue-and-white delftware, reflecting the contemporary taste for Dutch fashions

Note: Due to the fragile nature of the contents, it is necessary to control the light levels in certain rooms

O **Park:** all year: daily 12–5.30 or dusk if earlier (opens 11 on days when garden open). Last admission 5. Closed Christmas Day. **House & garden:** 3 April to 1 Nov: daily except Wed & Thur 12–5.30 (garden opens at 11). Last admission 5 or dusk if earlier. *Note:* Property closed 3/4 July 1998 for jazz concerts. **Events:** 3/4 July, Jazz Festival and 50s, 60s & 70s music; also opera in West Garden; for details tel. 01985 843601

£ House, garden & park £5.40, children £2.70; family ticket £13.30 (2 adults & 3 children). Park only £1.70, children 80p. Park & garden only £2.80. Party rate available weekdays only. Please contact Property Manager. Coaches by prior arrangement

◻ Shop open same days as house, 12–5.30; also Nov to 20 Dec: weekends only 12–4 (tel. 0117 937 4300)

♿ Access to ground floor, orangery and terrace, stable restaurant and small shop; disabled drivers may park near house; disabled passengers may be set down and collected from front door. Photograph album of inaccessible rooms available. WC. Manual wheelchairs only in house. Wheelchairs available. Sympathetic Hearing Scheme

◉ Taped guide to house; Braille guide and menu

◧ Coffee, lunches and teas in licensed stable restaurant. Open 3 April to 1 Nov: daily except Wed & Thur, 11–5.30, last orders 5; 8 Nov to 20 Dec & March 1999: weekends only 12–4 (but may not open in adverse weather - please tel. to check); also available for functions and meetings all year round (tel. 0117 937 4293). Special winter programme in restaurant. Picnics welcome in park, but parties over 20 please advise. No barbecues

🚶 Children's guide

▦ School parties by appointment only; below stairs activities may be arranged

🐕 Dog-walking area: no dogs in deer park. No shaded areas in main car park

→ (1: K3) 8ml N of Bath,12ml E of Bristol; approached from Bath–Stroud road (A46), 2ml S of Tormarton interchange with M4, exit 18 [172: ST743757] *Bus:* Ryans Coaches from ≋ Bath Spa, Fri & Sat only (tel. 01225 424157) *Station:* Bath Spa 8ml

---

ELIZABETHAN HOUSE ▦ *Devon*

32 New Street, The Barbican, Plymouth PL1 2NA Tel: 01752 253871

A typical Tudor sea captain's timber-framed house, set in the heart of Plymouth's historic Barbican and a rare survival. Now a NT shop and information centre

Note: The property is managed by the National Trust in partnership with Plymouth City Council, which owns it

O 1 April to 1 Nov: daily except Mon & Tues 10–5

£ £1 (including NT members). No WC

Open as house

In Barbican area (not NT)

→ (1: F8) Near the Barbican, which overlooks Plymouth Harbour *Bus:* Plymouth Citybus 25 from ⊠ Plymouth (tel. 01752 222221) *Station:* Plymouth ¼ml

---

FINCH FOUNDRY 🚗 🚃 🚶   *Devon*

Sticklepath, Okehampton EX20 2NW Tel: 01837 840046 Fax: 01837 840046

A fascinating 19th-century water-powered forge, which produced agricultural and mining hand tools. Still in working order with regular demonstrations, the foundry has three water wheels driving the huge tilt hammers and grindstone

⭕ 1 April to 1 Nov: daily except Tues 11–5.30. Last admission 30min before closing

£ £2.60. Note: access to car park is narrow and therefore unsuitable for coaches and wide vehicles

Open as foundry

♿ Disabled drivers may park in front of building. Access to shop; foundry may be viewed through shop windows. Workshop and museum difficult

Braille guide; objects can be touched; volunteers will explain history of foundry

Light refreshments tea-room open same times as foundry

→ (1: F7) 4ml E of Okehampton off the A30 *Bus:* Western National X9 Exeter–Bude; Stagecoach Devon 51 Exeter–Okehampton; Western National 187 Exeter–Gunnislake. All pass ⊠ Exeter St David's (tel. 01392 382800) *Station:* Okehampton (Sun, Jun–Sept only) 4½ml

---

FYNE COURT 🚗 🛗 🚶 🚶   *Somerset*

Broomfield, Bridgwater TA5 2EQ Tel: 01823 451587

Formerly the pleasure grounds of the now demolished home of the pioneer electrician, Andrew Crosse (1784-1855), this nature reserve is now the headquarters of the Somerset Wildlife Trust and a visitor centre for the Quantocks

⭕ All year: daily 9–6 or sunset if earlier

£ Free. Car park charge. Coach-parking by prior arrangement only

Shop (not NT) open Easter to Christmas daily 2–5

♿ Trail for disabled visitors. Access to patio outside tea-room in fine weather. WC

Teas on Sun and BH, May to Sept (not NT). Picnic sites

🐕 Strictly no dogs allowed

→ (1: H5) 6ml N of Taunton; 6ml SW of Bridgwater [182: ST222321] *Station:* Taunton 6ml

GLASTONBURY TOR 🖼️ 🚹 *Somerset*

near Glastonbury   Tel: (Regional Office) 01985 843600

The dramatic and evocative Tor dominates the Somerset Levels and offers spectacular views over Somerset, Dorset and Wiltshire. At the summit an excavation has revealed the plans of two superimposed churches of St Michael, of which only the 15th-century tower remains

What's new in 1998: Information leaflet, price 50p, available from mobile recruitment Land Rover or at NT Wessex Regional Office (please add 50p for p&p)

O All year

£ Free

🛍️ NT shop in Wells

🍴 Refreshments available in nearby Glastonbury (not NT)

🐕 Dogs must be kept on leads at all times

→ (1: J5) Signposted from Glastonbury, from where seasonal park-and-ride (not NT) operates *Bus:* Badgerline 163 from 🚆 Taunton (not Sun), 173 from 🚆 Bath Spa (Sun only), 376 from 🚆 Bristol Temple Meads & Yeovil (not Sun) (tel. 0117 955 3231); Southern National 29A 🚆 Bristol Temple Meads–Taunton (Sun only) (tel. 01823 272033). All pass within ½ml of the Tor

GLENDURGAN GARDEN ✿ *Cornwall*

Mawnan Smith, nr Falmouth TR11 5JZ
Tel: 01326 250906 (opening hours only) or 01208 74281

A valley garden of great beauty, created in the 1820s and running down to the tiny village of Durgan and its beach. There are many fine trees and rare and exotic plants, with outstanding spring displays of magnolias and camellias. The laurel maze, dating from 1833, has recently been restored. The house is privately occupied

What's new in 1998: A restored path and new viewpoint on Manderson's Hill provide a wonderful westward view of the garden and maze. New children's guide

O 3 March to 31 Oct: Tues to Sat & BH Mon (closed Good Fri) 10.30–5.30. Last admission 4.30

£ £3.20. Family ticket £8. Pre-arranged parties £2.70 per person

🛍️ Shop and plant sales open as garden

♿ All access paths are steep, a viewing point is accessible but a strong companion is needed

👁 Braille guide

🍽 Snacks and light refreshments

🚹 Giant's Stride (a pole with ropes to swing from) and the maze

🐴 No dogs allowed in the garden

→ (1: C9) 4ml SW of Falmouth, ½ml SW of Mawnan Smith, on road to Helford Passage [204: SW772277] *Bus:* Truronian T4 from Falmouth (passing close ✉ Penmere) (tel. 01872 73453) *Station:* Penmere (U) 4ml

---

GREAT CHALFIELD MANOR 🏠 ✝ ⚘   *Wiltshire*

nr Melksham SN12 8NJ Tel: 01225 782239 Fax: 01225 783379

A charming manor house, encircled by a moat and defensive wall and with beautiful oriel windows and a great hall. Completed in 1480, the manor and gardens were restored earlier this century by Major R. Fuller, whose family live here and manage the property

◯ 1 April to 29 Oct: Tues, Wed, Thur by guided tours only, starting 12.15, 2.15, 3, 3.45 & 4.30. Guided tours of the manor take 45min and numbers are limited to 25. It is suggested that visitors arriving when a tour is in progress visit the adjoining parish church and garden first. Closed on public holidays.
Note: Groups are welcome to visit the Manor in organised parties on Fri & Sat, by prior written arrangement with Mrs Robert Floyd. Organisers of coach parties should plan to allow 2hrs because of limits on numbers in house

£ £3.50. No reduction for children or parties. No WC

♿ Limited access to garden only

→ (1: K4) 3ml SW of Melksham via Broughton Gifford Common (sign for Atworth, drive on left) [166: ST860630] *Bus:* Badgerline 237 Melksham–Trowbridge (passing close ✉ Trowbridge), alight Holt, 1ml by footpath (tel. 01225 464446) *Station:* Bradford-on-Avon, 3ml

---

HARDY MONUMENT 🏠 🗻   *Dorset*

Black Down, Portesham   Tel: (Regional Office) 01985 843600

A monument erected in 1844 in memory of Vice-Admiral Sir Thomas Masterman Hardy, Flag-Captain of HMS Victory at the Battle of Trafalgar. It has been recently restored by the Trust

What's new in 1998: New guide

◯ 4 April to 27 Sept: Sat & Sun only 11–5. Staffed by volunteers. Numbers at the top of the monument are limited. Children must be accompanied by an adult. No WC

£ £1; no reduction for children

♿ No wheelchair access

→ (1: K7) From the B3157 Weymouth–Bridport road, turn off at Portesham; the road climbs steeply to a car park signposted 'Hardy Monument' [194: SY613876] *Bus:* Weybus 6 Weymouth–Abbotsbury (passing close ⚑ Weymouth), alight Portesham, thence 2ml (tel. 01305 767023) *Station:* Dorchester South or Dorchester West (U), both 6ml

---

HARDY'S COTTAGE 🏠 ✿   *Dorset*

Higher Bockhampton, nr Dorchester DT2 8QJ Tel: 01305 262366

The small cob and thatch cottage where novelist and poet Thomas Hardy was born in 1840 and from where he would walk to school every day in Dorchester, six miles away. It was built by his great-grandfather and is little altered since. The interior has been furnished by the Trust (see also Max Gate, p.79)

○ 5 April to 1 Nov: daily except Fri & Sat (but open Good Fri) 11–5 (or dusk if earlier). Approach only by 10min walk from car park through woods

£ £2.60. No reduction for children or parties. School parties and coaches by prior arrangement only. No WC. Hardy's works on sale

💳 Shop at 65 High West St, Dorchester (tel. 01305 267535)

♿ Access to garden only; special car-parking arrangement with Custodian

→ (1: K7) 3ml NE of Dorchester, ½ml S of A35 [194: SY728925] *Bus:* Wilts & Dorset X84, 184–6 Weymouth–Salisbury, 187/9 Poole–Dorchester (all pass ⚑ Dorchester South & close Dorchester West), alight Bockhampton Lane, ½ml (tel. 01202 673555) *Station:* Dorchester South 4ml; Dorchester West (U) 4ml

---

HEDDON VALLEY SHOP 🚶 🗺 🚶   *Devon*

Heddon Valley, Parracombe, Barnstaple EX30 4PX Tel: 01598 763402

An information centre and gift shop, set in a spectacular NT owned wooded valley in Exmoor. The area offers many beautiful coastal and woodland walks

○ 29 March to 30 Sept: daily 10–6; Oct: daily 10–5. Open BHols

£ Free, voluntary contributions welcome. Car park

🚶 See local listings for programme of guided walks on the surrounding coastal estate. Walks leaflet available from shop

💳 Gift shop

🍱 Confectionery, ice-cream and cold drinks

🏠 By arrangement with the Warden (tel. 01598 763476)

→ (1: F5) Halfway between Combe Martin and Lynton, off the A39 at Hunters Inn *Bus:* Filers 311 Barnstaple–Lynton (passing close ⚑ Barnstaple), alight just N of Parracombe, thence 2ml (tel. 01392 382800)

HORTON COURT 🏠 🔎

South Gloucestershire

Horton, nr Chipping Sodbury, Bristol BS17 6QR
Tel: (Regional Office) 01985 843600

A magnificent Norman hall and an exceptionally fine detached loggia are all that remain of what is probably the oldest rectory in England. There are interesting early Renaissance features, including stucco caricatures of classical figures

🅾 1 April to 31 October: Wed & Sat 2–6 or dusk if earlier. Other times by written appointment with tenant

💷 £1.70, children 80p. Unsuitable for coaches. No WC

♿ Ambulatory only accessible; allocated parking on application to tenant

➡ (1: K3) 3ml NE of Chipping Sodbury, ¾ml N of Horton, 1ml W of the Bath–Stroud road (A46) [172: ST766851] *Station:* Yate 5ml

KILLERTON 🏠 🔎 ✝ ❀ ✿ ♟ 🏛 🚶 🎭

Devon

Broadclyst, Exeter EX5 3LE Tel: 01392 881345

The house, home of the Aclands, was rebuilt in 1778 to the design of John Johnson. Furnished as a comfortable family home, it houses the Paulise de Bush costume collection, displayed in period rooms, and a Victorian laundry. There is an introductory exhibition in the stable courtyard and an interesting 19th-century chapel. The delightful hillside garden features rhododendrons, magnolias, herbaceous borders and rare trees, as well as an ice house and early 19th-century rustic style summer-house known as The Bear's Hut. The surrounding parkland and woods offer a number of beautiful circular walks and there is a discovery centre offering historical and environmental activities

What's new in 1998: New leaflet describing circular walks around Killerton

🅾 **House:** 14 March to 1 Nov: daily except Tues 11–5.30. Special pre-Christmas opening from 12 Dec. Last admission 5. **Park & garden:** open all year from 10.30 to dusk. **Events:** costume exhibitions: from mid June, "Glamour" (dress for special occasions) plus "Portrait of a Collector" featuring Paulise de Bush collection; 18/19 July, Exeter Festival open-air concerts. Full events programme from Property Manager, s.a.e. please. Note: on 18/19 July, only ticket holders to the Exeter Festival Concerts will be admitted to the garden after 4.30; house will close at 4.30

💷 £4.50; family ticket £12.50. Garden and park only £3.50. Garden and park reduced winter rate (Nov to Feb). Pre-booked parties £4

🚶 Introductory talks by arrangement with Property Manager

🛍 Shop and plant centre in stable courtyard. 14 March to end Sept: open daily 11–6 (closes 5 on Tues); Oct: open daily 11–5; 1 Nov to 21 Dec: Wed to Sun 11–5, plus special opening 21 to 24 Dec 11–5; Jan 1999: weekends only 11–4; Feb to mid March 1999: Wed to Sun 11–4. The shop may not open during adverse weather conditions in winter - please ring to check (tel. 01392 881912)

♿ Three steps to house (ramp available on request), wheelchairs available. Wheelchair stairclimber for access to costume displays, but please check availability in advance. Lower levels of garden accessible, but gravel paths and grass. Volunteer-driven buggies available for tour of garden on days when house open; by arrangement at other times. WCs. Designated parking for disabled drivers and transfer by buggy to house and garden. Wheelchair lift to upper level of shop

👁 Braille guides for house and costume collection; scented plants. Grand piano and organ may be played by visually impaired musicians

🍽 Licensed restaurant open same days as house 12–5 and for pre-booked Christmas lunches (tel. 01392 882081). Tea-room in stable courtyard open 14 March to end Sept: daily 10.30–5.45; Oct: 10.30–4.30; 1 Nov to 24 Dec: Wed to Sun 11–4.30, plus 21 to 24 Dec 11–4.30; Jan to 14 March 1999: Sat & Sun only 11–4. The tea-room may not open in adverse weather conditions in winter - please ring to check (tel. 01392 881345)

🚼 Table & chair in women's WCs near stable courtyard, and at house; children's guide; quiz sheet for house; children's menu and highchairs available; babies in back carriers and single pushchairs admitted to all areas. Discovery centre open most weekends when house open

📖 Discovery centre for pre-booked parties; teachers' resource guide (£2.50). Orienteering course. Play area. Victorian Days and guided walks with warden

🐕 In park only; parking in shade available in overflow car park

→ (1: G6) Off Exeter–Cullompton road (B3181, formerly A38); from M5 northbound, exit 29 and follow A30 Exeter/Honiton road for 3ml, then take left turn signed 'Broadclyst & Killerton'; from M5 southbound, exit 28 (192: SX9700) *Bus:* Stagecoach Devon 54/A, DevonBus 327, 375 from Exeter (all passing close ⚽ Exeter Central), some pass the house, but on most alight Killerton Turn ¾ml (tel. 01392 382800) *Station:* Pinhoe (U), not Sun, 4½ml; Whimple (U), not Sun, 6ml; Exeter Central & St David's, both 7ml

KING JOHN'S HUNTING LODGE 🏠 *Somerset*

The Square, Axbridge BS26 2AP Tel: 01934 732012

An early Tudor merchant's house, extensively restored in 1971

Note: The property is run as a local history museum by Sedgemoor District Council in cooperation with Somerset County Museums Service and Axbridge Archaeological and Local History Society

🅾 Easter to end Sept: daily 2–5

£ Free. School parties by arrangement. Council car park, 2min walk

♿ Access limited to ground floor

🖥 In Axbridge (not NT)

➔ (1: J4) In the Square, on corner of High Street [182: ST431545] *Bus:* Badgerline 126, Weston-super-Mare–Wells (passing close ⇄ Weston-super-Mare) (tel. 0117 955 3231) *Station:* Worle (U) 8ml

KINGSTON LACY 🏠 ❀ 🖥 🐟 🚹 🎖 *Dorset*

Wimborne Minster BH21 4EA Tel: 01202 883402

A 17th-century house, designed by Sir Roger Pratt for Sir Ralph Bankes to replace his ruined family seat at Corfe Castle (see p.57). Altered by Sir Charles Barry in the 19th century, the house contains the outstanding collection of paintings and other works of art accumulated by William Bankes. It is famous for its dramatic Spanish Room, with walls hung in magnificent gilded leather. The house and garden are set in a wooded park with attractive waymarked walks and a fine herd of Red Devon cattle. The surrounding estate is crossed by many paths (leaflet available from shop) and dominated by the Iron Age hill-fort of Badbury Rings. The botanically rich rings are managed by grazing and dogs are not permitted. Point-to-point races are held early in the year and on these days a charge is made for car-parking

What's new in 1998: Park, garden, shop and restaurant now open every day 28 March to 1 Nov (but park and garden closed on Fri 17 & 31 July and 14 Aug for events)

🅾 **House**: 28 March to 1 Nov: daily except Thur & Fri, 12–5.30; last admission 4.30. **Park and garden**: 28 March to 1 Nov: daily 11–6. 2 Nov to 21 Dec: house closed, but park, garden, shop and restaurant open Fri, Sat & Sun 11–4. Special snowdrop days and spring flower opening in early 1999; for details tel. Infoline 01202 880413. **Events**: 17 July, Bournemouth Sinfonietta; 31 July, jazz; 14 Aug, Palm Court (all with fireworks); to book tel. 01985 843601; for other events and talks, tel. 01202 883402

£ House, garden & park: £6, child £3. Park & garden only £2.50, child £1.25; family ticket (2 adults and up to 5 children to house, garden & park) £15. Pre-booked parties (15+) £5.

🎖 Parties of 15+; for details tel. 01202 883402

🖥 28 March to 1 Nov: daily 11.30–5.30. Also open Fri, Sat & Sun in Nov & Dec and on special garden open days (tel. for details): 11–4 (tel. 01202 841424)

⌖ Park (Centenary walk), garden, restaurant and shop all accessible; some thick gravel. Wheelchairs and self-drive buggy available. WC. House not suitable for wheelchairs, except for two days (May & Sept) which are reserved for special access to main state rooms only; for details tel. 01202 883402

⌖ Braille guide. Bronzes, wood carvings and some marblework may be touched

⌖ Coffee, lunches & teas in licensed stable restaurant, open as shop. Party bookings, special occasions and Christmas lunches (tel. 01202 889242). Picnics in park only

⌖ Baby-changing facilities in ladies' and disabled WCs. Highchairs in restaurant

⌖ Frizzell Study Centre & active education programme. Children's guide

⌖ In park and woods only, under strict control when near livestock and picnickers

→ (1: L6) On B3082 Blandford–Wimborne road, 1½ml W of Wimborne [19: SY980019] *Bus:* Wilts & Dorset X13, 132/3/9 from Bournemouth, Poole, Shaftesbury (passing ⬛ Bournemouth & close ⬛ Poole). On all alight Wimborne Square 2½ml. An occasional service from Bournemouth to the house operates in the summer (tel. 01202 673555) *Station:* Poole 8½ml

---

KINGSTON LACY ESTATE: LODGE FARM 🏠 *Dorset*

Kingston Lacy Estate Office Tel: 01202 882493

A stone first-floor hall house of the early 15th century, built for Henry V or VI. Documentary sources suggest that it was the residence of the head park keeper, warrener and forester of Kingston Lacy manor

🅾 By appointment only; please tel. Estate Office

£ £1.50

→ (1: L6) *Bus:* Wilts & Dorset X20 from Bournemouth & Poole, Wed only, Aug only; otherwise X13, 132/3/9 from Bournemouth, Poole, Shaftesbury (passing ⬛ Bournemouth & close ⬛ Poole), alight Wimborne Square, 3ml. (tel. 01202 673555) *Station:* Poole 9ml

---

KNIGHTSHAYES COURT 🏠 ❈ ♠ 🕇 ♥ *Devon*

Bolham, Tiverton EX16 7RQ Tel: 01884 254665 Fax: 01884 243050

Designed by William Burges and begun in 1869, Knightshayes is a rare survival of his work. The rich interiors combine medieval romanticism with lavish Victorian decoration, and the smoking and billiard rooms, elegant boudoir and drawing room all give an atmospheric insight into grand country house life. The celebrated garden features a water lily pool and topiary 'hunt' complete with fox and hounds, as well as fine specimen trees, rare shrubs and delightful seasonal colours. Attractive woodland walks lead through the grounds

What's new in 1998: Minstrels Gallery now restored and accessible; partial restoration of original bookcases in Library

⭕ 1 April to 1 Nov: **House** open daily except Fri (but open Good Fri) 11–5.30; please note that some items normally on view may not be displayed due to conservation work. **Garden** open daily 11–5.30. Last admission 5. Nov & Dec: Sun 2–4 for pre-booked parties only. **Events**: for details please tel. 01884 254665

💷 £5.10. Garden & grounds only £3.50. Pre-booked parties £4.40. Parking 400m. Visitor reception: (tel. 01884 257381)

🎟 By appointment with the Property Manager (tel. 01884 254665)

🛍 Shop and plant centre open 14/15 March, then Wed to Sun 11–4.30 until 29 Mar; 1 April to 1 Nov: open daily 10.30–5.30. 4 Nov to 20 Dec: open Wed to Sun 11–4.30; from mid March 1999: open Wed to Sun 11–4.30 (tel. 01884 259010)

♿ Ground floor of house, shop and restaurant accessible. Small lift to first floor of house unsuitable for wheelchairs, unless user can stand while chair is folded for carriage in lift. Some gravel paths in garden, but recommended signed routes. Access to picnic area in car park. Disabled drivers may park near house, or passengers may be set down by house entrance. Note: please show membership cards or purchase tickets at stables first. WC

👁 Scented plants. Audio and Braille house guides; audio guide indicates many tactile objects, including pianos and a spinet, which may be played by musicians

🍽 Licensed restaurant open for coffee, lunches and teas: 14/15 March, then Wed to Sun 11–4.30 until 29 March; 1 April to 1 Nov: daily 10.30–5.30; 4 Nov to 20 Dec: Wed to Sun 11–4.30; from mid March 1999: Wed to Sun 11–4.30. Also open for pre-booked Christmas lunches and candlelit dinners (tel. 01884 259416). Picnic area in car park. Restaurant opening hours during Oct may vary from those printed, although light refreshments will always be available during opening hours. If in doubt, please telephone when you are planning a visit

👶 Changing facilities in women's WC; children's menu; highchair available; children's guide and quizzes for house and garden; baby back carriers admitted to all areas

🐕 In park only, on leads

➡ (1: G6) 2ml N of Tiverton; turn right off Tiverton–Bampton road (A396) at Bolham [181: SS960151] *Bus:* East Devon 216/7, 717 Tiverton–Dulverton, alight Bolham, thence ¼ml; otherwise Tiverton & District 373/4 from 🚋 Tiverton Parkway; Devon General 55/A/B Exeter–Tiverton (passing close 🚋 Exeter Central), alighting Tiverton, 1¼ml (tel. 01392 382800) *Station:* Tiverton Parkway 8ml

---

LACOCK ABBEY, FOX TALBOT MUSEUM & VILLAGE
🏰 ✝ 🏵 🛡   *Wiltshire*

Lacock, nr Chippenham SN15 2LG
Tel: Abbey 01249 730227 Museum 01249 730459 Fax: 01249 730501

Founded in 1232 and converted into a country house c.1540, the fine medieval cloisters, sacristy, chapter house and monastic rooms of the abbey have survived largely intact. The handsome 16th-century stable courtyard has half-timbered gables, a clockhouse brewery and bakehouse. The wooded garden boasts a fine display of spring flowers, magnificent trees, an

18th-century summer-house, Victorian rose garden and ha-ha. The Museum of Photography commemorates the achievements of a former resident of the abbey, William Fox Talbot (1800–77), inventor of the modern photographic negative and whose descendants gave the abbey and village to the Trust in 1944. The village, which dates from the 13th century and has many limewashed half-timbered and stone houses, featured in the recent TV and film productions of Pride and Prejudice, Moll Flanders *and* Emma

What's new in 1998: Exhibition of historic and contemporary photographs in the museum gallery

◐ **Museum, cloisters & grounds**: 1 March to 1 Nov: daily (closed Good Fri) 11–5.30. **Abbey**: 1 April to 1 Nov: daily, except Tues, 1–5.30; last admission 5. Museum open some winter weekends; tel. for details. **Events**: leaflet available on request

£ Abbey, grounds, cloisters and museum £5.50, children £3; family ticket (2 adults + 2 children) £15; parties £5, children £2.50. Grounds, cloisters and museum only £3.50, children £2; family ticket (2 adults + 2 children) £10

𝍫 Guided tours by arrangement

▣ Shop in village: 1 April to 1 Nov: daily 10–5.30; 2 Nov to 22 Dec: daily 11–4; 4 Jan to end March 1999: daily 11–4 (tel. 01249 730302). Museum shop selling photographic books, films, postcards; open as museum

♿ All areas of grounds, cloisters and museum are accessible (stairlift in museum). Abbey is difficult with 4 sets of steps; limited parking at abbey by arrangement; wheelchairs and Batricar available at museum; WC at abbey and at Red Lion car park (RADAR lock). Sympathetic Hearing Scheme

☜ Braille and taped guides; pre-booked guided tours

▣ In village (not NT)

𝍖 Children's guide to abbey

▤ Pre-booked school parties welcome

🐕 No dogs in abbey or grounds

➔ (1: L4) 3ml S of Chippenham, just E of A350 [173: ST919684]; signposted to car park *Bus:* Badgerline 234/7 Chippenham–Trowbridge (passing close **▣** Chippenham & Trowbridge) (tel. 01225 464446) *Station:* Chippenham 3½ml

---

LANHYDROCK 🏰 ❀ ♠ ⚓ 𝍖 🛡 *Cornwall*

Bodmin PL30 5AD Tel: 01208 73320 Fax: 01208 74084

One of the most fascinating late 19th-century houses in England, full of period atmosphere and the trappings of a high Victorian country house. Although the gatehouse and north wing (with magnificent 32m-long gallery with plaster ceiling) survive from the 17th century, the rest of the house was rebuilt following a disastrous fire in 1881 and featured the latest in contemporary living, including central heating. The garden features a stunning collection of magnolias, rhododendrons and camellias, and offers fine colours right through into autumn

Note: A total of 49 rooms are open to visitors, who should allow at least 1½ hours to tour the house. The car park is 600m from the house

What's new in 1998: An adventure play area for children near the car park

🅾 **House:** 1 April to 1 Nov: daily except Mon, but open BH Mon, 11–5.30 (closes 5 in Oct). Last admission to house 30min before closing. **Garden:** 1 March to 1 Nov: daily 11–5.30 (closes 5 in March & Oct); Nov to end Feb: daily during daylight hours. **Events:** 11 July, open-air jazz concert; programme details available from the Property Manager

£ House, garden & grounds £6.20; family ticket £15.50. Garden & grounds only £3.10. Pre-arranged parties £5.50

🛍 Shop open: March, weekends only 11–4; 1 April to 1 Nov, daily 11-5.30 (5 in Oct); Nov & Dec, daily 11–4. Plant sales (in the car park), open March: daily 11–4; 1 April to 1 Nov: daily 11–5.30 (5 in Oct) (tel. 01208 74099)

♿ Disabled visitors may be driven to house; close parking, for assistance please ask at Reception Building. Information leaflet available. Access for manual wheelchair users to house via ramp to restaurant; most ground-floor rooms easily accessible; small lift to first floor; WC. No powered wheelchairs allowed in house. Shop has some steps. Garden has a few steps and sloping gravel paths, steep in places – access via steps; ramp available. Powered self-drive buggy available if booked. Indoor and outdoor wheelchairs available

👁 Aromatic plants; water sounds. Braille guides for house & garden; large print guide for house. Tactile route guide sheet (with handcloth) for house. Piano may be played by musicians, but access is via a few steps

☕ Refreshments available daily 1 March to 1 Nov. Licensed restaurant open daily except Mon (but open BH Mon) 1 April to 1 Nov. Limited opening in Nov & Dec (tel. 01208 74331)

🚼 Parent and baby room; baby slings and harnesses available; pushchair storage area in house

🎒 Schools' resource book. Schools' base; children's guide; handling collection; education stewards

🐕 In park and woods only, on leads

➔ (1: D8) 2½ml SE of Bodmin, overlooking valley of River Fowey; follow signposts from either A30, A38 Bodmin–Liskeard or B3268 Bodmin–Lostwithiel roads [200: SX085636] *Bus:* Western National 55, from ➤ Bodmin Parkway (tel. 01209 719988) *Station:* Bodmin Parkway 1¼ml by original carriage-drive to house, signposted in station car park; 3ml by road

---

LAWRENCE HOUSE 🏠 *Cornwall*

9 Castle Street, Launceston PL15 8BA Tel: 01566 773277/774518

A Georgian house given to the Trust to help preserve the character of the street, and now leased to Launceston Town Council as a museum and civic centre

What's new in 1998: Victorian-style garden

🅾 April to early Oct: Mon to Fri 10.30–4.30. Open BH Mon. Other times by appointment

£ Free, but visitors are invited to contribute towards museum expenses

🛍 Small shop, open as museum

♠ Braille guide

➜ (1: E7) [201: SX330848] *Bus:* Western National 76 from Plymouth (passing
🚆 Plymouth); Tilleys from Exeter (tel. 01392 382800)

THE LEVANT STEAM ENGINE 🔧 🎨   *Cornwall*

Trewellard, Pendeen, nr St Just
Tel: 01736 786156 (opening hours only) or 01736 788662 (Geevor)

*In its tiny engine house perched on the cliff edge, the famous Levant beam engine is steaming
again after sixty idle years. The sight, sounds and smells of this 155-year-old engine conjure
up the feel of Cornwall's industrial past. ½ml along the cliff is Geevor mine (not NT) and a
mining museum*

Note: This property is managed by the Trevithick Trust

O Open Easter, May & Spring BH Sun & Mon; June: Wed, Thur, Fri & Sun; July to
5 Oct: daily except Sat 11–5

£ £3. Family ticket £7.50, concessions £2.50, students £1.50. Stewarded by
volunteer members of the Trevithick Society. Members are invited to contribute
to the cost of the project

🎨 Available

♿ Limited access – assistance if required

♠ Recommended to accompanied visually impaired visitors; machinery sounds,
smells, and atmosphere; old boiler and controls may be touched

☕ At Geevor mine or Pendeen village

🔊 Suitable for small groups only (max. 40) by prior arrangement

➜ (1: A9) 1ml W of Pendeen, on B3306 St Just–Zennor road [203: SW368346]
Bus: Western National 10A from 🚆 Penzance (tel. 01209 719988)
Station: Penzance 7ml

LITTLE CLARENDON 🏠   *Wiltshire*

Dinton, Salisbury SP3 5OZ Tel: (Regional Office) 01985 843600

*A Tudor house, greatly altered in the 17th century. The three principal rooms on the ground
floor are open to visitors*

O 4 April to 31 Oct: Mon 1–5 & Sat 9–1

£ £1.50. No reduction for children or parties. House not suitable for pushchairs or
prams. No coaches

➜ (1: L5) ¼ml E of Dinton church [184: SU015316] *Bus:* As for Philipps House, p.82

LOUGHWOOD MEETING HOUSE ✠ — *Devon*

Dalwood, Axminster EX13 7DU Tel: 01392 881691

Built c.1653 by the Baptist congregation of Kilmington, who attended services here at the risk of imprisonment or transportation. A simple but interesting building, with an interior fitted in the early 18th century

◙ All year

£ Free (donation box provided)

➜ (1: H6) 4ml W of Axminster; turn right on Axminster–Honiton road (A35), 1ml S of Dalwood, 1ml NW of Kilmington [192/193: SY253993] *Bus:* Red Bus 380 Axminster–Ottery St Mary (passing close ⊠ Axminster) (tel. 01392 382800) *Station:* Axminster 2½ml

LUNDY 🏰 🏠 ✠ ♨ 🏞 ⓣ 📷 🐦 🚶 — *Devon*

Bristol Channel EX39 2LY Tel: 01237 431831 Fax: 01237 431832

A unique and unspoilt island, undisturbed by cars and home to a fascinating array of wildlife amidst dramatic scenery. There is a small village with an inn and Victorian church, and nearby the 13th-century Marisco Castle keeps guard

Note: The island is financed, administered and maintained by the Landmark Trust

◙ Always. Sea passages from Bideford all year round, also from Ilfracombe in summer season, by the island vessel MS *Oldenburg* (300 tons, 267 passengers, refreshments on board). For sailing details tel. 01237 470422. Groups and passenger ships by prior arrangement

£ Entrance fee included in fare price for passengers on MS *Oldenburg*, but £3.50 per person for those arriving by other means. Discount for NT members who book in advance and arrive on *Oldenburg*

⌂ Shop selling the famous Lundy stamps, souvenirs and postcards, along with general supplies and groceries

♿ Disabled visitors are very welcome but should telephone in advance so that disembarking arrangements may be made

◗ Food and drink at the Marisco Tavern. Accommodation: 23 holiday cottages; camping site for up to 40 people. For bookings, apply to: The Landmark Trust, Shottesbrooke, Maidenhead, Berkshire SL6 3SW (tel. 01628 825925)

⚹ Baby-changing facilities in women's WC. Children in particular find Lundy a fascinating place

→ (1: D5) 11ml N of Hartland Point, 25ml from Ilfracombe, 30ml S of Tenby [180: SS1345] *Bus:* Bus services available from ⊞ Barnstaple to Bideford or Ilfracombe (tel. 01392 382800) *Station:* Barnstaple: 8½ml to Bideford, 12ml to Ilfracombe

---

LYDFORD GORGE ⛴ ⚹   *Devon*

The Stables, Lydford Gorge, Lydford, nr Okehampton EX20 4BH
Tel: 01822 820441/820320

This famous gorge is 1½ml long and can be viewed from a circular walk, which starts high above the river and passes through attractive oakwoods before dropping down to the spectacular 30m-high White Lady waterfall. The path then proceeds along an enchanting riverside walk through the steeply sided ravine, scooped out by the River Lyd as it plunges into a series of whirlpools, including the thrilling Devil's Cauldron

◯ 1 April to 1 Nov: daily 10–5.30, last admission 5; also 2 Nov to end March 1999: daily 10.30–3, but from waterfall entrance as far as waterfall only; also top path open from main entrance shop 7 Nov to 20 Dec: Sat & Sun only 11–4. There are delays at the Devil's Cauldron during busy periods. The walk is arduous in places; visitors should wear stout footwear. *Note:* Not suitable for visitors with heart complaints or walking disabilities. Free car parks at both entrances

£ £3.20. Pre-arranged parties £2.60

⌂ Shop and information at main entrance open as gorge, but 7 Nov to 20 Dec: Sat & Sun 11–4. Small shop at end of gorge (waterfall entrance) 1 April to 1 Nov, open same times as gorge

♿ Gorge unsuitable for disabled visitors. Accessible picnic area; WC

◗ Main entrance; tea-room serving morning coffee, hot meals, home-made cakes and ice-cream, open 1 April to 1 Nov: daily 10.30–5.30; 3 Nov to 21 Dec: Sat & Sun 11–4

⚹ Children's guide; baby-changing facilities; babies in back carriers welcome; difficult for pushchairs in places due to terrain and width of some paths

▥ Teachers' geology pack and guide

⚐ Must be kept on leads at all times

→ **(1: F7)** At W end of Lydford village; halfway between Okehampton and Tavistock, 1ml W off A386 opposite Dartmoor Inn; main entrance at W end of Lydford; second entrance near Mucky Duck Inn [191 & 201: SX509846] *Bus:* Western National 86, Plymouth–Barnstaple (most passing ▆ Plymouth); 187 ▆ Gunnislake–▆ Okehampton, Sun, June to Sept only (tel. 01392 382800); bus stop at main entrance and waterfall entrance to gorge. Reduction on entry charge on production of valid bus ticket and for those arriving by cycle

LYTES CARY MANOR 🏠 ✝ ❀ *Somerset*

near Charlton Mackrell, Somerton TA11 7HU Tel: Regional Office 01985 843600

A charming manor house with a 14th-century chapel and Tudor Great Hall, much added to in the 18th-century and rescued from dereliction this century by Sir Walter Jenner. The interiors were refurnished in period style and are complemented by the attractive hedged garden, full of typical 16th-century plants and trees

🅾 1 April to 31 Oct: Mon, Wed & Sat 2–6 or dusk if earlier; last admission 5.30

£ £4, children £2. No reduction for parties. Large coaches cannot pass the gate piers so must stop in narrow road, ¼ml walk. Coaches strictly by appointment only

♿ Access to garden only. Scented plants in herbaceous borders. WC

📖 Braille guide

🚻 Children's trail

🐕 In car park only

→ **(1: J5)** Signposted from Podimore roundabout at junction of A303, A37 take A372 [183: ST529269] *Bus:* Badgerline 376 Bristol–Yeovil (passing ▆ Bristol Temple Meads) (tel. 0117 9553231); Southern National 54 Yeovil–Taunton (passing close ▆ Taunton) (tel. 01823 272033). Both pass within ¼ml ▆ Yeovil Pen Mill. On both, alight Kingsdon, 1ml *Station:* Yeovil Pen Mill 8½ml; Castle Cary 9ml; Yeovil Junction 10ml

MARKER'S COTTAGE 🏠 *Devon*

Broadclyst, Exeter EX5 3HR Tel: 01392 461546

A fascinating medieval cob house, containing a cross-passage screen decorated with a painting of St Andrew and his attributes

🅾 29 March to 1 Nov: Sun, Mon, Tues 2–5

£ £1. House unsuitable for coach parties. WC. Please park in village car park

♿ Access difficult; four steps into house

→ **(1: G6)** Off Exeter–Cullompton road (B3181) in village of Broadclyst. Turn right opposite church (coming from Exeter direction) and then second right [192:SX985973] *Bus:* Stagecoach Devon 54 Exeter–Cullompton (passes close ▆ Exeter Central) (tel. 01392 427711) *Station:* Pinhoe (U), not Sun, 2½ml; Polsloe Bridge (U) 4ml; Whimple (U) 4½ml; Exeter Central 5½ml; Exeter St David's 6ml

MAX GATE 🏠 ✿ *Dorset*

Alington Avenue, Dorchester DT1 2AA Tel: 01305 262538 Fax: 01305 250978

Novelist and poet Thomas Hardy designed and lived in this house from 1885 till his death in 1928. Here he wrote Tess of the d'Urbervilles, Jude the Obscure *and* The Mayor of Casterbridge, *as well as much of his poetry. The house contains several pieces of his furniture*

🅾 **Dining & drawing rooms:** 5 April to 30 Sept: Mon, Wed & Sun 2–5. Open at other times for private visits, tours and seminars by schools, colleges and literary societies, by appointment with the tenants, Mr & Mrs Andrew Leah

£ Dining & drawing rooms and garden £2.10, children £1.10. No WC

🛍 Shop at 65 High West St, Dorchester (tel. 01305 267535)

♿ Some level access to ground floor

◐ Braille guide

➡ (1: K7) 1ml E of Dorchester on the A352 Wareham road. From Dorchester follow A352 until you reach the roundabout named Max Gate (at the junction of the A35 Dorchester bypass). Turn left and left again into the cul-de-sac outside the house *Bus:* Southern National D from town centre (tel. 01305 783645) *Station:* Dorchester South 1ml; Dorchester West (U) 1ml

MOMPESSON HOUSE 🏠 ✿ *Wiltshire*

The Close, Salisbury SP1 2EL Tel: 01722 335659

An elegant and spacious 18th-century house in the Cathedral Close, featured in the award-winning film Sense and Sensibility, *and with magnificent plasterwork and a fine oak staircase. As well as pieces of good quality period furniture, the house also contains the Turnbull collection of 18th-century drinking glasses. Outside, the delightful walled garden has a pergola and a notable specimen magnolia*

🅾 1 April to 1 Nov: daily except Thur & Fri 12–5.30. Last admission 5

£ £3.40, children £1.70. Parties £2.90. Garden only 80p. Visitor sitting room. Parking in Cathedral Close (a charge is made by the Dean & Chapter). Coach-parking in Central Car Park

🎭 Out of hours tours of house and/or garden, by prior arrangement

🛍 Shop at 41 High Street, Salisbury (tel. 01722 331884)

♿ Access to ground floor, garden and tea-room. WC

◐ Braille guide; scented plants

☕ Teas in Garden Room 12–5

🐕 No dogs permitted

➡ (1: L5) On N side of Choristers' Green in the Cathedral Close, near High Street Gate [184: SU142295] *Bus:* From surrounding areas (tel. 01722 336855) *Station:* Salisbury ½ml

MONTACUTE HOUSE 🏠 ♣ ♠ 🎭

Somerset

Montacute TA15 6XP Tel: 01935 823289

A glittering Elizabethan house, adorned with elegant chimneys, carved parapets and other Renaissance features, including contemporary plasterwork, chimney-pieces and heraldic glass. The magnificent state rooms, including a long gallery which is the largest of its type in England, are full of fine 17th- and 18th-century furniture and Elizabethan and Jacobean portraits from the National Portrait Gallery. There are also good quality textiles, including an exhibition of 17th-century samplers. The formal garden includes mixed borders and old roses and is surrounded by a landscaped park. Montacute featured in the award-winning film Sense and Sensibility

Note: For conservation reasons some rooms in the house do not have electric light. Visitors wishing to make close study of tapestries, textiles or paintings should avoid visiting on dull days

House: 1 April to 1 Nov: daily except Tues 12–5.30. Last admission 5. **Garden & park:** 1 April to 1 Nov: daily except Tues 11–5.30 (dusk if earlier); also open 4 Nov to March 1999: Wed to Sun 11.30–4. **Events:** 19 June, open-air theatre; 11/12 July, horse trials; for further details of all events tel. 01985 843601

House, garden & park: £5.20, children £2.60; family ticket (2 adults & 2 children) £13. Pre-booked parties (15+) £4.80, children £2.30. Limited parking for coaches which must be booked in advance. Garden and park only, 1 April to 1 Nov: £2.90, children £1.30; from 4 Nov to March 1999: £1.50. No reduction for parties; party organisers please book in writing with s.a.e. to the Property Manager

Open same days as house 11–5.30; also for Christmas shopping, 4 Nov to 20 Dec: Wed to Sun 11–4; March 1999: Wed to Sun 11–4 (tel. 01935 824575)

Designated parking for disabled drivers. Disabled visitors are very welcome, but access to garden, restaurant & shop only; we regret there is no access to house for wheelchair users (many steps and stairs). WC. 2 wheelchairs available

Braille guides for house, garden and park; Braille restaurant menu. Fragrant plants & shrubs

■ Licensed restaurant open as shop; light refreshments only 11–12, lunches 12–2 & teas 2–5.30 (tel. 01935 826294). Christmas menu and pre-booked parties catered for: 4 Nov to 20 Dec: Wed to Sun 11–4; March 1999: Wed to Sun 11–4 (light refreshments only). Limited seating available so party organisers please book lunches & teas in writing to the Property Manager. Picnic area adjacent to car park

■ Children's guidebook and quiz sheets. Parent & baby room. Children's portions and highchairs available

■ Teachers' resource book

■ In park only, on leads. not allowed in garden. Shaded parking limited

→ (1: J6) In Montacute village, 4ml W of Yeovil, on S side of A3088, 3ml E of A303; signposted [183 & 193: ST499172] *Bus:* Safeway 681 Yeovil–South Petherton/Crewkerne (passing within ¾ml ₪ Yeovil Pen Mill) (tel. 01460 240309) *Station:* Yeovil Pen Mill 5½ml; Yeovil Junction 7ml; Crewkerne 7ml

---

THE OLD MILL 🏠 🖼 🚹 *Devon*

Wembury Beach, Wembury PL9 0HP Tel: 01752 862314

A cafe housed in a former mill house, standing on a small beach near the Yealm estuary

£ Free, but parking charge for non-members

🚹 Regular guided rock pool rambles and other marine-related events are led by the Devon Wildlife Trust wardens from Wembury Marine Centre (open Easter to end Sept), tel. 01752 862538 for details

🛍 1 April to end Oct: Beach goods and souvenirs (not NT), peak periods only. Car park beside beach, parking charge to non-members

♿ Access difficult, several stone steps

■ 1 April to 31 Oct: daily (but closed in bad weather). Limited opening Mar, Nov & Dec. Drinks, refreshments, ice-cream (not NT)

■ Not admitted to café at any time or on beach from 1 April to 30 Sept

→ (1: F8) At Wembury, nr Plymouth [201: SX517484] *Bus:* Western National 48 from ₪ Plymouth, thence ½ml (tel. 01752 222666) *Station:* Plymouth 10ml

---

OVERBECKS MUSEUM AND GARDEN 🏠 ❀ 🖼 🚹 🚹 🎭 *Devon*

Sharpitor, Salcombe TQ8 8LW Tel: 01548 842893

This elegant Edwardian house contains the eclectic collections of the scientist who lived here from 1928–37, Otto Overbeck. Among the items on show are late 19th-century photographs of the area, local shipbuilding tools, model boats, toys, shells, animals, a nautical collection and some of Mr Overbeck's drawings. The beautiful and luxuriant garden, with spectacular views over the Salcombe estuary, enjoys a micro-climate and so is home to many rare plants, trees and shrubs

🅾 **Museum:** 1 April to end July: Sun to Fri 11–5.30; Aug: daily 11–5.30; Sept: Sun to Fri 11–5.30; Oct: Sun to Thur 11–5. Last admission 30min before closing. **Garden:** daily throughout year 10–8 or sunset if earlier. WC open same days as museum. **Events:** please tel. for details

£ Museum & garden £3.80; garden only £2.60. No party reduction. Small car park near house; charge refundable on admission. Roads leading to Overbecks are steep single track and therefore unsuitable for coaches or large vehicles

👤 By arrangement, outside normal opening hours

🛍 Shop open as museum

♿ Garden is steep with some gravel paths, but largely accessible with a strong companion; details of parking and other facilities available from Property Manager. Ground floor, shop and tea-room accessible via ramp into museum. Wheelchair available

👁 Braille guides to museum for adults and children; also Braille ghost hunt certificate!

🍴 Tea-room for snacks and light refreshments same days as museum 12–4.15. Picnics allowed in parts of garden

👶 Secret room with dolls, toys and other collections; quiz guide; ghost hunt for children; baby-changing facilities, single pushcairs admitted to house and garden

📕 Teachers' pack

🐕 No dogs in garden. Estate walks from car park

➔ **(1: F9)** 1½ml SW of Salcombe, signposted from Malborough and Salcombe [202: SX728374] *Bus:* Tally Ho! 606 from Kingsbridge (with connections from Plymouth, Dartmouth & ⊠ Totnes), Western National 164 from Totnes (Sun only); on both alight Salcombe, 1½ml (tel. 01392 382800)

PHILIPPS HOUSE AND DINTON PARK 🏠 ♠ 👤   *Wiltshire*

Dinton, Salisbury SP3 5HJ Tel: 01985 843600

A restrained neo-Grecian house by Jeffry Wyatville, completed in 1816. The principal rooms on the ground floor are open to visitors. The surrounding landscape park has recently been restored and offers many attractive walks

What's new in 1998: A new walks leaflet 'Welcome to Dinton Park' guides the visitor on a choice of lakeland or park and woodland walks. It costs 50p and is available from Dinton Post Office or the NT Wessex Regional Office (please add 50p for p&p)

🅾 **Park:** open all year; **House:** 4 April to 31 Oct: Mon 1–5 & Sat 9–1. Visitors should park at the house when open, otherwise use car park off St Mary's Road, next to church

£ Access to the park is free; house £2

👤 A series of recommended walks around the park starts from the car park; leaflets are available from the village shop/post office and the NT shop in Salisbury

♿ Access to the park is limited, but good views of the lake can be obtained from the main access point from the car park. Access to principal ground floor rooms in house

◉ Braille guide available

◐ Penruddocke Arms and Swordsman Inn, Dinton (not NT)

➔ (1: L5) 9ml W of Salisbury, on N side of B3089 [184: SU004319]
Bus: Wilts & Dorset 25, 26, 27 from Salisbury (passing ⊠ Salisbury & Tisbury) (tel. 01722 336855) *Station:* Tisbury 5ml

PRIEST'S HOUSE 🏠   *Somerset*

Muchelney, Langport TA10 0DQ Tel: 01458 252621

A late medieval hall house, much altered but retaining some interesting original features, such as the Gothic doorway, mullioned windows and magnificent two-tiered window. It was originally the residence of priests serving the church across the road. The house is occupied by tenants and has recently been extensively repaired

🅾 5 April to 28 Sept: Sun & Mon 2.30–5.30; last admission 5.15

💷 £1.60. No reductions for parties or children. No WC. Unsuitable for coaches and trailer caravans

➔ (1: J5) 1ml S of Langport [193: ST429250] *Bus:* Southern National 54 Yeovil–Taunton (passing close ⊠ Taunton & within ¼ml Yeovil Pen Mill), alight Huish Episcopi, ½ml (tel. 01823 272033)

PRIOR PARK LANDSCAPE GARDEN �   *Bath & NE Somerset*

Ralph Allen Drive, Bath BA2 5AH
Tel: 01225 833422; Recorded information (24hrs): 0891 335242

A beautiful and intimate 18th-century landscape garden, created by local entrepreneur Ralph Allen with advice from the poet Alexander Pope and 'Capability' Brown, and set in a sweeping valley with magnificent views of the City of Bath. The many interesting features include a Palladian Bridge and three lakes. The restoration of the garden is continuing. Prior Park College, a co-educational school, operates from the mansion (not NT)

Note: Planning permission to open the property was granted until Sept 1998 only; renewal is likely to be conditional on the success of the 'green transport' scheme, as no car park can be provided. See details below

🅾 Daily, except Tues 12–5.30 (or dusk if earlier). Closed 25/26 Dec & 1 Jan 1999

💷 £3.80, children £1.90. To thank visitors for using public transport, all those who produce a valid bus or train ticket will receive £1 off admission; NT members will receive a £1 voucher (to be used towards the cost of a guidebook, cream tea or a purchase of £1 or more at the NT shops in either Bath centre or Dyrham Park). There is a bus and coach drop-off point outside the gates to the garden. Coach parties should book in advance on tel. 01225 833422; every passenger qualifies for a discount

⬜ In Abbey Churchyard, Bath (tel. 01225 460249)

♿ There are three parking bays for disabled drivers. It is essential to reserve these in advance on tel. 01225 833422. The garden is extremely steep in places, but offers good views from the top, which is easily accessible

👁 Braille guide

🐕 No dogs allowed due to grazing cattle

➔ (1: K4) All visitors must use public transport as there is no parking at Prior Park or nearby. To obtain a leaflet explaining how to reach the garden, tel. 01225 833422 *Bus:* Badgerline 2, 4, 733 ▣ Bath–Combe Down (tel. 01225 464446). As Bath is very congested, use park-and-ride to centre *Station:* Bath Spa 1ml

---

ST MICHAEL'S MOUNT 🏰 🏠 ✝ 🏛 🔏 *Cornwall*

Marazion, nr Penzance TR17 0EF Tel: 01736 710507 Fax: 01736 711544

Originally the site of a Benedictine priory and approached by a causeway at low tide, the dramatic castle on top of this famous rocky island dates from the 12th century. It was converted into a private house in the 17th century and contains fascinating early rooms, an armoury, a rococo Gothic drawing room and, at the highest point, a 14th-century church. There are magnificent views towards Land's End and The Lizard

Note: Sensible shoes are advised, as many walking surfaces are uneven. Owing to narrow passages within the castle, visitors are warned that some delays may occur at the height of the season. On Sun from June to Sept a short non-denominational service is held in the church at 11; seating is limited

🕐 1 April to 30 Oct: Mon to Fri 10.30–5.30. Last admission 4.45. Nov to end March: It is essential to telephone the property before setting out, in order to ascertain the opening arrangements for that day. The times stated above apply from the visitors' entrance on the island and ample time should be allowed for travel from the mainland. *Note:* The Mount is also open most weekends during the season; these are special charity open days, when NT members are asked to pay for admission

💷 £3.90; family ticket £10. Pre-arranged parties £3.50 per person. No NT car park; public car park in Marazion

🔏 Audio tour available. Introductory video in cinema

⬜ Shop open 1 April to 30 Oct daily (tel. 01736 711067)

♿ The causeway and paths are cobbled, and therefore unsuitable for wheelchairs, prams and pushchairs

👁 Braille and taped guides

☕ Island café (not NT), open daily 1 April to end Oct. Coffee, lunches and teas in The Sail Loft restaurant, 1 April to 30 Oct: daily; limited out of season service (tel. 01736 710748)

🏛 Special educational visits for schools and organisations on Tues from March to end May, weather permitting, by prior arrangement with The Manor Office, Marazion (tel. 01736 710507). Schools' resource pack available

🐕 No dogs allowed

➤ (1: B9) ½ml S of A394 at Marazion, whence there is access on foot over the causeway at low tide or, during summer months only, by ferry at high tide [203: SW515298]. Tide and ferry information only: tel. 01736 710265/710507 *Bus:* Western National 2, 2X Penzance–Falmouth; 17/A Penzance–St Ives. All pass ⊟ Penzance. (tel. 01209 719988) *Station:* Penzance 3ml

---

SALTRAM 🏠 🏡 ✝ ✿ 🌳 👤 🎭   *Devon*

Plympton, Plymouth PL7 3UH Tel: 01752 336546

A remarkable survival of a George II mansion, complete with its original contents and set in an attractive landscape park. Robert Adam worked here on two occasions to create the magnificent state rooms. There is exquisite plasterwork throughout and several rooms are decorated with original Chinese wallpaper. The house contains fine period furniture, china and pictures, including many portraits by Reynolds and Angelica Kauffmann. The superb 18th-century gardens contain an orangery, chapel and several follies, as well as beautiful shrubberies and imposing specimen trees

What's new in 1998: Early opening of house on Sun and BHols at 11.30

⭘ **House:** 1 April to 30 Sept: daily except Fri & Sat (but open Good Fri) 12.30–5.30 (open 11.30 on Sun & BHols); 1 Oct to 1 Nov: daily except Fri & Sat 12.30–4.30. **Garden:** 2–23 March: Sat & Sun only 11–4; from 28 March as house but from 10.30. **Art gallery & Great Kitchen:** open as house but from 10.30. Last admission 30min before closing. Timed tickets may be issued at busy times. **Events:** full programme, including open-air concerts and theatre during summer, and traditional candlelight concerts in Adam Saloon in Nov & Dec (tel. 01752 336546 to join mailing list)

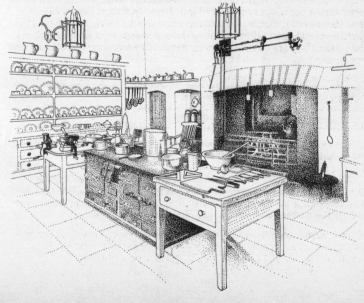

£ £5.60; garden only £2.60. Parking 500m, £1.50. Discount for pre-booked parties, rates on application

🚶 Walks with the Warden throughout the year. Tel. 01752 336546 for programme

🛍 Shop in stable block. Open same days as house 10.30–5.30 (closes 5 in Oct); 2 Nov to 21 Dec: daily except Fri 11–5; Jan 1999: daily except Fri 11–4; Feb & March 1999: Sat & Sun 11–4 (tel. 01752 330034). Work by West Country artists on sale in art gallery; open same days as house

♿ House, ground floor of art gallery, and garden accessible; disabled visitors may be set down at front door by prior arrangement; lift (66cm wide by 86.5cm deep) to first floor. Information from ticket office in stable block. Wheelchairs at house and also at ticket office for use in garden. WC on ground floor

👁 Scented plants; Braille and audio guides

🍽 Licensed restaurant open same days as house 12.30–5.30 (closes 4.30 in Oct), last admission 5 (4 in Oct) (entrance from garden at garden admission price); also for pre-booked Christmas lunches (tel. 01752 340635). Coach house tea-room in stable block near car park, open same days as house 10.30–5. Nov to end March 1999: open as shop

👶 Pushchairs, children's guide, baby-changing facilities available on request from entrance hall. Highchairs, children's menu and baby foods available in restaurant

🏫 Education room available; advance bookings essential. For details contact Property Manager (tel. 01752 336546)

🐕 In park only. Dogs must be on leads in areas being grazed by cattle. Shaded 'dog park' near stable block entrance

➡ (1: F8) 3½ml E of Plymouth city centre, between Plymouth–Exeter road (A38) and Plymouth–Kingsbridge road (A379); take Plympton turn at Marsh Mills roundabout [201: SX520557] *Bus:* Plymouth Citybus 19/A, 20/A, 21, 22, 51 from Plymouth, alight Plymouth Road–Plympton Bypass Jn, ¾ml footpath (tel. 01752 222221). Visitors arriving by public transport receive reduced price entry on production of valid ticket *Station:* Plymouth 3½ml

---

SELWORTHY VILLAGE 🏠 ✚ 🚹 *Somerset*

Tel: (Holnicote Estate Office) 01643 862452

Situated below Selworthy Woods, seven thatched cottages with cream cob walls are grouped around a traditional village green and overlooked by its white-painted church. The surrounding Holnicote Estate includes the high tors of Dunkery and Selworthy Beacons, with breathtaking views in all directions, as well as fifteen farms and many small hamlets and villages. The estate also covers 4½ml of coastline between Porlock Bay and Minehead, where the South West Peninsula Coastal Path begins. There are over 100ml of footpaths to enjoy through the fields, woods, moors and villages of this most attractive part of the country

Note: The church is not NT

What's new in 1998: Two new walks leaflets guide the visitor around Horner Wood, part of the Dunkery and Horner Wood National Nature Reserve. Priced at 50p each, they are available from local NT shops and the NT Wessex Regional Office (please add 50p for p&p)

O At any reasonable time throughout the year. Parking available 100m past the village

⌂ Shop & information centre located on the green, open 1 to 31 March daily 10–4; 1 April to 1 Nov: daily 10–5; Nov: weekends only 10–4. Closed for lunch 1–1.30. Spring and autumn opening reduced in bad weather

⛶ Tea-room (not NT) on the green; closed Mon. Refreshments also at Bossington & Horner on Holnicote Estate

→ (1: G5) Off A39 Minehead–Porlock, 3ml W of Minehead *Bus:* Southern National 38, 300, Exmoor Bus 285 Minehead–Porlock, alight Holnicote, thence ½ml (tel. 01823 358299) *Station:* Minehead (West Somerset Rly) 5ml

---

SHUTE BARTON 🏠 🏠 ⓘ   *Devon*

Shute, nr Axminster EX13 7PT Tel: 01297 34692

One of the most important surviving non-fortified manor houses of the Middle Ages. Commenced in 1380 and completed in the late 16th century, then partly demolished in the late 18th century, the house has battlemented turrets, late Gothic windows and a Tudor gatehouse

O The house is tenanted; there is access to most parts of the interior for conducted tours only: 1 April to 31 Oct: Wed & Sat 2–5.30. Last admission 5

£ £1.60. No party reduction; unsuitable for coaches or large groups. No WC

→ (1: H7) 3ml SW of Axminster, 2ml N of Colyton on Honiton–Colyton road (B3161) [177/193: SY253974] *Bus:* Red Bus 380 Axminster–Honiton (passes close ⊠ Axminster and Honiton), alight Shute Cross, ¾ml; Axe Valley 885/Red Bus 378 ⊠ Axminster–Seaton, alight Whitford, thence 1½ml (tel. 01392 382800) *Station:* Axminster 3ml

---

STEMBRIDGE TOWER MILL 🏠   *Somerset*

High Ham TA10 9DJ Tel: (Regional Office) 01985 843600

The last thatched windmill in England, dating from 1822 and in use until 1910

O 1 April to 30 Sept: Sun, Mon & Wed 2–5; special arrangements may be made for coach and school parties

£ £1.70, children 80p. Parties by prior arrangement with the tenant; no reduction. Parking for coaches ¼ml. No WC

🐕 No dogs allowed

➔ (1: J5) 2ml N of Langport, ½ml E of High Ham [182: ST432305]; take the Somerton road from Langport and follow High Ham signs. Take road opposite cemetery in High Ham. Mill is ¼ml along on right *Bus*: Southern National 54 Yeovil–Taunton (passing close ⊠ Taunton & within ¼ml Yeovil Pen Mill), alight Langport, 2½ml (tel. 01823 272033) *Station*: Bridgwater 10ml

STOKE-SUB-HAMDON PRIORY 🏠 *Somerset*

North Street, Stoke-sub-Hamdon TA4 6QP Tel: (Regional Office) 01985 843600

A complex of buildings begun in the 14th century for the priests of the chantry chapel of St Nicholas (now destroyed)

🅾 1 April to 31 Oct: daily 10–6 or dusk if earlier. Great Hall only open

£ Free

🐕 No dogs allowed

➔ (1: J6) Between A303 and A3088. 2ml W of Montacute between Yeovil and Ilminster *Bus*: Safeway 681 Yeovil–South Petherton/Crewkerne (passing within ¾ml ⊠ Yeovil Pen Mill) (tel. 01460 240309) *Station*: Crewkerne or Yeovil Pen Mill, both 7ml

STONEHENGE DOWN 🐾 🏚 🚶 *Wiltshire*

Amesbury, nr Salisbury SP4 7DE Tel: (English Heritage) 01980 623108

The Trust owns 587ha (1450 acres) of downland surrounding the famous monument, including some fine Bronze Age barrow groups and the Cursus, variously interpreted as an ancient racecourse or processional way. There are recommended walks and an archaeological leaflet, available at Stonehenge shop, at the NT shop in Salisbury, or from the leaflet dispenser in the car park

Note: The monument itself is owned and administered by English Heritage

🅾 Monument opening details are obtainable from English Heritage at the address and tel. no. above. NT members free. NT land open at all times, but may be subject to closure at the Summer Solstice (21 June) for up to 2 days

🏚 Shop run by EH adjacent to the monument

♿ Wheelchair access to the monument but not to land. WC

🔊 Taped guide available for monument only; also refers to the landscape

🍴 Refreshments available adjacent to the monument (not NT)

🐕 No dogs on archaeological walks

➔ (1: M5) Monument 2ml W of Amesbury, at junction of A303 & A344/A360 [184: SU1242] *Bus*: Wilts & Dorset 3 ⊠ Salisbury–Stonehenge (tel. 01722 336855) *Station*: Salisbury 9½ml

STOURHEAD 🏚 ❀ 🌳 ♨ 🚶 🛡 *Wiltshire*

The Estate Office, Stourton, Warminster BA12 6QD Tel: 01747 841152;
Recorded information 0891 335205

*An outstanding example of the English landscape style, this splendid garden was designed by
Henry Hoare II and laid out between 1741 and 1780. Classical temples, including the
Pantheon and Temple of Apollo, are skilfully located around the central lake at the end of a
series of vistas, which change as the visitor moves around the paths and through the
magnificent mature woodland. The house, begun in 1721 by Colen Campbell, contains
furniture by the younger Chippendale and fine paintings. King Alfred's Tower, an intriguing
red-brick folly built in 1772 by Henry Flitcroft, is almost 50m high and gives breathtaking
views over the estate. Much of the estate woodland and downland is managed for nature
conservation and there are two interesting Iron Age hill-forts, Whitesheet Hill and Park Hill
Camp. Waymarked walks lead visitors through the estate*

What's new in 1998: Level walk from house to King Alfred's Tower along Terrace
Walk, 1½ml; the Pelargonium House, a glass house which will contain the Stourhead
Pelargonium Collection is to be built in lower walled garden, summer 1998

🅾 **Garden:** all year daily 9–7 or sunset if earlier (except 23–25 July when garden
will close at 5; last admission 4). **House:** 28 March to 1 Nov: daily except Thur &
Fri 12–5.30 or dusk if earlier; last admission 30min before closing (tel. 01747
840348). **King Alfred's Tower:** 28 March to 1 Nov: Tues, Wed, Thur & Fri
2–5.30; Sat & Sun 11.30–5.30 or dusk if earlier. Closed Mon except BHMon
(tel. 01985 844785). **Events:** 23–25 July, Fête Champêtre; midsummer event,
open-air Shakespeare and other events, tel. 0891 335203. Regional Box Office
01985 843601/2 or Stourhead Events Office 01747 840142

£ Garden or house: March to Oct; £4.40, children £2.40; family ticket £10.30, pre-
booked parties (15 or more) by written appointment £3.80. Garden only, Nov to
end Feb: £3.40, children £1.50; family ticket £8.20, no reduction for parties.
Combined garden & house ticket: £7.90, children £3.70; family ticket, £20.60,
parties £7.60. King Alfred's Tower: £1.50, children 70p

⏰ Exhibition about Stourhead Estate in reception building in the main car park

▣ Open daily 28 March to 1 Nov 11–6; 2 Nov to end March 1999 11–4 (tel. 01747 840591). Plant centre open daily 1 to 27 March 12–4; 28 March to 27 Sept 12–6 (tel. 01747 840894)

♿ Wheelchairs and parking at house and garden for disabled drivers. WCs available at main car park and in Spread Eagle courtyard. Garden: 1½ml path around lake accessible to wheelchair users, but steep in places and more than one strong companion essential. Wheelchairs available. House: 13 steps up to house accessible by stairclimber (must be booked in advance), all showrooms on one level accessible by wheelchair. Sympathetic Hearing Scheme. House congested at weekends and in May & June. Shop and refreshments in Spread Eagle courtyard accessible; plant centre off main car park accessible. King Alfred's Tower: level walk across grass and along 1½ml terrace walk to house

👁 'Touch tour' guide available. Braille garden guide; scented azaleas in early summer

🍴 Village Hall self-service tea-toom serving coffee, light lunches, teas and ice-creams, open daily 28 March to 1 Nov 10.30–5.30 (tel. 01747 840161). Picnics near car parks and in garden. Spread Eagle Inn, situated close to garden entrance, provides en-suite accommodation and home-cooked food to guests and visitors. Open all year with log fires in winter. Weekend and mid-week breaks available 1 Nov to end Feb. Special party bookings welcome (tel. 01747 840587).

🚼 Parent & baby room next to reception building in main car park

▣ Special events and projects can be organised by contacting the Estate Office

🐕 From Nov to end Feb dogs are allowed in the garden on lead and on wider estate throughout year. Please keep your dog on a lead whenever near farming stock. Dogs are not allowed in King Alfred's Tower, but may be tied up outside

➔ (1: K5) At Stourton, off B3092, 3ml NW of Mere (A303), 8ml S of Frome (A361) [183:ST7834]. Parking 400m from house, garden and catering facilities. King Alfred's Tower: 3½ml by road from Stourhead House; parking 350m *Bus:* Wilts & Dorset 26, Wakes 125 Salisbury–Stourhead (Wed & Fri only); otherwise Southern National 59 from ⊞ Gillingham, some to garden, but on others alight Zeals, 1¼ml (tel. 0345 090899) *Station:* Gillingham 6½ml; Bruton (U) 7ml

---

STUDLAND BEACH & NATURE RESERVE 🦆 🏛 🚼 🚶   *Dorset*

Countryside Office, Studland, Swanage BH19 3AX Tel: 01929 450259

Fine sandy beaches stretch continuously for 3ml from South Haven Point to the chalk cliffs of Handfast Point and Old Harry Rocks, and include Shell Bay and a designated naturist area. The heathland behind the beach is a National Nature Reserve and a haven for many rare birds and other forms of wildlife. There are several public paths and two nature trails here. Spyway Farm and Blackers Hole, near Langton Matravers, support important bird and butterfly habitats, as well as rare plants, and give access to the sea at Dancing Ledge. There are NT car parks at Spyway Farm and Acton village, and information boards at Spyway farm buildings. Hartland Moor, part-owned by English Nature, is currently being restored from farmland to lowland heath and new footpaths have been created

What's new in 1998: Please note new arrangements for dogs; Purbeck Walks pack describes walks in the surrounding countryside. It is priced at £2.45 and available from local NT shops and the NT Wessex Regional Office (please add 50p for p&p)

[O] All year. **Car parks:** Shell Bay: all year; The Knoll & Middle Beach: 9–8 summer months only (reduced parking area in winter); South Beach: 9–11pm

[£] Car parks (Shell Bay, The Knoll, Middle Beach and South Beach): April: £2, £1 after 2; May & June: £2.50, £2 after 2, £1 after 4; July & Aug: £3.50, £2.50 after 2, £1.50 after 4; Sept: £2, £1.50 after 2, £1 after 4. Rest of year donations only. NT members free. Coaches £9. Motorcycles £1. Boat launching: powered craft £14 per day, catamarans £9. Others, incl. sail boards, £4.50 per day (incl. NT members). WCs at Knoll & Middle Beach. Bicycle racks are sited at all car parks

[Ⲕ] Guided tours of nature reserve given by NT wardens and English Nature wardens. Information from the Countryside Office (tel. 01929 450259)

[🖻] Knoll visitor centre: shop open daily 1 March to 30 June 11–4; 1 July to 7 Sept 10–5; 8 Sept to Feb 1999 11–4, weather permitting. Longer opening in fine weather (tel. 01929 450500)

[♿] Knoll car park has good access. In summer, boardwalks for wheelchairs along part of Knoll Beach and to visitor facilities. RADAR WC at Knoll Beach; RADAR WC at Middle Beach car park. New Hartland Moor walk, described in 'Purbeck Walks' leaflet, offers some wheelchair access

[🍴] NT beach café at Knoll Beach open same days and times as Knoll visitor centre shop (tel. 01929 420305). Concessionary cafés at Middle Beach and Shell Bay

[👶] Baby-changing facilities in WC at Knoll visitor centre

[📖] Information in Knoll visitor centre and old coastguard hut at Middle Beach

[🐕] Welcome on main beaches 8 Sept to 25 June (must be on leads from 1 May), but prohibited from the Knoll and Middle Beach 26 June to 7 Sept. Access to Shell Bay beach and South Beach is permitted 26 June to 7 Sept. No fouling on beach – 'Poop Scoops' are on sale at visitor centre and car park kiosks. Dogs are welcome all year on nature reserve footpaths

[→] (1: L7) [195: SZ036835] *Bus:* Wilts & Dorset 150 Bournemouth–Swanage (passing ≋ Branksome) to Shell Bay and Studland; 152 Poole–Sandbanks (passing close ≋ Parkstone) (tel. 01202 673555); Yellow Buses 12 Christchurch–Sandbanks, summer only (tel. 01202 557272). Vehicle ferry from Sandbanks to Shell Bay *Station:* Branksome or Parkstone, both 3½ml to Shell Bay or 6ml to Studland via vehicle ferry

---

TINTAGEL OLD POST OFFICE [🏠]   *Cornwall*

Tintagel PL34 0DB Tel: 01840 770024 (opening hours only)

A small and fascinating 14th-century stone house, built to the plan of a medieval manor house and with a large hall. It was used in the 19th century for nearly fifty years as the letter-receiving office for the district and is now restored to that period and function

[O] 1 April to 1 Nov: daily 11–5.30 (closes 5 in Oct)

£ £2.20. Pre-arranged party rate £1.60

Shop open as property

Unsuitable for disabled visitors

Braille guide

→ (1: D7) In centre of village [200: SX056884] *Bus:* Western National 122/4/5, X4 Wadebridge–Bude (with some from Bodmin Parkway) (tel. 01209 719988); Fry's service from Plymouth (tel. 01840 770256)

TINTINHULL HOUSE GARDEN ✤   *Somerset*

Farm St, Tintinhull, Yeovil BA22 9PZ Tel: 01935 822545

A delightful formal garden, created this century around a 17th-century manor house. Small pools, varied borders and secluded lawns are all neatly enclosed within walls and clipped hedges, and there is also an attractive kitchen garden

○ 1 April to 30 Sept: daily except Mon & Tues 12–6 (open BHMon)

£ £3.70; children £1.80. No reduction for parties. Coach parties by arrangement in advance with the Gardener

In advance with the Gardener

Parking in courtyard by arrangement; some access for wheelchair users but cobbles, uneven paths and steps make progress difficult

Roses, honeysuckles and other scented plants

Tea-room in stable block; open same days as property. Light refreshments and teas 12–5.30

No dogs in courtyard or garden

→ (1: J6) 5ml NW of Yeovil, ½ml S of A303, on E outskirts of Tintinhull [183: ST503198] *Bus:* Southern National 52 Yeovil–Martock (passing within ¼ml Yeovil Pen Mill) (tel. 01935 76233) *Station:* Yeovil Pen Mill 5½ml; Yeovil Junction 7ml

---

TREASURER'S HOUSE 🏠   *Somerset*

Martock TA12 6JL Tel: 01935 825801

A small medieval house, recently refurbished by the Trust. The two-storey hall was completed in 1293 and the solar block is even earlier. There is also a kitchen, added later, and an interesting wallpainting

○ 5 April to 29 Sept: Sun, Mon & Tues 2–5. Parking is limited and unsuitable for coaches and trailer caravans

£ Medieval hall, wallpainting and kitchen £1.60. No reduction for children. Parties (no reduction) only by prior arrangement with tenant; please tel. for details. No WC

🗁 In Martock (not NT)

➜ (1: J6) Opposite church in middle of village; 1ml NW of A303 between Ilminster and Ilchester [193: ST462191] *Bus:* Southern National 52 Yeovil–Martock (passing within ¼ml ⮫ Yeovil Pen Mill) (tel. 01935 76233) *Station:* Crewkerne 7½ml; Yeovil Pen Mill 8ml

---

TRELISSICK GARDEN 🏵 🌲 🛥 🏛 🧍 🎭 *Cornwall*

Feock, nr Truro TR3 6QL Tel: 01872 862090 Fax: 01872 865808

Beautifully located at the head of Fal estuary, the estate commands panoramic views over the area and has extensive park and woodland walks beside the river. At its heart sits the tranquil garden, set on many levels and containing a superb collection of tender and exotic plants which bring colour throughout the year. The display of spring blossom is particularly delightful. The house is not open, but there is an art and craft gallery, shop, two restaurants and fine Georgian stable block

What's new in 1998: New shop extension specialising in Cornish foodstuffs. New children's guide

🅾 Garden open 1 March to 1 Nov: daily 10.30–5.30 (opens 12.30 on Sun and closes 5 in March & Oct). The woodland walks are open throughout the year. **Events:** programme of theatrical and musical events; details from the Property Manager (tel. 01872 862090)

💷 £4; family ticket £10. Pre-arranged parties £3.40 per person. £1.50 car park fee refundable on admission

🗁 Shop and plant sales, open daily 1 March to 1 Nov (tel. 01872 865515). Art and craft gallery open as shop (tel. 01872 864084). Shop and gallery also open daily 3 Nov to Christmas

♿ Upper parts of garden reasonably flat with loose gravel paths; parking near shop & restaurant, both accessible. Wheelchairs and special guide available from reception. Access to ground floor of gallery. WC near shop & car park

👁 Small walled garden with aromatic plants near entrance. Braille guide.

☕ Coffee, lunches and teas in Trelissick Barn. Light refreshments in the Courtyard Room, 1 March to 1 Nov: Mon to Sat 10.30–5.30, Sun 12–5.30 (closes at 5 in Mar & Oct); additional limited daily opening in Nov & Dec (tel. 01872 863486)

📕 Schools' resource pack

🐕 In woodland walks and park only

➡ **(1: C9)** 4ml S of Truro, on both sides of B3289 above King Harry Ferry [204: SW837396] *Bus:* Truronian 311 from Truro (tel. 01872 273453); Western National 51B Truro–St Mawes via King Harry Ferry, Sun only (tel. 01209 719988). Both pass close ⊞ Truro *Station:* Truro 5ml; Perranwell (U), not Sun, except July & Aug, 4ml

---

TRENGWAINTON GARDEN ❁   *Cornwall*

nr Penzance TR20 8RZ
Tel: 01736 362297 (during opening hours) Fax: 01736 68142

A unique garden, perhaps more favoured for the cultivation of exotic trees and shrubs than any other on mainland Britain. The walled garden in particular contains many species which cannot be grown in the open anywhere else in the country. Intimate and closely linked to the stream running through its valley, the garden opens out in front of the house (not open) to give splendid views of Mount's Bay and The Lizard

What's new in 1998: New ornamental pond and new tea-room

🅾 1 March to 29 Oct: daily except Fri & Sat (but open Good Fri) 10–5.30 (closes 5 in March & Oct). Last admission 30min before closing

£ £3; family ticket £7.50. No reduction for parties

🏠 Shop and plant sales in reception lodge

♿ Jubilee Garden and Lower Stream area best for wheelchair users. One wheelchair and one powered self-drive buggy available; please pre-book. Some access to walled garden. Shop and plant sales accessible. WC

👁 Fragrant plants, stream, pools, water sounds; Braille guide

🍽 Tea-room opening 1998. Undercover seating, light refreshments

🐕 Dogs allowed on leads

➡ **(1: B9)** 2ml NW of Penzance, ½ml W of Heamoor off Penzance–Morvah road (B3312), ½ml off St Just road (A3071) [203: SW445315] *Bus:* Western National 10/A Penzance–St Just (tel. 01209 719988) *Station:* Penzance 2ml

---

TRERICE 🏠 ❁   *Cornwall*

nr Newquay TR8 4PG Tel: 01637 875404 Fax: 01637 879300

This delightful small Elizabethan manor house enjoys a secluded location and contains fine fireplaces, plaster ceilings, oak and walnut furniture, interesting clocks and Stuart portraits. The highlight of the interior is the magnificent great chamber with its splendid barrel ceiling. The attractive garden has some unusual plants and an orchard with old varieties of fruit trees, and in the barn there is an exhibition on the history of the lawnmower

🅾 1 April to 1 Nov: daily except Tues & Sat (but open daily 27 July to 6 Sept), 11–5.30 (closes 5 in Oct). Last admission 30min before closing.
Events: programme available from the Property Manager (s.a.e. please)

£ £4; family ticket £10. Pre-arranged parties £3.40

Shop and plant sales open as house

Ground & upper (via grass slope) floors of house, tea-room & shop accessible; some loose gravel and cobbles. Parts of garden accessible. Close parking by prior arrangement with Property Manager. WC. *Note*: Winner of British Gas ADAPT award for Historic Houses, 1992

Braille guide and taped tour available. Access leaflet. Many items can be touched

Coffee, lunches and teas in the Barn. Organisers of parties should arrange for meals beforehand (tel. 01637 875404)

Parent & baby room

Schools may visit the house from 10.30 by prior arrangement with the Property Manager. School hut available. Schools are welcome to picnic in the orchard

Dogs in car park only

→ (1: C8) 3ml SE of Newquay via A392 and A3058 (turn right at Kestle Mill) [200: SW841585] *Bus*: Western National 50 Newquay–Trerice (May to Sept only); otherwise 90, X90 Newquay–Truro, alight Kestle Mill, ½ml (tel. 01209 719988) *Station*: Quintrell Downs (U), not Sun, except July & Aug, 1½ml

---

WATERSMEET HOUSE 🐘 🏊 🏞 🚶 *Devon*

Watersmeet Road, Lynmouth EX35 6NT Tel: 01598 753348

A fishing lodge, built c.1832 in a picturesque valley at the confluence of the East Lyn and Hoar Oak Water, and now serving as a NT shop, with refreshments and information. The site has been a tea-garden since 1901 and is the focal point for several beautiful walks

O 1 April to 30 Sept: daily 10.30–5.30; Oct: daily 10.30–4.30

£ Free. Pay-and-display car park, or free car parks at Combepark Wood, Hillsford Bridge and Countisbury

🚶 See local listings for programme of guided walks on Watersmeet Estate. Walks leaflet available from shop

🏠 1 April to 30 Sept: daily 10.30–5.30; Oct: daily 10.30–4.30

♿ Limited access arrangements for disabled visitors strictly by appointment with Catering Manager (tel. 01598 753348)

🍽 Morning coffee, lunches and cream teas in tea-garden beside the river; 1 April to end Sept: daily 10.30–5.30; Oct: 10.30–4.30. Party catering by arrangement

🚼 Baby-changing facilities in both men's and women's WCs

📷 By arrangement with the Warden (tel. 01598 753580)

🐕 Admitted, but not to restaurant or shop

➜ (1: G4) 1½ml E of Lynmouth, in valley on E side of Lynmouth–Barnstaple road (A39) [180: SS744487] *Bus:* Filers 311, Red Bus 295 Barnstaple–Lynmouth (passing close ⊞ Barnstaple), 300 Minehead–Ilfracombe. On both, alight Lynmouth, thence walk through NT Gorge (tel. 01392 382800)

WEST PENNARD COURT BARN 🏠

Somerset

West Pennard, nr Glastonbury   Tel: (Regional Office) 01985 843600

A 15th-century barn of five bays with a roof of interesting construction. Repaired and given to the Trust by the Society for the Protection of Ancient Buildings in 1938

O Visitors to collect key from Mr P. H. Green, Court Barn Farm, West Bradley, Somerset; prior telephone arrangement is welcomed (tel. 01458 850212)

£ Free

➜ (1: J5) 3ml E of Glastonbury, 7ml S of Wells, 1½ml S of West Pennard (A361) [182/183: ST547370] *Bus:* Badgerline 160 Wells–Street, to within 1ml (tel. 0117 955 3231) *Station:* Castle Cary 8ml

WESTBURY COLLEGE GATEHOUSE 🏠

Bristol

College Road, Westbury-on-Trym, Bristol   Tel: (Regional Office) 01985 843600

The 15th-century gatehouse of the College of Priests (founded in the 13th century), of which John Wyclif was prebend. There is an interesting church (not NT) nearby

O Access by key only, to be collected by prior written or telephone (0117 962 1536) arrangement with the Rev. G. M. Collins, The Vicarage, 44 Eastfield Road, Westbury-on-Trym, Bristol BS9 4AG

£ £1.10, children 50p

➜ (1: J3) 3ml N of the centre of Bristol [172: ST572775] *Bus:* Frequent from surrounding areas (tel. 0117 955 3231) *Station:* Clifton Down (U) not Sun, 2ml

WESTWOOD MANOR 🏠 ❀ *Wiltshire*

Bradford-on-Avon BA15 2AF Tel: 01225 863374

A 15th-century stone manor house, altered in the early 17th century, with late Gothic and Jacobean windows and fine plasterwork. There is a modern topiary garden and attractive views over the Frome valley

Note: Westwood Manor is administered for the National Trust by the tenant

🅾 1 April to 30 Sept: Sun, Tues & Wed 2–5. At other times parties of up to 20 by written application with s.a.e. to the tenant

£ £3.50. No reduction for parties or children. No WC

♿ No wheelchair access

➔ (1: K4) 1½ml SW of Bradford-on-Avon, in Westwood village, beside the church; village signposted off Bradford-on-Avon to Rode road (B3109) [173: ST812590] *Bus:* MC Travel 96, Trowbridge Taxibus 97 from Trowbridge (passes close ☒ Trowbridge); otherwise from surrounding areas to Bradford-on-Avon, thence 1½ml (tel. 0345 090899) *Station:* Avoncliff (U), 1ml; Bradford-on-Avon 1½ml

WHITE MILL ⛫ 🚹 *Dorset*

Sturminster Marshall, nr Wimborne BH21 4BX Tel: 01258 858051

Rebuilt in 1776 on a site marked as a mill in the Domesday Book, this cornmill was extensively repaired in 1994 and still retains its original elm and applewood machinery (now too fragile to be operative). The setting, next to the River Stour, is delightful and there is a riverside picnic area nearby

🅾 28 March to 1 Nov: weekends & BHols 12–5. Pre-booked parties welcome at other times (subject to additional charge) (tel. 01258 857184)

£ £2, children £1. Parties by arrangement

🚹 The mill is shown by guided tour and numbers within the building must be restricted for safety reasons. No WC

♿ Limited parking in front of mill. Access around the mill is via narrow steps, but wheelchair access is available to most of the ground floor via ramps. A viewing platform and internal mirrors enable visitors to view much of the remainder of the mill

👁 Handling collection, audio guide. Large-print guide available

🐕 No dogs in mill, but access to Stour Valley Way from White Mill (south) to Wimborne

➔ (1: L6) On the River Stour north of Sturminster Marshall. From B3082 Blandford to Wimborne road take right-hand turn signposted Sturminster Marshall. Mill is 1ml on right. Car park nearby *Bus:* Wilts & Dorset 129, X13 Poole–Blandford (passes close ☒ Poole); 139, X13 Bournemouth–Shaftesbury (passes ☒ Bournemouth), alight Sturminster Marshall, 1½ml (tel. 01202 673555) *Station:* Hamworthy 7ml; Poole 8½ml

Introduction to the South & South East

Although this is one of England's most densely populated and urbanised areas, there remain some remarkably extensive and beautiful open spaces here, as well as miles of dramatic coastline. Much of this is due to the work of the Trust, which over many decades has acquired and protected land threatened by development and insensitive use.

The Trust owns many properties within easy reach of London, including most of the delightful village of **Chiddingstone** in Kent, complete with cobbled streets and the famous Chiding Stone, from which it takes its name. Nearby are **Chartwell**, Sir Winston Churchill's former home, the beautiful moated **Ightham Mote** and the enchanting **Emmetts Garden**. The Trust's founder, Octavia Hill, knew this area well, and a woodland is named after her at **Toys Hill**, from where there are magnificent views.

One of the South East's most mysterious areas is Romney Marsh, still peaceful and relatively inaccessible. Here the Trust owns 3½ miles of the **Royal Military Canal**, between Appledore and Warehorne. The canal was built in 1804–7 as a defence against Napoleonic invasion and there are pleasant walks along its banks. On the edge of the Marsh is **Smallhythe Place**, former home of the great Victorian actress, Ellen Terry.

The White Cliffs of Dover need no introduction. They offer miles of outstanding coastline and walking country, as well as the chance to visit a real lighthouse at **South Foreland**. Recent years have seen much development in this part of Kent due to the Channel Tunnel, but man's presence has been felt here for many thousands of years – at **Coldrum Long Barrow**, near Trottiscliffe, the Trust owns a Neolithic burial chamber, in which skeletal remains have been found.

Much of the Sussex coast is now under tarmac and concrete, but Trust-owned land on the **Seven Sisters**, including **Birling Gap** and **Crowlink**, offers delightful walks over open downland with spectacular coastal views. Further inland, **Frog Firle Farm** at Alfriston is classic South Downs country, rich in natural history and with splendid views over the Cuckmere valley. Nestling in the gentle countryside just north of the Downs is the charming manor house **Bateman's**, Rudyard Kipling's former home. West along the South Downs Way are important areas of downland, such as **Devil's Dyke** and **Harting Down**. Both are rich in downland flora and fauna, and reward those who leave the beaten track.

The Trust cares for a further 16 miles of beautiful coastline on the Isle of Wight, including the **Needles Headland** with the **Old Battery**, overlooking the famous stacks of rock. From here there are excellent walks to enjoy as far as **Tennyson Down**, where the great poet once strolled. The ancient port of **Newtown**, with its Old Town Hall, is also an interesting place to visit.

The Surrey and Hampshire heaths are one of the most depleted habitats in Britain, and the Trust owns several of the last remaining areas of what was once a large expanse of wilderness. At **Hindhead** there are splendid walks through heath and woodland, including trails to the dramatic **Devil's Punch Bowl**, and nearby is **Frensham Common**, home to a wide variety of interesting birds, plants and insects. The Trust's heathland management work is explained at **Witley Common Information Centre.** The Trust also cares for some 800ha (2000 acres) in the magnificent New Forest, including **Hale Purlieu** and **Bramshaw Commons**, which offer excellent walking.

The Surrey Hills, rising to **Box Hill** and **Leith Hill** at their highest point, provide a picturesque backdrop to some of the Trust's classic country estates, including **Polesden Lacey** and the exquisite **Clandon Park**. This is idyllic countryside, offering a variety of walks with breathtaking views. Running for nearly 20 miles between Guildford to Weybridge are the **River Wey Navigations**, once a busy transportation system. Information on the history of this important waterway is available at **Dapdune Wharf** in Guildford.

The Chilterns offer some of the finest scenery in southern England and from their highest point, **Coombe Hill**, there are spectacular views over three counties. There are some beautiful villages around here, among them **West Wycombe** and **Bradenham**, as well as **Hughenden Manor**, the former home of Benjamin Disraeli and a wonderful centre for good walking through typical Chiltern beechwoods.

Highlights for Disabled Visitors

Particularly recommended are the wheelchair route at **Toys Hill** in Kent and accessible trails at **Witley Common**; **Pinkney's Green**, a nature reserve near Maidenhead, has specially adapted paths and viewing platforms, as well as a tapping rail (access by RADAR key).

... and for Families

Plenty of space to run around and play at **Coombe Hill**, the **White Cliffs of Dover** and the **Seven Sisters**. **Devil's Dyke** offers a wide range of activities for children. Also, the lighthouse at **South Foreland** and spectacular **Bodiam Castle** have much to offer families on a day out.

Further Information

NT Regional Offices:

- **Kent & East Sussex** (tel. 01892 890651)
- **Southern** (01372 453401) – for properties in Surrey, West Sussex, Hampshire and the Isle of Wight .
- **Thames & Chilterns** (tel. 01494 528051) – for properties in Hertfordshire, Bedfordshire, Buckinghamshire and Berkshire.

Please contact any of the above for a free copy of the NT Countryside Guide to the South East, sponsored by Barclays, which gives full details of a range of Trust coast and countryside properties in the area.

Leaflets on walks in Kent and East Sussex are available from the NT Kent & East Sussex Office and for details of Countryside Events in those counties, please tel. 01892 891001.

Leaflets on walks and events in Surrey, West Sussex, Hampshire and the Isle of Wight are available from the NT Southern Office (tel. 01372 453401).

There is also a North Downs Countryside Pack, available from Box Hill Shop (tel. 01306 888793) and West Weald countryside leaflets, available from Witley Common (tel. 01428 683207).

A free leaflet on 'Walks & Places to Visit on the Isle of Wight' is available, free of charge, from the NT IoW Office (tel. 01983 873945).

ALFRISTON CLERGY HOUSE 🏠 ❊ 🛡 *East Sussex*

The Tye, Alfriston, Polegate BN26 5TL Tel: 01323 870001

Bought in 1896 for the princely sum of £10, this was the first building to be acquired by the Trust. A 14th-century half-timbered and thatched hall house, it is little altered and typical of the Wealden vernacular style. The interior contains a fine medieval hall and exhibition and there is a charming cottage garden, with many typical countryside flowers, once common but rarely seen today

O 1 April to 1 Nov: daily except Tues & Fri (but open Good Fri) 10–5 or sunset if earlier. Last admission 30min before closing. **Events:** for details tel. 01892 891001

£ £2.20, children £1.10. WCs and parking in car park at other end of village (not NT)

🛍 Shop open as house. Also Christmas shop until 20 Dec: daily except Mon & Tues 11–4; tel. Custodian for details

♿ House unsuitable for wheelchair users

👁 Braille guide

🎫 In village (not NT)

🐕 No dogs in garden or house

➔ (2: H8) 4ml NE of Seaford, just E of B2108, in Alfriston village, adjoining The Tye and St Andrews Church [189: TQ521029] *Bus:* Autopoint 125 from Lewes, 126 from Eastbourne & Seaford (pass close ≋ Lewes, Polegate and Seaford) (tel. 01273 474747) *Station:* Berwick (U) 2½ml

ASCOTT 🏠 ❊ *Buckinghamshire*

Wing, nr Leighton Buzzard LU7 0PS Tel: 01296 688242 Fax: 01296 681904

Originally a half-timbered Jacobean farmhouse, Ascott was bought in 1876 by the de Rothschild family and considerably transformed and enlarged. It now houses a quite exceptional collection of fine paintings, Oriental porcelain and English and French furniture. The extensive gardens are a mixture of the formal and natural, containing specimen trees and shrubs, as well as an herbaceous walk, lily pond, Dutch garden and remarkable topiary sundial

O **House and garden:** 1 April to 7 May & 1 to 30 Sept: daily except Mon 2–6 (open Good Fri but closed BH Mon); **Garden only:** 13 May to 30 Aug: every Wed & last Sun in each month 2–6. Last admission to house 5

£ House and garden £5.40. Garden only £4. Children half-price. No reduction for parties, which must book in advance. Parking 220m

♿ Access to ground floor only. 3 wheelchairs available; limited access to garden; close parking by prior arrangement. WC in car park

🐕 In car park only

→ **(2: E2)** ½ml E of Wing, 2ml SW of Leighton Buzzard, on S side of A418 [165:SP891230] *Bus:* Aylesbury & The Vale/Wycombe Bus X15, 65, 325, Aylesbury–Milton Keynes (passing close ≋ Aylesbury & Leighton Buzzard) (tel. 0345 382000) *Station:* Leighton Buzzard 2ml

ASHRIDGE ESTATE 🏠 🎋 🚹 🛡   *Hertfordshire*

Ringshall, Berkhamsted HP4 1LT Tel: 01442 851227 Fax: 01442 842062

This magnificent and varied estate runs across the borders of Herts and Bucks, along the main ridge of the Chiltern Hills. There are woodlands, commons and chalk downland, supporting a rich variety of wildlife and offering splendid walks through outstanding scenery. The focal point of the area is the Monument, erected in 1832 to the Duke of Bridgwater. There are also breathtaking views from Ivinghoe Beacon, accessible from Steps Hill

O **Estate:** open all year, incl. 16ml boundary trail & six self-guided walks. Guide leaflets available from visitor centre shop. **Monument, visitor centre & shop:** 10 April to 1 Nov: Mon to Thur & Good Fri 2–5, Sat, Sun & BH Mon 2–5.30. WCs closed on Good Fri. Last admission to monument 30min before closing. **Events:** for details of events please send s.a.e. to Box Office, PO Box 180, High Wycombe, Bucks HP14 4XT

£ Monument £1, children 50p. *Note:* For further information, shop and party bookings tel. 01442 851227; Estate Office tel. 01442 842488). Riding permits available from riding warden (tel. 01442 842716)

🛍 Shop open 10 April to 1 Nov: Mon to Thur & Good Fri 2–5, Sat, Sun & BH Mon 2–5.30. 7 Nov to 13 Dec: Sat & Sun 12–4 (or dusk if earlier)

♿ Monument area, monument drive and visitor centre accessible. WC (RADAR lock). Parking near visitor centre. Self-drive powered vehicles and one manual wheelchair free of charge from visitor centre; advance booking advisable. Extensive routes with fine views. Some routes may be difficult in poor weather

👁 Volunteer Base Camp used by groups of visually impaired people with sighted companions; details available from Estate Office

☕ Tea kiosk next to visitor centre, summer weekends

📖 Full educational programme, study base and residential visits. Details from the Education Warden (tel. 01442 851227)

🐕 Admitted if kept under control

→ **(2: E3)** Between Northchurch & Ringshall just off B4506 [165: SP970131] *Bus:* Monument; Seamarks 27; Lucketts 30/1 from ≋ Tring, alight Aldbury, ½ml. Beacon; Aylesbury & The Vale 61 Aylesbury–Luton (passing close ≋ Aylesbury & Luton); Seamarks 327 from Tring to Monument Drive and Beacon, Sun, June to Sept only (tel. 0345 244344) *Station:* Monument: Tring 1¾ml. Beacon: Cheddington 3½ml

BASILDON PARK 🏛 ❄ ♠ ♟ *Berkshire*

Lower Basildon, Reading RG8 9NR Tel: 0118 984 3040 Fax: 0118 984 1267

*This beautiful Palladian mansion was built in 1776–83 by John Carr for Francis Sykes, who had made his fortune in India. The interior is notable for its original delicate plasterwork and elegant staircase, as well as for the unusual Octagon Room. The house fell on hard times in the early part of this century, but was rescued by Lord & Lady Iliffe, who restored it and filled it with fine pictures and furniture. The early 19th-century pleasure grounds are currently being restored and there are waymarked trails through the parkland. At the top of Streatley Hill nearby is a car park giving access to **The Holies** and **Lardon Chase**, an outstanding area of downland and woodland with many beautiful walks and breathtaking views*

◉ **House:** 1 April to 1 Nov: daily except Mon & Tues (but open BH Mon) 1–5.30 (closed Good Fri). **Park, garden & woodland walks:** 1 March to 27 March: Sat & Sun 12–5; 1 April to 1 Nov: same days as house 11.30–5.30. *Note:* House and grounds will close at 5 on 15 August 1998 for jazz concert. **Events:** for details please send s.a.e. marked 'Events' to Box Office, P O Box 180, High Wycombe, Bucks HP14 4XT

£ House, park & garden £4, children £2; family ticket £10. Park & garden only £1.60, children 80p; family ticket £4. Parties of 15+ £3 per person, only on application to Property Manager. Parking in grounds, 400m from house

𝆑 Special guided tours by arrangement with the Property Manager; please tel. for details

🏠 Shop open 1–22 March: Sat & Sun 12–5; 1 April to 1 Nov: Wed to Fri 2–5.30, Sat & Sun 12.30–5.30. 2 Nov to 20 Dec: Fri, Sat & Sun 12–4 (tel. 01491 671738)

♿ Access to garden via firm gravel paths; tea-room accessible via ramps. Shop in stable yard; level access. Parking facilities for disabled drivers near house; please contact ticket office near car park; disabled passengers may be set down at house. Adapted WC in stable yard near car park

👁 Braille guide

☕ Tea-room open 1 April to 1 Nov, same days as house 1–5.30; 2 Nov to 20 Dec: Sat & Sun 12–4. Groups by prior arrangement (tel. 0118 9844080). Picnics in grounds except on main lawns near house

👶 Highchair available in tea-room

🐕 In park, woodland and grounds only, not on main lawns near house; dogs must be on leads at all times

➔ (2: D5) Between Pangbourne and Streatley, 7ml NW of Reading, on W side of A329; leave M4 at exit 12 [175: SU611782] *Bus:* Reading Buses 105 Oxford–Reading (passing ⊜ Pangbourne) (tel. 0118 959 4000) *Station:* Pangbourne 2½ml; Goring & Streatley 3ml

---

BATEMAN'S 🏠 🏠 ✕ ✿ 🔧 🛡

East Sussex

Burwash, Etchingham TN19 7DS Tel: 01435 882302 Fax: 01435 882811

The home of Rudyard Kipling from 1902–36, the interior of this beautiful Jacobean house reflects the author's strong associations with the East. There are many Oriental rugs and artefacts, and most of the rooms – including his book-lined study – are much as Kipling left them. The delightful grounds run down to the small River Dudwell, where there is a water-mill, and are maintained much as they were in Kipling's time, with roses, wild flowers and herbs. Kipling's Rolls-Royce is also on display

🅾 House, **mill and garden:** 4 April to 1 Nov: daily except Thur & Fri 11–5.30 (but open Good Fri). Last admission 4.30. The mill grinds corn every Sat at 2 in the open season. **Events:** for details tel. 01892 891001

💷 £4.70, children £2.35; family ticket £11.75. Pre-booked parties £4 except on Sun, BH Mon & Good Fri when £4.70

🏪 Shop open same days as house 11.30–5.30. Also Christmas shop until 20 Dec: daily except Mon & Tues 11–4; tel. Administrator for details

♿ The mill and shop are not suitable for wheelchair users. Access to ground floor of house, tea-room and garden; there are routes which avoid the steps. WC in car park. Map available

👁 Braille introduction to house. Scented plants & flowers; water-mill sounds (Sat only)

☕ Morning coffee, light lunches and teas in tea-room (licensed) open 11–5. Picnicking in copse adjacent to car park; no picnicking in garden

👶 Baby-changing facilities. Children's guide

📕 Teachers' resource booklet

🐕 On leads in car park only. Dog crèche

➔ (2: H7) ½ml S of Burwash (A265); approached by road leading S from W end of village or N from Woods Corner (B2096) [199: TQ671238] *Bus:* RDH 318 Hurst Green–Heathfield (passing ⊜ Etchingham) (tel. 01273 474747) *Station:* Etchingham 3ml

BEMBRIDGE WINDMILL ☒

Isle of Wight

Enquiries to NT Estate Office, Longstone Farm, Strawberry Lane, Mottistone, Newport, Isle of Wight PO30 4EB Tel: 01983 873945

Built c.1700 and still with its original wooden machinery, the windmill is the only one surviving on the Island

O 1 April to 30 Oct: daily except Sat (but open Easter Sat & daily in July & Aug) 10–5. Last admission 4.45

£ £1.30. No reduction for groups. All school groups are conducted by a NT guide; special charge applies. Parking 100m. No WC. Picnic field

↑ Conducted school groups and special visits March to end Oct (but not July or Aug), by written appointment

🏠 Small shop

♿ Mill not accessible to visitors with disabilities; grab ropes are provided for those able to climb the steep stairs. Area around mill is accessible

◉ Braille and large-print guides

📖 Educational quiz sheets

➔ (2:D9) ½ml S of Bembridge on B3395 [196: SZ639874] *Bus:* Southern Vectis 1 Cowes–Sandown (passing ⟰ Ryde Esplanade) (tel. 01983 827005) *Station:* Brading (U) 2ml by footpath. *Ferry:* Ryde (Wightlink Ltd) 6ml (tel. 0990 827744). E Cowes (Red Funnel) 13ml (tel. 01703 334010)

BOARSTALL DUCK DECOY 🦆 🚶

Buckinghamshire

Boarstall, nr Aylesbury HP18 9UX Tel: 01844 237488

A rare survival of a 17th-century decoy in working order, set on a tree-fringed lake, with nature trail and exhibition hall

Note: Nearby Boarstall Tower is closed during 1998 for major building repairs

O 29 March to 31 Aug: Wed 4–7; Sat, Sun & BH Mon 10–5. School parties by arrangement. Talk/demonstration when Warden is available, Sat, Sun & BH Mon at 11 & 3

£ £2.10; family ticket £5. Parties of six or more, which must book, £1 per person

♿ Nature trail, exhibition hall, bird hide and decoy accessible in dry weather; ramps; wheelchair available

🐕 In car park only

➔ (2:D3) Midway between Bicester and Thame, 2ml W of Brill [164 or 165: SP624151] *Station:* Bicester Town (U), not Sun, 6½ml; Bicester North, 7½ml

BODIAM CASTLE 🏰 🎣 🎭 *East Sussex*

Bodiam, nr Robertsbridge TN32 5UA Tel: 01580 830436 Fax: 01580 830398

One of the most famous and evocative castles in Britain, Bodiam was built in 1385, both as a defence and a comfortable home. The exterior is virtually complete and the ramparts rise dramatically above the moat below. Enough of the interior survives to give an impression of castle life, and there are spiral staircases and battlements to explore. An audiovisual presentation and small museum provide social and historical background

Note: Please note that Bodiam Castle is widely used by education groups during term-time mornings

🅾️ 14 Feb to 1 Nov: daily 10–6 or dusk if earlier; 3 Nov to 3 Jan: Tues to Sun 10–4 or dusk if earlier (closed 24/25/26 Dec, open New Year's Day). Last admission 1hr before closing. **Events:** for details tel. 01892 891001

💷 £3.30, children £1.65; family ticket £8.25. Parties £2.80. Car park ¼ml, £1 (NT members free); coaches £5

📷 Shop open 14 Feb to end Oct: same days as castle 11–5 (or dusk if earlier). Nov to Dec: Wed to Sun 11–4; tel. Administrator for details

♿ Access to car park, shop and restaurant function room; WC in car park. Castle (but not its towers) is accessible to wheelchair users, but it is ½ml from car park over uneven ground; for alternative access details please tel. Administrator before visiting

👁️ Adult and children's braille guides available from ticket office

☕ Lunches, teas and snacks in car park tea-room, open 14 Feb to end Oct: daily 11–5 (or dusk if earlier); Nov to Dec : Wed to Sun 11–4

🚼 Parent and baby room. Children's guide. Highchairs & children's menu in restaurant

🎒 Teachers' resource books. Education rooms with hands-on resources; pre-booked tours available, tel. Administrator for details

🐕 On leads in grounds only, not in castle

➡️ (2: J7) 3ml S of Hawkhurst, 2ml E of A21 Hurst Green [199: TQ782256]
Bus: Fuggles/Stagecoach South Coast 349 from 🚉 Hastings; Hastings & District RE Group 🚉 Rye–🚉 Battle, Sun, July to Aug only (tel. 01273 474747)
Station: Robertsbridge 5ml

BOX HILL 🏠 🛏 🚶 🎭 *Surrey*

The Old Fort, Box Hill Road, Box Hill, Tadworth, nr Dorking KT20 7LB
Tel: 01306 885502 Fax: 01306 875030

An outstanding area of woodland and chalk downland, long-famous as a destination for day-trippers from London, but surprisingly extensive and with much to offer the rambler and naturalist. There are many beautiful walks, and spectacular views towards the South Downs. On the summit there is an information centre, shop with plant sales, servery and a fort dating from the 1890s (which is partly open to the public)

🅾 All year. **Events:** 28 June, Country Day (extra charge for cars, incl. NT members); 1 Dec, special late-night opening in shop (up to 8pm), especially for visitors with disabilities, free glass of sherry and mince pie

£ Countryside free. Coaches must not use the zig-zag road from Burford Bridge on W side of the hill as a weight restriction applies, but must approach from E side of the hill B2032 or B2033; car/coach parks at top of hill; pay-and-display £1.50 (free to NT members displaying membership cards). Annual car park pass available

🚶 Guided walks at intervals throughout the year. Groups by prior arrangement with the Warden (tel. 01306 885502)

🛍 Shop & information centre: open all year, daily 11–4 (later in summer weather permitting); closed 25 & 26 Dec (tel. 01306 888793). Plant sales at back of shop, available March to Sept; Christmas trees on sale from 1 Dec

♿ Access to summit area, including shop & servery. Parking behind servery. Wheelchair path to viewpoint and beyond. WCs opposite main car park at summit

👁 Braille guides for short walk and nature walk

🍴 Servery. Hot & cold snacks & drinks: open all year, daily 11–4 (closed 25 & 26 Dec); longer hours (weather permitting) (tel. 01306 888793)

🏫 Educational room. Educational groups for day visits and residential groups by prior arrangement with North Downs Education Officer (tel. 01306 742809)

🐕 Must be kept under control (sheep grazing)

➔ (2: F6) 1ml N of Dorking, 2½ml S of Leatherhead on A24 [187: TQ171519] *Bus:* London & Country 516, ⊟ Leatherhead–Dorking (tel. 01737 223000) *Station:* Boxhill & Westhumble ½ml

BRADENHAM VILLAGE 🏠 🛏 🚶 *Buckinghamshire*

near High Wycombe   Tel: (Regional Office) 01494 528051

The church and 17th-century manor house (not open) provide an impressive backdrop to the sloping village green. The manor was once the home of Isaac D'Israeli, father of Benjamin Disraeli, who lived nearby at Hughenden Manor (see p.115). A network of paths provides easy access for walkers to explore the delightful surrounding countryside, which includes hills, farmlands and classic Chiltern beechwoods

🅾 All year; parking available on the village green

£ Free

◉ The Red Lion pub (not NT), in the village

→ **(2: E3)** 4ml NW of High Wycombe, off the A4010 [165:SU825970]
Bus: Wycombe Bus 321, 332 High Wycombe–Princes Risborough
(tel.0345 382000) *Station:* Saunderton 1ml

BRIGHSTONE SHOP AND MUSEUM   *Isle of Wight*

Enquiries to the Manager, National Trust Shop, North Street, Brighstone
PO30 4AX Tel: 01983 740689

*An attractive terrace of thatched vernacular cottages, containing a NT shop and Village
Museum (run by Brighstone Museum Trust)*

◯ 5 Jan to 9 April: Mon to Sat 10–1. Good Fri to 31 May: daily 10–4. 1 June to
1 Nov: daily 10–5. 2 Nov to 31 Dec: Mon to Fri 10–4, Sat 10–1. Closed 25/26
Dec & 1 Jan

£ Free entry, donations welcome

→ **(2: C9)** *Bus:* Southern Vectis 12 Newport–Alum Bay (tel. 01983 827005)
Ferry: Yarmouth (Wightlink Ltd) 8ml (tel. 0990 827744); E Cowes (Red Funnel)
12ml (tel. 01703 334010)

BUCKINGHAM CHANTRY CHAPEL ✠   *Buckinghamshire*

Market Hill, Buckingham

*A 15th-century chapel, the oldest building in Buckingham and incorporating a fine Norman
doorway. Later used as a school, it was restored by Gilbert Scott in 1875*

◯ All year: by written appointment with the Buckingham Heritage Trust, c/o Old
Gaol Museum, Market Hill, Buckingham MK18 1EN

£ Free. No WC

♿ Wheelchair access

→ **(2: D2)** On Market Hill [152 or 165: SP693340] *Bus:* Paynes 32, MK Metro 51/A
from Milton Keynes (passing close ≷ Milton Keynes Central); Aylesbury & The
Vale 66 from Aylesbury (passing close ≷ Aylesbury) (tel. 0345 382000)
Station: Wolverton 10ml

CHARTWELL 🏠 ❀ 🚶 🛡   *Kent*

Westerham TN16 1PS Tel: Information 01732 866368 Shop 01732 867837
Restaurant 01732 863087 Office 01732 868381 Fax: 01732 868193

*The home of Sir Winston Churchill from 1924 until the end of his life. An unpretentious
Victorian country house, with stunning views over the Weald, this became the place from*

which Sir Winston drew inspiration. *The rooms remain much as he left them, with pictures, maps and personal mementoes strongly evoking the career and wide-ranging interests of this great statesman. The beautiful terraced gardens contain the pond where Sir Winston fed his fish, and his garden studio in which many of his paintings can be seen*

Note: Entry to the house is by timed ticket for all visitors (incl. NT members). Very occasionally there may be a delay in gaining admission to the house. The waiting time may be spent in the garden, shop or restaurant

What's new in 1998: Now open Tues in July & Aug only, 11–5

O **House, garden & studio:** 1 April to 1 Nov: daily 11–5 (except Mon & Tues, but open BH Mon and see What's new above); last admission 4.30. **Events:** for details tel. 01892 891001

£ House, garden & studio £5.20, children £2.60, family ticket £13; Garden & studio only £2.60. Coaches and groups please book. No reductions

🚶 Guided tours (Wed am only) by arrangement

🛍 Shop open same days as house 11–5.30. Also Christmas shop till 20 Dec: daily except Mon & Tues 11–4

♿ Contact visitor reception on arrival for close parking to house; information sheet and wheelchairs available. Limited wheelchair access in garden, with fine views across the High Weald. Ground floor accessible, two steps to small lift (no motorised chairs) to first floor which is limited to one wheelchair at a time. Access to shop and restaurant with close parking. 2 WCs in car park

👁 Rose garden; scented plants; Braille guide

🍴 Coffee, lunches and teas; licensed self-service restaurant. Open same days as house 10.30–5. Also Christmas opening as shop 11–4. Function room enquiries 01732 863087

👶 Children's guidebook and quiz; children's meals available. No pushchairs in house. Baby-changing facility

🐕 In grounds only, on leads please

➔ (2: G6) 2ml S of Westerham, fork left off B2026 after 1½ml [188: TQ455515] *Bus:* London Links 320, 🚆 Bromley N–Westerham (passing 🚆 Bromley S); 410 Reigate–Sevenoaks (passing 🚆 Oxted and 🚆 Sevenoaks), on both alight Westerham, 2ml (tel. 0345 696996) *Station:* Edenbridge (U) 4ml; Edenbridge Town 4½ml; Oxted 5½ml; Sevenoaks 6½ml

---

CLANDON PARK 🏛 🦌 ✥ ♣ 🎭 *Surrey*

West Clandon, Guildford GU4 7RQ
Tel: 01483 222482; Infoline: 01483 223479 Fax: 01483 223479

A grand Palladian mansion, built in the early 1700s by the Venetian architect Leoni, and notable for its magnificent two-storeyed Marble Hall. The house is filled with the superb collection of 18th-century furniture, porcelain, textiles and carpets acquired in the 1920s by the connoisseur Mrs David Gubbay. The attractive gardens contain a parterre, grotto, sunken Dutch garden and a Maori house with a fascinating history

Note: The Queen's Royal Surrey Regiment Museum (tel. 01483 223419) is based at Clandon and open to visitors

What's new in 1998: Disabled WC; nursing room

House: 1 April to 29 Oct: Tues, Wed, Thur & Sun, plus Good Fri, Easter Sat & BH Mons 11.30–4.30; last admission 4. **Garden:** daily 9–dusk. **Museum:** 1 April to 29 Oct: same days as house 12–5. **Events:** concerts are held in the Marble Hall and in the grounds; contact Regional box office (tel. 01372 451596). The Saloon is available for civil wedding ceremonies and the Marble Hall for wedding receptions, as well as private and corporate functions; all enquiries are welcome on tel. 01483 224912

£ House & garden £4.20; family ticket £10.50. Special group rate £3.50 Tues, Wed & Thur only. Combined ticket with Hatchlands Park £6. Parking 300m

Coach parties welcome. Groups and morning guided tours by prior arrangement

Shop open: March (weekends only 1–5); 1 April to 29 Oct: same days as house 12–5; 1 Nov to 23 Dec: daily 1–5; tel. 01483 211412

Parking near front of house for three disabled drivers only; disabled visitors may be set down at house. Access limited to ground floor and lower-ground floor (accessible from north courtyard); no steps. Adapted WC on lower-ground floor. Ramp to garden. Electric stairclimber available to lift chairs up entrance steps to ground floor only, which is then completely level; upper floor (porcelain collections) only accessible via 40 stairs. Restaurant and shop accessible. 3 wheelchairs and 1 seatwalker available.

Braille guide

Licensed restaurant in vaulted undercroft of house for coffees, lunches and teas, same days as house 11–5. March (Sun only), Nov (Tues, Wed, Thur & Sun) and Dec (daily until 23rd) 12–5. Advance bookings for lunch advisable, especially on Sun; tel. 01483 222502. Picnicking in grounds and gardens. Tables in car park area. Refreshment kiosk in car park open Sun

Changing table available. Children's quizzes for house and garden, children's menus and highchairs. Pushchairs allowed in house Tues, Wed & Thur. No back carriers allowed

On leads in car park area only

➜ (**2**: F6) At West Clandon on A247, 3ml E of Guildford; if using A3 follow signposts to Ripley to join A247 via B2215 [186: TQ042512] *Bus:* London & Country 563 Guildford–Addlestone (passing ⌷ Clandon); otherwise London & Country 408 Guildford–Croydon, 479 Guildford–Kingston, Surrey Hills Leisure Bus 433 Guildford–Dorking (all pass close ⌷ Guildford), alight W Clandon Cross Roads, ¼ml (tel. 01737 223000) *Station:* Clandon 1ml. Turn left on main road

---

CLAREMONT LANDSCAPE GARDEN � ⌷   *Surrey*

Portsmouth Road, Esher KT10 9JG Tel: 01372 467806/469421

Claremont's creation and development involved some of the great names in garden history - Sir John Vanbrugh, Charles Bridgeman, 'Capability' Brown and William Kent were all involved. The first gardens were begun c.1715 and later that century the delights of Claremont were famed throughout Europe. The Trust has been restoring this layout following years of neglect. The many features include a lake, island with pavilion, grotto, turf amphitheatre, viewpoints and vistas

Note: The house (Claremont Fancourt School) is not NT

🅾 All year: Jan to end March: daily (except Mon) 10–5 or sunset if earlier; April to end Oct: Mon to Fri 10–6; Sat, Sun & BH Mon 10–7. *Note*: Garden closed all day 14 July and closed at 2 on 15 to 19 July. Nov to end March 1999: daily (except Mon) 10–5 or sunset if earlier. Last admission 30min before closing. Closed 25 Dec. **House (not NT):** open first weekend each month from Feb to Nov 2–4.30. **Events**: 15 to 19 July, Fête Champêtre and open-air concert; send s.a.e. for booking form to Claremont Box Office, c/o Southern Regional Office, or tel. 01372 459950 for information. Telephone bookings taken from 15 April

💷 £3 (50p discount if arriving on public transport - please present valid ticket). Family ticket (2 adults & 2 children) £8. Groups of 15+ £2.50. All coach parties must book; no coaches on Sun. Parking at entrance

🚶 Guided tours (min. 15 persons) £1.50 extra per person by prior booking (tel. 01372 469421)

🛍 Shop open 17 Jan to end March: Sat & Sun 11–4.30; April to end Oct: daily (except Mon) 11–5; Nov to 13 Dec: daily (except Mon & Tues) 11–4; 16 Jan to end March 1999: Sat & Sun 11–4. Open BH Mon

♿ Level firm gravel pathway around lake, and level grassland. Wheelchairs available. Access to tea-room and shop. WC in car park. Parking by entrance. Accessible events; for details see above

👁 Braille guide

🍴 Tea-room serving morning coffee, home-made lunches (12–2) and teas. Open as shop. In adverse weather conditions tea-room and shop may be closed

🚼 Baby-changing facilities available in WC. Highchairs in tea-room

🐕 On leads Nov to end March but not admitted April to end Oct

➜ (**2**: F6) On S edge of Esher, on E side of A307 (no access from Esher bypass) [187: TQ128634] *Bus:* London & Country 415 Victoria–Guildford (passing close ⌷ Esher) (tel. 01737 223000) *Station:* Esher 2ml; Hersham 2ml; Claygate 2ml

CLAYDON HOUSE 🏛 ✛ 🎭 *Buckinghamshire*

Middle Claydon, nr Buckingham MK18 2EY
Tel: 01296 730349 Fax: 01296 738511

One of England's most extraordinary houses. In continuous occupation by the Verney family for over 350 years, Claydon was originally a Jacobean manor house, but was remodelled in the 1750s at a time when the craze for chinoiserie was at its height. The result was the remarkable series of rooms we see today, lavishly decorated in intricately carved white woodwork covered with motifs based on Oriental birds, pagodas and summer-houses

Note: All Saints' Church (not NT) in the grounds is also open to the public Evensong: 28 June, 26 July, 23 Aug, all at 5

What's new in 1998: Collection of illustrations in water colour and other media by Sir John Verney, late cousin of Sir Ralph Verney 5th Bt of Claydon; display of uniforms and memorabilia of the citizen soldiers of Buckinghamshire presented by Bucks Military Museum Trust

🅾 4 April to 1 Nov: daily except Thur & Fri 1–5. Last admission 4.30. Closed Good Fri. Leaflets available in French, German and Spanish. **Events:** August, lantern-light concert; for details please send s.a.e. Box Office, P O Box 180, High Wycombe, Bucks HP14 4XT

💷 £4; family ticket £10. Parties of 15+ welcome Sat & Mon to Wed, £3.50; lunches available on application to Custodian

🔏 Privileged view with guide and coffee £10; please tel. for details

♿ Wheelchairs available. Car-parking close to front door; 3 steps to front door; ramps; then all ground-floor rooms accessible. Access to garden via ramps. WC. Tea-room accessible

👁 Braille guide. Guided tours by arrangement

☕ Teas open 2–5 (open at 1 on Sun & BH Mon)

🚼 Baby-changing facilities

🐕 In park on leads only

➡ (2: D2) In Middle Claydon 13ml NW of Aylesbury, 3½ml SW of Winslow; signposted from A413, A421 & A41; entrance by N drive only [165: SP720253] *Bus:* Red Rose 17 and Classic Coaches 78 from Aylesbury (passing close 🚉 Aylesbury) (tel. 0345 382000)

CLIVEDEN 🏛 ✽ ♠ 🎭 *Buckinghamshire*

Taplow, Maidenhead SL6 0JA Tel: 01628 605069 Fax: 01628 669461

Perched on cliffs above the Thames, this Italianate palace, the third house on this site, was built for the Duke of Sutherland by Charles Barry in 1850-1 and was once the home of Nancy, Lady Astor. It is now let as an hotel. The spectacular grounds include a magnificent parterre and water garden, with many miles of walks giving splendid views of the river below

What's new in 1998: New woodland walks and car park open; restaurant closed for refurbishment from 2 Nov 1998 to March 1999

O **Woodlands only**: 1 March to 1 Nov. **Entire estate**: 28 March to 1 Nov: daily 11–6; Nov & Dec: daily 11–4. **House** (three rooms open): April to Oct: Thur & Sun 3–6. Last admission 5.30. Entry by timed ticket from information kiosk. Octagon Temple open same days as house. **Events**: for details please send s.a.e. to Property Manager

£ Grounds £4.80; family ticket £12. House £1 extra. Party rates on application to the Property Manager; parties must book (no parties on Sun or BH Mon). Car-parking 400m from house. New woodland car park £2; family ticket £5. *Note:* Mooring charge on Cliveden Reach £6 per 24hrs (up to 4hrs £2) (incl. NT members) but excl. admission fee to Cliveden. Tickets available from River Warden. Mooring at suitable locations for more than ½ml downstream from Cliveden boathouse

⬛ Shop in walled garden open 28 March to 1 Nov: Wed to Sun & BH Mon (incl. Good Fri) 1–5.30; Nov to 20 Dec: Wed to Sun 12–4 (tel. 01628 665946)

♿ Garden & grounds largely accessible; route-maps, 2 self-drive powered vehicles, plus one two-seater and 4 wheelchairs available. Wheelchair access to house, but some steps; ramped access to terrace. Restaurant and shop accessible. WC. Car park 200m from house but other arrangements available

⬛ Scented rose garden

⬛ Morning coffee, light lunches, teas and vegetarian dishes, open same days as shop 11–5 in licensed Conservatory restaurant, which closes for refurbishment 2 Nov to March 1999. Parties of more than 20 must book (tel. 01628 661406). Refreshment kiosk in walled garden open Mon, Tues & Sun 11–5. No picnics in formal gardens

⬛ Highchairs available. Baby-changing facilities in WCs near main car park

⬛ In specified woodlands only; not in garden

➔ (2: E4) 3ml upstream from Maidenhead, 2ml N of Taplow; leave M4 at exit 7 onto A4, or M40 at exit 4 onto A404 to Marlow and follow signs. Entrance by main gates opposite Feathers Inn [175: SU915851] *Station:* Taplow (not Sun) 2½ml; Burnham 3ml

---

DORNEYWOOD GARDEN ✤   *Buckinghamshire*

Dorneywood, Burnham SL1 8PY

The house was given to the Trust as an official residence for either a Secretary of State or Minister of the Crown. Only the garden is open, with herbaceous borders, a rose garden, cottage and kitchen gardens, maintained in the style of the 1930s

O Garden open by written appointment only on Wed 10 June & 1 July, Sat 1 & Sun 2 Aug: 2–5. Application to the Secretary, Dorneywood Trust, at above address

£ £2.70. No reduction for parties

♿ Access to part of garden only

 (**2**: E4) Located on Dorneywood Road, SW of Burnham Beeches, 1½ml N of Burnham village, 2ml E of Cliveden [175: SU938848] *Bus:* Chiltern Rover/Bee Line 3, 44, 74, 444 High Wycombe–Heathrow Airport (passing close ⊞ Slough & Beaconsfield), alight Farnham Common, 1½ml walk through Burnham Beeches (tel. 0345 382000) *Station:* Burnham 2½ml

---

EMMETTS GARDEN ❖ 🛉 🛡 *Kent*

Ide Hill, Sevenoaks TN14 6AY
Tel: 01732 750367 Enquiries 01732 868381 Fax: 01732 868193

This charming and informal garden at the highest point in Kent was laid out in the late 19th century, with many exotic and rare trees and shrubs from across the world. There are glorious shows of daffodils and bluebells in spring, and also a rose garden and rock garden. The area was transformed by the 1987 storm and dramatic new vistas opened up, which can be enjoyed from the hilltop tea-garden

🅞 1 April to 1 Nov: Sat, Sun & Wed, plus BH Mon & Good Fri 11–5.30. Last admission 4.30. **Events:** for details of concerts and other events tel. 01892 891001

💷 £3, children £1.50; family ticket £7.50. Pre-booked parties £2.20

🛉 Guided pre-booked parties by arrangement; please tel. 01732 868381

📷 Small shop in tea-room, open same days as garden 11.30–4.30

♿ Most parts of garden accessible; volunteer-driven golf buggy (seats 3) available from car park to ticket hut only; three wheelchairs available for garden. WC. Access to shop and tea-room

🐾 Fountain and waterfall; scented azaleas and bluebells in spring, roses in summer. Beware sheer drop at end of shrub garden

🍴 Tea-room open same days as garden 11.30–4.30

🛉 Baby-changing facilities

🌲 Tree trail

🐕 On leads please

➔ (**2**: G6) 1½ml S of A25 on Sundridge to Ide Hill road, 1½ml N of Ide Hill off B2042, leave M25 at exit 5, then 4ml [188: TQ477524] *Bus:* East Surrey 404 from ⊞ Sevenoaks, alight Ide Hill, 1½ml (tel. 0345 696996) *Station:* Sevenoaks 4½ml; Penshurst (U) 5½ml

HATCHLANDS PARK 🏛 🏠 ❀ 🌳 🚶 🛡 *Surrey*

East Clandon, Guildford GU4 7RT
Tel: 01483 222482; Infoline: 01483 223479 Fax: 01483 223176

Built in 1758 for Admiral Boscawen, hero of the Battle of Louisburg, and set in a beautiful Repton park offering a variety of park and woodland walks, Hatchlands contains splendid interiors by Robert Adam, decorated in appropriately nautical style. It also houses the Cobbe collection, the world's largest group of keyboard instruments associated with famous composers, eg Purcell, J.C. Bach, Mozart, Chopin, Mahler and Elgar. There is also a small garden by Gertrude Jekyll, flowering from late May to early July

What's new in 1998: New shop entrance and layout

🅾 **House:** 1 April to 29 Oct: Tues, Wed, Thur, Sun & BH Mon (and Fri in Aug) 2–5.30. Last admission 5. **Garden:** open same as house. Park walks April to Oct: daily 11.30–6. No dogs on walks. **Events:** NT open-air summer concerts, please contact Regional Box Office (tel. 01372 451596); Cobbe Foundation concerts on selected Wed lunchtimes (for details/bookings tel. 0181 944 6316)

💷 House and grounds £4.20; family ticket £10.50. Special group rate £3.50 (Tues to Thur only). Combined ticket with Clandon Park £6. Park walks and garden only £1.70. Parking 300m

🚶 Guided tours are not available but stereo audio tour of house and keyboard instruments available for hire, £1 (incl. NT members)

🛍 Shop open same days as house 1.30–5.30 (tel. 01483 224523)

♿ Staff-driven buggy service available from car park to house (ask at kiosk on arrival). Access to ground floor, terrace and part of garden. WC. Wheelchairs and wheeled walker/seat available. Access to restaurant in courtyard for wheelchair users. Fanny Boscawen walk (short and relatively flat)

👁 Braille and audio guides (hire fee £1); also Standard and Basic language versions

🍽 Licensed restaurant for lunches and home-made teas 12.30–5.30 same days as house (tel. 01483 211120). Limited advance booking for lunch available, especially advisable on concert days (usually Wed). Picnicking in grounds

🚼 Facilities in ladies' WC for nursing mothers; changing table. Children's menu; highchairs

🐕 On lead in car park area only

➡ (2: F6) E of East Clandon, N of A246 Guildford–Leatherhead road [187: TQ063516] *Bus:* London & Country 408 Guildford–Croydon, 479 Guildford-Kingston, Surrey Hills Leisure Bus 433 Guildford–Dorking (all pass close ⊠ Guildford) (tel. 01737 223000) *Station:* Clandon 2½ml, Horsley 3ml

HINTON AMPNER GARDEN 🏠 ❀ 🛡 *Hampshire*

Bramdean, nr Alresford SO24 0LA Tel: 01962 771305 Fax: 01962 771305

Scented plants, unexpected vistas and glorious countryside combine to provide year-round interest in this splendid 20th-century shrub garden. The garden achieves the vision of tranquility of its creator, Ralph Dutton, by uniting a formal design with various informal plantings in pastel shades. The house, restored after a fire in 1960, displays his fine collection of Regency furniture and Italian paintings

Note: The house is privately tenanted and is open by arrangement with the tenant

○ **Garden:** 15 & 22 March, then 28 March to end Sept: Tues, Wed, Sat, Sun & BH Mon 1.30–5.30; last admission 5. **House:** 28 March to end Sept: Tues & Wed only, plus Sat & Sun in Aug 1.30–5.30. No access to grounds before 1.15. **Events:** 17 May, Spring Plant Fair 11–5; details on application

£ House & garden £4, garden only £3. Special entrance for coaches; please book in advance. No group bookings in Aug. Party rate on application

♿ Most of house, garden and tea-room accessible; map of wheelchair route available. Four wheelchairs available. Parking in front of house on request at kiosk. WCs by house

◉ Braille guides to house and garden. Scented plants

▣ Tea-room open same days as garden 1.30–5; light lunches served until 2. Picnics in grass car park only

🐕 No dogs

➔ **(2: D7)** On A272, 1ml W of Bramdean village, 8ml E of Winchester, leave M3 at exit 9 and follow signs to Petersfield [185: SU597275] *Bus:* Stagecoach Hampshire Bus 67 Winchester–Petersfield (passing close ⇌ Winchester & ⇌ Petersfield) (tel. 01256 464501) *Station:* Alresford (Mid Hants Rly) 4ml; Winchester 9ml

HUGHENDEN MANOR 🏠 ❀ 🌷 🛡 *Buckinghamshire*

High Wycombe HP14 4LA Tel: 01494 532580

The home of Victorian prime minister and statesman Benjamin Disraeli from 1847 until his death in 1881. Most of his furniture, books and pictures remain, and there are beautiful walks through the surrounding park and woodland. The garden is a re-creation of the colourful design of his wife, Mary Anne.

Note: Certain rooms have little electric light. Visitors wishing to make close study of interior of the house should avoid dull days, particularly early and late in the season

○ **House:** 1 to 30 March: Sat & Sun only; 1 April to 31 Oct: daily except Mon & Tues (closed Good Fri, but open BH Mon) 1–5. Last admission 4.30. Closed Good Fri. On BH weekends and other busy days entry is by timed ticket only, on a first come, first served basis. **Garden:** same days as house 12–5. **Park & woodland:** open all year. **Events:** for details please send s.a.e. to The Box Office, PO Box 180, High Wycombe, Bucks HP14 4XT

£ House & garden: £4; family ticket £10. Garden only £1, children 50p. Park & woodland free. Parties must book in advance – rates on application to the Estate Office; no parties Sat, Sun or BH Mon. Coach-parking: space for one coach only; car park 200m from house. Please show membership cards and purchase tickets from the stableyard ticket office

⚔ Guided tours available for pre-booked parties on request

🛍 Shop open as house. Also Nov to 20 Dec: Wed to Sun 11–3 (tel. 01494 440718)

♿ Access to all ground-floor rooms; close car-parking arrangements; garden has some steep paths, best seen from terrace; park and woodland very hilly. WC. Wheelchairs available. Good access to shop and tea-room

👁 Braille and taped guides. Large-print short guides available on loan

🍴 Tea-room open same days as house: Wed to Fri 1–5, Sat, Sun & BH Mon 12–5. Also Nov to 20 Dec, Sat & Sun 11–3

👶 Children's guidebook available during 1998. Baby-changing facilities. Children's menu and highchairs. Loan of all-terrain buggy for outdoors. Baby front slings and toddler reins available

📖 Study base available for pre-booked groups. Guided tours linked to Victorian history and environmental education can also be arranged. Handling collection available. Rates and details from Estate Office

🐕 Dogs welcome except in house and formal gardens, where only guide dogs are permitted. Dog rings in stableyard and shady parking in car park

➔ (2: E4) 1½ml N of High Wycombe; on W side of the Great Missenden road (A4128) [165: SU866955] *Bus*: Chiltern Rover 323/4 High Wycombe–Aylesbury (passing close ⊞ High Wycombe) (tel. 0345 382000). *Note*: long and steep walk to entrance *Station*: High Wycombe 2ml

IGHTHAM MOTE 🏠 ✝ ✿ 🐾 👶 ⚔ *Kent*

Ivy Hatch, Sevenoaks TN15 0NT Tel: 01732 810378 Fax: 01732 811029

A superb moated manor house, nestling in a sunken valley and dating from 1340 onwards. A comprehensive programme of repair was begun in 1988. The main features of the house span many centuries and include the Great Hall, old chapel and crypt, Tudor chapel with painted ceiling, drawing room with Jacobean fireplace, frieze and 18th-century wallpaper, and the Robinson Library. There is an extensive garden and interesting walks in the surrounding woodland

What's new in 1998: Re-opening of the North West Quarter and upper floor of the house following completion of extensive conservation and repair work, including the Tudor Chapel and ceiling panels and the refurbished Billiards Room and Drawing Room

🕐 1 April to 1 Nov: daily except Tues & Sat 11–5.30. Last admission 5. Car park open dawn to dusk throughout the year. Estate walks leaflet available. **Events:** for details tel. 01892 891001

£ £4.50, children £2.25; family ticket £11.25. Pre-booked parties of 20 or more weekday afternoons £3.50 (no reduction Sun & BH)

⟨K⟩ Free introductory talks. Pre-booked special guided conservation tour for groups of 20 or more on open weekday mornings only; tel. 01732 810378 for details (group reductions only apply after noon). Guided walks to Old Soar Manor

⟨🗁⟩ Shop open same days as house, 11.30–5.30 (tel. 01732 811203)

⟨♿⟩ Access to most of ground floor, garden (some gravel paths), cobbled courtyard, conservation exhibition, tea pavilion and part of shop only; two wheelchairs available. Woodland estate walk accessible. Contact Property Manager in advance or enquire at ticket office on arrival for closer parking to house. WC

⟨◉⟩ Braille guide. Some contents may be touched on request

⟨▮⟩ Tea pavilion open same days as house, 11.30–5. Oct hours vary – weather dependent. Picnic area in car park. No picnics in gardens

⟨🛉⟩ Baby-feeding/changing facilities available; children's quiz

⟨▮⟩ Teachers' resource book. Special tours for schools, contact Property Manager for details. Woodland shelter in grounds for use by groups

⟨🐕⟩ No dogs in gardens or house, but welcome on leads on estate walks

→ (2: H6) 6ml E of Sevenoaks, off A25, and 2½ml S of Ightham, off A227 [188: TQ584535] *Bus:* Wealden Beeline 220–2 ⊠ Borough Green–⊠ Tunbridge Wells, alight Fairlawne, thence ½ml (footpath); East Surrey 404 Sevenoaks-Plaxtol (passing ⊠ Sevenoaks), alight Ivy Hatch, ¾ml; otherwise Kentish Bus 306 ⊠ Sevenoaks–⊠ Gravesend (passing ⊠ Borough Green), alight Ightham Common, 1½ml (tel. 0345 696996). *Station:* Borough Green & Wrotham 3½ml; Hildenborough 4ml

KING'S HEAD 🏨   *Buckinghamshire*

The Market Square, Aylesbury HP20 1TA
Tel: (Regional Office) 01494 528051 Fax: 01494 463310

A coaching inn, dating from 1450 and of particular interest for its large mullioned window, which contains fragments of 15th-century glass carrying the arms of Henry VI and his wife, Margaret of Anjou

🅾 This property is to be re-let, and at time of going to press opening times are not yet finalised. Please contact above number for information about opening arrangements

➡ (**2**: E3) At NW corner of Market Square *Bus:* from surrounding areas (tel. 0345 382000) *Station:* Aylesbury 400m

KNOLE 🏠 ✤ 🍴 🕴 🛡   *Kent*

Sevenoaks TN15 0RP
Tel: 01732 462100 Infoline: 01732 450608 Fax: 01732 465528

One of the great houses of England, set in a magnificent deer park. The original 15th-century house was enlarged and embellished in 1603 by the 1st Earl of Dorset, one of Queen Elizabeth's 'favourites', and has remained unaltered ever since - a rare survival. The thirteen state rooms open to the public contain magnificent collections: 17th-century Royal Stuart furniture, including three state beds, silver furniture and the prototype of the famous Knole Settee, outstanding tapestries and textiles, and important portraits by Van Dyck, Gainsborough, Lely, Kneller and Reynolds

What's new in 1998: New hours of opening; display on the history of country house brewing in the Brewhouse where NT Foundation for Art Interiors are now also on view

○ **House**: 1 April to 1 Nov: Wed, Thur, Fri & Sat 12–4; last admission 3.30 (but 1hr recommended for visit); Sun, Good Fri & BH Mon 11–5; last admission 4.30. Pre-booked groups on Wed, Thur, Fri & Sat 12–3. **Park**: open daily to pedestrians by courtesy of Lord Sackville. **Garden**: May to Sept: first Wed in each month only, by courtesy of Lord Sackville, 11–4; last admission 3. **Events**: programme of concerts and lectures; for details tel. 01892 891001

£ **House**: £5, children £2.50; family ticket £12.50. Pre-booked parties £4. Parking (NT members free) £2.50. Park free to pedestrians. Only vehicles carrying visitors to the house are allowed in the park. **Garden (note limited opening times)**: £1, children 50p

⫟ Guided tours for pre-booked parties on Thur 10–12 throughout season; normal admission price plus £2 guiding fee per head

⌂ Shop open as house, except Wed to Sat 11–4.30. Christmas shop 11–4. (tel. 01732 743748)

♿ Access to Great Hall, Stone Court, Green Court, shop, restaurant, garden (only open on first Wed in month: May to end Sept) and park; WCs in Green Court and near restaurant; wheelchair available

◉ Braille guide; several items to touch. Herb and wilderness gardens, subject to limited opening (see above)

◗ Tea-room open as house (except Wed to Sat, when open 11–4.30), serving morning coffee, lunch and tea

⫟ Children's guide, worksheets and objects of the month. Highchairs in tea-room, children's portions. Baby-changing facilities

▦ Education room, handling and costume collections. Strong links to Tudor and Stuart aspects of curriculum, living history, teacher's guide. Excellent collection of historical portraits. Contact Education Assistant for details (tel. 01732 462100)

⫟ In park only, on lead. Please do not feed the deer; they can be dangerous

→ (**2**: H6) Off M25 London Orbital at S end of Sevenoaks town; just E of A225 [188: TQ532543] *Bus*: Special connecting service from ⊞ Sevenoaks (tel. 0345 484950), with combined transport/admission tickets available and concessions for NT members, families and rail-card holders; otherwise from surrounding areas to Sevenoaks, thence ¾ml (tel. 0345 696996) *Station*: Sevenoaks 1½ml

---

LAMB HOUSE 🏠 ✿   *East Sussex*

West Street, Rye TN31 7ES
Tel: (Regional Office) 01892 890651 Fax: 01892 890110

A delightful brick-fronted house, dating from the early 18th century and typical of the attractive town of Rye. This was the home of writer Henry James from 1898 to 1916, and later of author E. F. Benson. Some of James's personal possessions can be seen, and there is a charming walled garden

Note: The house is administered and largely maintained on the Trust's behalf by a tenant

○ 1 April to 31 Oct: Wed & Sat only 2–6. Last admission 5.30

£ £2.50, children £1.25. No reduction for parties. WCs and car park available in Rye

🐾 No dogs in house or garden

➔ (2: J7) In West Street, facing W end of church [198: TQ920202]
Bus: From surrounding areas to Rye (tel. 01273 474747) *Station:* Rye ½ml

---

LANGDON CLIFFS 🏞 🖼 🚶

Kent

near Dover | Tel/fax: 01304 202756

The gateway to Britain, the White Cliffs of Dover are internationally famous. The Trust owns 5½ml in total, mainly east of Dover town and featuring chalk downland designated a Site of Special Scientific Interest, with breathtaking views. This is an excellent place from which to watch ferry and shipping traffic in the Straits of Dover, and is also the start of a 2ml coastal walk to South Foreland Lighthouse (see p.138)

○ All year, daily. Car park open 10–6, sometimes closing later in summer.

£ Car park £1.20 (NT members free)

🍴 Refreshment kiosk

🐾 Welcome, but must be kept under strict control at all times

➔ (2: L6) *Bus:* Stagecoach East Kent 100, 200 Dover–Margate to within ½ml (tel. 0345 696996) *Station:* Dover Priory 2½ml

---

LEITH HILL 🏛 🏞 🚶

Surrey

Coldharbour | Tel/fax: 01306 711777

The highest point in south-east England, crowned by an 18th-century Gothic tower, from which there are magnificent views. The surrounding woodland contains ancient stands of hazel and oak, and there is a splendid display of rhododendrons in May–June

○ **Tower:** 1 April to end Sept: Wed 12–5; Sat, Sun & BH 11–5. Last admission 4.30. Also open weekends Oct to end March 11–3.30. Last admission 3 (tel. 01306 712434)

£ Tower: 80p. No reduction for groups. Rhododendron wood: £1.50 per car. Parking in designated areas along road at foot of the hill, ½ml walk from tower, some steep gradients. No direct vehicular access to summit. No coaches. Information room and telescope in tower. Circular trail guide available from dispenser £1

🚶 Guided walks at intervals throughout the year. Groups by prior arrangement with the Warden (tel. 01306 711777)

♿ Access path to upper part of rhododendron wood; car park

🍴 Light refreshments open same times as tower. Picnic areas alongside tower and within rhododendron wood

■ Educational groups for day visits and residential groups catered for by prior arrangement with North Downs Education Officer (tel. 01306 742809)

🐕 Dogs not allowed in rhododendron wood picnic area; elsewhere in rhododendron wood on leads. No dogs in tower

➔ (2: F6) On summit of Leith Hill, 1ml SW of Coldharbour A29/B2126 [187: TQ139432]. Rhododendron wood: [187: TQ131427] *Bus:* Surrey Hills Leisure Bus 433 from ⊛ Guildford & ⊛ Dorking, Sun, May to Sept only; otherwise Tillingbourne 21, 31 Guildford–Dorking (passing close ⊛ Guildford and passing ⊛ Chilworth and Dorking), alight Holmbury St Mary 2½ml (tel. 01737 223000) *Station:* Holmwood (U), not Sun, 2½ml; Dorking 5½ml

LONG CRENDON COURTHOUSE 🏠 *Buckinghamshire*

Long Crendon, Aylesbury HP18 9AN

A 14th-century two-storeyed building, partly half-timbered and probably first used as a wool store. The manorial courts were held here, from the reign of Henry V until Victorian times

O Upper floor only April to end Sept: Wed 2–6; Sat, Sun & BH Mon 11–6

£ £1. No reduction for parties. No WC

➔ (2: D3) 2ml N of Thame, via B4011, close to the church [165: SP698091] *Bus:* Aylesbury & The Vale 260/1, Aylesbury–Thame (not Sun) (passing ⊛ Haddenham & Thame Parkway) (tel. 0345 382000) *Station:* Haddenham & Thame Parkway 2ml by footpath, 4ml by road

MONK'S HOUSE 🏠 ✿ *East Sussex*

Rodmell, Lewes BN7 3HF
Tel: (Regional Office) 01892 890651 Fax: 01892 890110

A small weather-boarded house, the home of Leonard and Virginia Woolf until Leonard's death in 1969. The rooms inside reflect the life and times of the literary circle in which Virginia moved

Note: The house and garden are administered and largely maintained by the tenant on the Trust's behalf

O 1 April to 31 Oct: Wed & Sat 2–5.30. Last admission 5

£ £2.50, children £1.25. No reduction for parties; max. 15 people in house at a time. Parties only by prior arrangement with the tenant. Car park 50m; village street too narrow for coaches; drivers please set passengers down at main road junction, and park elsewhere

🐕 No dogs in house or garden

➔ (2: G8) 4ml SE of Lewes, off former A275 in Rodmell village, near church (no access from A26) [198: TQ421064] *Bus:* Leisurelink 123 Lewes–Newhaven (passing ⊛ Lewes) (tel. 01273 474747) *Station:* Southease (U) 1¼ml

MOTTISFONT ABBEY GARDEN, HOUSE & ESTATE

Hampshire

Mottisfont, nr Romsey SO51 0LP Tel: 01794 340757 Fax: 01794 341492

Set amidst glorious countryside along the River Test, this 12th-century Augustinian priory was converted into a private house after the Dissolution, and still retains the spring or 'font' from which its name is derived. The abbey contains a drawing room decorated by Rex Whistler and Derek Hill's 20th-century picture collection, but the key attraction is the grounds, with magnificent trees, walled gardens and National Collection of Roses. The estate includes Mottisfont village and surrounding farmland and woods

What's new in 1998: The rose garden is currently undergoing a phased programme of soil and plant renovation; several beds will be replanted each year

Garden & grounds : 28 March to 28 Oct: daily except Thur & Fri 12–6 (or dusk if earlier). Rose season mid-June to mid-July; check recorded message for state of roses, 01794 341220. Extended opening 13–28 June, daily 11–8.30. Last admission to grounds 1hr before closing. **House: Whistler Room & cellarium:** same days as garden 1–5. **Derek Hill picture collection:** Sun & Mon 1–5. **Events:** open-air events in summer; for details contact Regional Box Office (tel. 01372 451596). Rooms in the house are available for private and commercial functions, seminars and civil wedding ceremonies; please contact Visitor Services Manager (tel. 01794 340757). Free parking

£ Garden, grounds & Whistler Room: £4; family ticket £10; when roses are at their best £5; family ticket £12. No reduction for parties; coaches please book in advance. *Note:* As the roses are renowned for their scent, please refrain from smoking in the walled garden during the rose season. To appreciate the roses evening viewing is recommended

⬛ Shop and plant sales open same days as garden,12.30–5.30, but 11–8 during 13–28 June and 12.30–4 in Oct (tel. 01794 341901)

♿ Extensive garden, lawns and gravel drive can be arduous. Rose garden is accessible to wheelchair users. Wheelchairs and two volunteer-driver buggies available. *Note*: paths not suitable for small-wheeled narrow wheelchairs. WC

◉ Braille guide. Many scents in rose garden

▣ Licensed restaurant (capacity 60). Lunches and home-made teas 12–5 same days as garden. Dining rooms available for pre-booked lunches, suppers and dinner parties; contact Visitor Services Manager (tel. 01794 340757). Tea garden open (in the tennis court) during busy periods 12–5, 11–7 during 13–28 June

♿ Baby-changing facilities; children's menus

🐕 Dogs in car park only (no shade). Delightful woodland walks may be enjoyed in Spearywell Woods and Great Copse; details from property

➡ (2: B7) 4½ml NW of Romsey, ¾ml W of A3057 [185: SU327270]
Station: Dunbridge (U) ¾ml

MOTTISTONE MANOR GARDEN ✿ ♥   *Isle of Wight*

Bookings and postal enquiries to the Gardener, Manor Cottage, Hoxall Lane, Mottistone PO30 4ED

A relatively recent garden, noted for its colourful herbaceous borders, grassy terraces planted with fruit trees and stunning sea views. The 16th- and 17th-century manor house lies at the heart of the Mottistone Estate, which offers delightful walks between the Downs and the coast

What's new in 1998: 'The Shack'. A 1930s timber summer-house, set out as a retreat and workroom by architects John Seely (2nd Lord Mottistone, donor of the Mottistone Estate to the NT) and Paul Paget; original fixtures and furniture. Teas in the garden, weather permitting

🅾 **Garden:** 1 April to 7 Oct: Wed & BH Mon 2–5.30. Also Sun in July & Aug 2–5.30. Last admission 5. Groups by written appointment. **House:** open Aug BH Mon only 2–5.30; guided tours for NT members 10.30–12. **Events:** summer open-air concerts

£ Garden £2. No reduction for groups. Parking 50m

♿ Not recommended for wheelchair users; steep slopes

▣ Teas available in garden

🐕 On leads

➡ (2: C9) At Mottistone, 2ml W of Brighstone on B3399 [196: SZ406838]
Bus: Southern Vectis 12 Newport–Alum Bay (tel. 01983 827005)
Ferry: Yarmouth (Wightlink Ltd) 6ml (tel. 0990 827744) E Cowes (Red Funnel) 12ml (tel. 01703 334010)

THE NEEDLES OLD BATTERY 🖼 🏞 🎭   *Isle of Wight*

West Highdown PO39 0JH Tel: 01983 754772 during opening hours

The threat of a French invasion prompted the construction in 1862 of this spectacularly sited fort, which still retains its original gun barrels. The laboratory, searchlight position and position-finding cells have all been restored and a 65m tunnel leads to stunning views of the Hampshire and Dorset coastline

O 22 March to 29 Oct: daily except Fri & Sat (but open Easter weekend and daily in July & Aug) 10.30–5. Last admission 4.30. *Note*: Property will be closed during adverse weather conditions; tel. property on day of visit to check. **Events**: send s.a.e. or tel. for information

£ £2.40; family ticket £6. No reduction for groups; school groups can be conducted by an NT guide by prior arrangement; a special charge applies. No vehicular access to Battery (visitors with disabilities by prior arrangement). Many paths are steep and not suitable for people with walking difficulties. Access to the searchlight is by narrow spiral staircase, with further steps to tea-room and headland beyond the Battery. Parking 1ml away at Alum Bay (not NT; charge £2.50), or park in Freshwater Bay (IOW Council) or Highdown car park (NT) and walk over Downs (or see bus services below). Children and dogs must be kept under strict control because of the cliffs

𝕏 School groups/special visits 22 March to 29 Oct (but not Aug) by appointment

🛍 Shop open same days as Battery 11–4.30

♿ Some access; car-parking 1ml from Battery, but accompanied wheelchair users may park nearer by prior arrangement only with the Administrator

🍽 Tea-room (spectacular views) open same days as Battery 11–5 (last admission 4.30)

👶 Children's guide and quiz sheets; the children's exhibition tells the story of 'The Needles at War' and cartoon information boards throughout explain how the Battery functioned

🐕 Dogs welcome on leads

➜ (2: B9) At Needles Headland, W of Freshwater Bay and Alum Bay (B3322) [196: SZ300848] *Bus*: Southern Vectis 42 Yarmouth–Needles, April to Oct only; otherwise any service to Alum Bay, thence 1ml (tel. 01983 827005) *Ferry*: Yarmouth (Wightlink Ltd) 5ml (tel. 0990 827744); E Cowes (Red Funnel) 16ml (tel. 01703 334010)

NYMANS GARDEN 🖼 ❖ 𝕏 🎭   *West Sussex*

Handcross, nr Haywards Heath RH17 6EB Tel: 01444 400321/400777

One of the great gardens of the Sussex Weald, and still retaining much of its distinctive family style in the historic collection of plants, shrubs and trees. This is reflected also in the surrounding estate, with its woodland walks and wild garden, and in the many rare and exotic species collected from overseas. The Messels family's creative character is much in evidence in Lady Rosse's library, drawing room and forecourt garden

What's new in 1998: In June & July the garden only will be open Sundays until 9

O **Garden:** 1 March to 1 Nov: daily except Mon & Tues (but open BH Mon) 11–6 or sunset if earlier; last admission 5.30. During June & July the garden only will be open on Sun till 9 – picnics welcome. Winter 1998/9: Sat & Sun, including restaurant & shop, 12–4 (last admission 3.30), but restricted according to ground conditions; tel. 01444 400321 for information. **House:** Lady Rosse's library, drawing room and forecourt garden will be open free of charge (as part of garden visit) 1 March to 1 Nov: same days as garden 12–4. Space is very limited and access cannot be guaranteed for every visitor; queuing likely and timed tickets may be in operation

£ £5; family ticket £12.50. Groups £4. Joint ticket which includes same day entry to Standen £7, available Wed to Fri. Car park at entrance; coaches *must* book in advance, with reduction available for groups of 15+ arriving by coach in Sept & Oct - tel. 01444 400321. Picnics welcome outside formal garden

🛍 Shop and plant sales open same days and times as garden. Also Nov daily (except Mon & Tues):11–4; Christmas shop 1 to 24 Dec: 11–4 (tel. 01444 400157)

♿ Garden, licensed tea-room and shop accessible; wheelchair route indicated around garden (map available); wheelchairs available on request. Limited wheelchair access to house during quieter periods only. WCs

👓 Braille guide. Old roses and other scented plants

🍽 Coffee, light lunches and home-made teas in licensed tea-room 11–5, same days as shop. Limited menu Nov to end Feb 1999. Open for Christmas lunches. Kiosk open (weather permitting) May to Sept 11–6. The Pavilion (restaurant) is available for private and commercial functions with limited associated use of the garden; please contact Property Manager for details

👶 Changing table in WCs at car park and tea-room. Highchair available in tea-room

🐕 In car park only, except guide dogs

➔ (**2**: G7) On B2114 at Handcross, 4½ml S of Crawley, just off London–Brighton M23/A23 [187: TQ265294] *Bus:* London & Country 773 Brighton–Crawley; Brighton & Hove 33 Haywards Heath–Crawley (tel. 0345 959099). Alight Handcross, ¼ml. All pass ☒ Crawley *Station:* Balcombe 4½ml; Crawley 5½ml

---

OAKHURST COTTAGE 🏠 👤 *Surrey*

Hambledon, nr Godalming GU8 4HF Tel: 01428 683207 (Witley Centre)

A small 16th-century timber-framed cottage, restored and furnished as a simple labourer's dwelling. There is a delightful garden containing typical contemporary plants

O 30 March to end Oct: Wed, Thur, Sat, Sun & BH Mon 2–5. Strictly by appointment only

£ £2.50, incl. guided tour. No reduction for groups. Schools & groups by special arrangement any day or evening. Parking 200m. No WC

→ (2: E6) *Bus:* Guildford & West Surrey 503 from Godalming (Wed only) (passes close ✠ Godalming); otherwise Stagecoach Hants & Surrey 71 Guildford–Hindhead (passes close ✠ Godalming), alight Lane End 1ml (tel. 01737 223000) *Station:* Witley 1½ml

OLD SOAR MANOR 🏠 *Kent*

Plaxtol, Borough Green TN15 0QX Tel: 01732 810378

The solar block of a late 13th-century knight's dwelling

O 1 April to 30 Sept: daily 10–6

£ Free. Exhibition on Manor and surrounding areas. No WCs

🚶 Guided walks from Ightham Mote; please tel. for details

🐕 No dogs please

→ (2: H6) 2ml S of Borough Green (A25); approached via A227 and Plaxtol; narrow lane, unsuitable for coaches [188: TQ619541] *Bus:* Wealden Beeline 220-2 ✠ Borough Green–✠ Tunbridge Wells; East Surrey 404 Sevenoaks–Plaxtol (passing ✠ Sevenoaks); on both alight E end of Plaxtol, thence ¾ml by footpath (tel. 0345 696996) *Station:* Borough Green & Wrotham 2½ml

OLD TOWN HALL, NEWTOWN 🏠 🚶 *Isle of Wight*

Ken Cottage, Upper Lane, Brighstone PO30 4AT Tel: 01983 741052

The small, now tranquil village of Newtown once sent two members to Parliament and the Town Hall was the setting for often turbulent elections. An exhibition inside depicts the exploits of 'Ferguson's Gang', an anonymous group of Trust benefactors

O 29 March to 28 Oct: Mon, Wed & Sun (but open Good Fri, Easter Sat and Tues & Thur in July & Aug) 2–5. Last admission 4.45

£ £1.20. No reduction for groups

🚶 Guided tours by written appointment

♿ Not recommended for wheelchair users; flights of steps. WC

👁 Braille and large-print guides

🏫 School groups welcome by appointment

🐕 No dogs

→ (2: C9) Between Newport and Yarmouth, 1ml N of A3054 [196: SZ424905] *Bus:* Southern Vectis 35 from Newport; otherwise 7 ✠ Ryde Esplanade–Freshwater (passing Yarmouth Ferry Terminal), alight Barton's Corner, 1ml (tel. 01983 827005) *Ferry:* Yarmouth (Wightlink Ltd) 5ml (tel. 0990 827744); E Cowes (Red Funnel) 11ml (tel. 01703 334010)

OWLETTS 🏠 ❀

Kent

The Street, Cobham, Gravesend DA12 3AP
Tel: (Regional Office) 01892 890651 Fax: 01892 890110

A modest red-brick Charles II house, with contemporary staircase and plasterwork ceiling; the former home of Sir Herbert Baker, the architect, famous for his work in India (where he worked with Lutyens) and South Africa

Note: The property is administered and maintained on the Trust's behalf by the tenant, who is a descendant of Sir Herbert Baker

🅾 1 April to 30 Sept: Wed & Thur only, 2–5. Last admission 4.30

💷 £2, children £1.10. Parties by arrangement; please write to tenant. No WC

🐕 No dogs in house or garden

➔ (2: H5) 1ml S of A2 at W end of village, at junction of roads from Dartford and Sole Street [177: TQ665687] *Station:* Sole Street 1ml

PETWORTH HOUSE AND PARK 🏠 ♣ 🎭

West Sussex

Petworth GU28 0AE
Tel: 01798 342207 Infoline: 01798 343929 Fax: 01798 342963

A magnificent late 17th-century mansion and beautiful park, landscaped by 'Capability' Brown and immortalised in Turner's paintings. The house contains the Trust's finest collection of pictures, with works by Turner, Van Dyck, Reynolds and Blake, as well as ancient and neo-classical sculpture, fine furniture and carving by Grinling Gibbons. The Servants' Block contains interesting kitchens and other servants' rooms. On weekdays, additional family rooms are open to visitors

What's new in 1998: Programme of special tours and conservation demonstrations on Mon (not July & Aug); please apply for details

🅾 **House:** 28 March to 1 Nov: daily except Thur & Fri (but open Good Fri) 1–5.30. Last admission to house 4.30; kitchens 5. Additional rooms shown weekdays (not BH Mon). **Pleasure grounds and car park** 12–6 (opens 11 on BH Mon and July & Aug) for walks, picnics and access to tea-room, shop and Petworth town. **Park:** all year, daily 8 to sunset (closed 26–28 June from 12). **Events:** 23–25 May, Craft Festival; 26–28 June, open-air concerts (NT members charged for these events). For details of exhibitions and other events please send s.a.e. or contact Regional Box Office (tel. 01372 451596)

💷 £5; family ticket £12.50. Pre-booked groups of 15+ £4.50. Coach parties alight at Church Lodge entrance, coaches then park in NT car park. Coach parties must book in advance due to limited parking; please contact Administration Office. Free entry to park

🚶 Guided tours by arrangement on Mon, Tues & Wed mornings (additional charge); contact Administration Office (tel. 01798 342207)

🛍 Shop open same days as house 12–5. BH Mon, July & Aug only open 11–5. Christmas shopping

♿ Car park is 800m from house. Vehicle available to take mobility impaired visitors to house; tel. for timetable. Alternatively they may be set down at the Church Lodge entrance; drivers should make arrangements with the Administration Office. All ground-floor public rooms accessible; wheelchairs available. Illustrated folder available of first floor bedrooms. WC in servants' block. Shop and tea-room accessible. Pleasure grounds accessible; parts of park possible, but mostly rough grass

⎆ Braille guides to house and servants' block

⚏ Coffee, light lunches and teas in licensed tea-room 12–5 same days as house; BH Mon, July & Aug only 11–5. Private functions catered for; also pre-booked Christmas lunches (tel. 01798 344080)

♿ Baby-feeding and changing facilities; highchair. No prams in house but pushchairs admitted. Children's guide and free quizzes

■ Details of educational programme from Education Officer (te. 01798 343748)

🐕 Dogs in park only, but must be kept under close control

➡ (2: F7) In centre of Petworth (A272/A283) [197: SU976218]; house car park well signposted, car park on A283; pedestrian access from Petworth town and from A272. No vehicles in park *Bus:* Stagecoach Coastline 1 Worthing-Midhurst, Brighton & Hove 1B Worthing–⏚ Petersfield (both pass ⏚ Pulborough) (tel. 0345 959099) *Station:* Pulborough 5¼ml

PITSTONE WINDMILL ✖   *Buckinghamshire*

Ivinghoe

One of the oldest post-mills in Britain, dating from 1627 and restored entirely by volunteers

◉ June to end Aug (Sun only) and May BH: 2.30–6. Last admission 5.30

£ £1, children 30p. For details of arrangements for parties, contact David Goseltine, Holland Cottage, Whipsnade, Dunstable, Beds LU6 2LG (tel. 01582 872303). Parking 200m (by B488). No WC

♿ Area around mill accessible but strong pusher needed to negotiate track from car park. Mill machinery not accessible; long flight of wooden steps

➡ (2: E3) ½ml S of Ivinghoe, 3ml NE of Tring, just W of B488 [165: SP946158] *Bus:* Aylesbury & The Vale 61 Aylesbury–Luton (passing close ⏚ Aylesbury & Luton) (tel. 0345 382000) *Station:* Tring 2½ml; Cheddington 2½ml

POLESDEN LACEY ⊞ ⎈ ⎆ ♿ ⛝   *Surrey*

Great Bookham, nr Dorking RH5 6BD Tel: Infoline: 01372 458203; House: 01372 452048; Restaurant: 01372 456190; Shop: 01372 457230 Fax: 01372 452023

In an exceptional setting on the North Downs, this Regency villa was extensively remodelled in 1906 by the Hon. Mrs Ronald Greville, a well-known Edwardian hostess. Her collection of fine paintings, furniture, porcelain and silver are displayed in the reception rooms and

corridors, as they were at the time of her celebrated house parties. There are extensive grounds, a walled rose garden, lawns and landscape walks. King George VI and Queen Elizabeth The Queen Mother spent part of their honeymoon here

What's new in 1998: Guided group tours of house and grounds Tues to Fri mornings by prior appointment – extra charge; wedding receptions may be held in marquees in the grounds

House: 1 April to 1 Nov: daily except Mon & Tues 1.30–5.30; also open BH Mon (starting with Easter) 11–5.30; last admission to house 30min before closing. **Grounds**: daily all year: 11–6 (or dusk if earlier). **Events**: 20 June to 5 July open-air theatre: send s.a.e. for booking form to Theatre Box Office, P.O. Box 10, Dorking, Surrey RH5 6FH; tel. 01372 451596. 5 July, Polesden Fair; additional charge for all visitors, incl. NT members. Variety of winter events, please tel. for details. Estate includes a YHA hostel (tel. 01372 452528)

Garden, grounds & landscape walks open all year round: £3; family ticket £7.50. House: £3 extra; family ticket £7.50 extra. Pre-booked groups £5. Parking 200m. Croquet lawn available; equipment for hire from the house. Picnics welcome outside formal garden

Shop and plant sales open from 17 Jan to 28 Feb: Sat & Sun only 11–4.30; 1 to 29 March: daily except Mon & Tues 11–4.30; 1 April to 1 Nov: daily except Mon & Tues, also BH Mon 11–5.30 (open daily July & Aug); 4 to 29 Nov: daily except Mon & Tues 11–4.30; 1 to 20 Dec: daily 11–4.30

Access to showrooms, restaurant, shop and parts of garden; fairly firm gravel paths. Disabled drivers' car park nearby. Wheelchairs available. Self-drive battery car available by prior appointment. WC near restaurant. A landscape walk through open farm and woodland has been built for wheelchair users (strong pusher recommended)

Braille guide to house; rose and lavender gardens (rose garden has crazy paving). The house steward will describe objects and indicate those that may be touched (prior appointment recommended)

Coffee, lunches and home-made teas in restaurant with table licence. 17 Jan to 28 Feb (light refreshments): Sat & Sun only 11–3; 1 to 29 March (light refreshments) daily except Mon & Tues 11–4; 1 April to 1 Nov: daily except Mon & Tues, also BH Mon 11–5; 4 Nov to 20 Dec (limited menu): daily except Mon & Tues 11–3. Light refreshments in the Old Stables July & Aug, Mon & Tues 11–4

⛹ Changing tables in men's and ladies' WCs. Highchairs available in restaurant. No prams, back carriers or pushchairs in house

🐕 No dogs in formal gardens, on paths or on lawns. Welcome in rest of grounds on leads and good walks on estate (under close control at all times)

➔ (2: F6) 5ml NW of Dorking, 2ml S of Great Bookham, off A246 Leatherhead–Guildford road [187: TQ136522] *Bus:* Surrey Hills Leisure Buses 433 from ≋ Guildford, (passing ≋ Dorking), Sun, May to Sept only; otherwise 408 Guildford–Croydon (passing close ≋ Guildford & Leatherhead), alight Great Bookham, 1½ml (tel. 01737 223000) *Station:* Boxhill & Westhumble 2ml

PRINCES RISBOROUGH MANOR HOUSE *Buckinghamshire*

Princes Risborough HP17 9AW

A 17th-century red-brick house with Jacobean staircase

🅾 House & front garden by written arrangement only with tenant, Wed 2.30–4.30. Last admission 4. Hall, drawing room and staircase shown

💷 £1.10. No reduction for parties. Public car park 50m

🐕 Admitted by arrangement with tenant

➔ (2: E3) Opposite church, off market square [165: SP806035] *Bus:* Aylesbury & The Vale 323/4 High Wycombe–Aylesbury (passing close ≋ Aylesbury) (tel. 0345 382000) *Station:* Princes Risborough 1ml

QUEBEC HOUSE 🏠 *Kent*

Westerham TN16 1TD Tel: (Regional Office) 01892 890651 Fax: 01892 890110

General Wolfe spent his early years in this gabled, red-brick 17th-century house. The low-ceilinged, panelled rooms contain memorabilia relating to his family and career and the Tudor stable block houses an exhibition about the Battle of Quebec (1759)

Note: The property is administered and maintained on the Trust's behalf by the tenant

🅾 5 April to 27 Oct: Tues & Sun only 2–6. Last admission 5.30. Parties by arrangement; please write to tenant

💷 £2.50, children £1.25. Pre-booked parties £1.80 (prices include exhibition). Public car park 150m E of house

♿ Difficult for wheelchair users, but some access to ground floor via ramps for single steps; garden accessible

🍴 Refreshments in village (not NT). No picnicking

➔ (2: G6) At E end of village, on N side of A25, facing junction with B2026 Edenbridge road [187: TQ449541] *Bus:* All services quoted for Chartwell pass close to the house *Station:* Sevenoaks 4ml; Oxted 4ml

RIVER WEY & GODALMING NAVIGATIONS AND
DAPDUNE WHARF 👤 🅟 👤

Surrey

Navigation Office and Dapdune Wharf, Wharf Road, Guildford GU1 4RR
Tel: 01483 561389/455056 Fax: 01483 531667

The Wey was one of the first British rivers to be made navigable, and opened to barge traffic in 1653. This 15.5ml waterway linked Guildford to Weybridge on the Thames, and thence to London. The Godalming Navigation, opened in 1764, enabled barges to work a further 4ml upriver. Dapdune Wharf in Guildford is the home of Reliance, *a restored Wey barge, as well as models and an interactive exhibition telling the story of the waterway, the people who lived and worked on it, and the barges built there*

What's new in 1998: Tea-room and ice-creams normally available at Dapdune Wharf and electric launch river bus service – from Dapdune Wharf to Guildford, operating during opening hours; additional charge (incl. NT members)

O **Dapdune Wharf:** 1 April to 1 Nov: Wed 12–5, Sat, Sun & BHols 11–5. Pre-booked groups and school parties welcome throughout the year

£ **Dapdune Wharf:** £2.50, family ticket £6; pre-booked groups £1.50.
Navigations: the entire 19½ml towpath is open to walkers and moorings for visiting boats: no charge. Navigation licences (including all lock tolls) payable on all powered and non-powered craft are issued for the year or for 7- or 21-day visits. There is a 10% reduction for visiting NT members on production of current membership card for 7 or 21 days only. There are insurance requirements and restrictions on engine size to protect the property. Please check with Navigation Office in advance of journey. Horse-drawn boat trips on narrow boat *Iona* (tel. 01483 414938); rowboats, punts, canoes and narrow boats at Farncombe Boat House (tel. 01483 421306); restaurant boats, excursion boats, rowboats and canoes at Guildford Boat House (tel. 01483 504494)

𝕏 Pre-booked guided tours of Dapdune Wharf available for groups. Please telephone for details

🦽 Wheelchair access to main exhibition at Dapdune Wharf; adapted WC. Accessible fishing sites; wheelchair access to some parts of towpath; contact Navigation Office for details

🕮 Braille guide

▣ Tea-room at Farncombe Boat House, nr Godalming (not NT) (tel. 01483 418769)

🚼 Baby-changing facilities at Dapdune Wharf

▦ Study centre and facilities available; please tel. for details

🐕 Must be kept under control. All dogs to be kept on leads within lock areas

→ (2: F5/E6) Dapdune Wharf is on Wharf Road, off Woodbridge Rd, Guildford. Car park, also easy access from town centre on foot via towpath or by river bus; tel. Navigation Office for details. Access to rest of Navigations from A3 & M25. Visiting craft can enter from the Thames at Shepperton or slipways at Guildford or Pyrford *Station:* 🚆 Addlestone, Byfleet & New Haw, Guildford, Farncombe & Godalming all lie close to the Navigation

RUNNYMEDE 🏊 🚶 🎭 *Surrey*

Egham **Tel: 01784 432891 Fax: 01784 470194**

An attractive area of riverside meadows, grassland and broadleafed woodland, rich in diversity of flora and fauna, and part-designated a Site of Special Scientific Interest. It was on this site, in 1215, that King John signed the Magna Carta, an event commemorated by the American Bar Association Memorial and John F. Kennedy Memorial. Also here are the Fairhaven Lodges, designed by Lutyens

🅾️ All year. Riverside grass car park open April to end Sept, daily when ground conditions allow, 10–7. Tea-room car park (hard-standing) open all year, April to Sept 9–7; Oct to March 10–5. **Events:** mid July Craft Fair; contact Four Seasons Events for information (tel. 01344 874787)

💷 Fees payable for parking, fishing and mooring. Fishing: day permits only; all year except during closed season (mid March to mid June); tickets available from riverbank. Mooring available for up to 24hrs only. Please note that mooring fees are also payable by members. *Note:* Seasonal boat trips to Windsor and Hampton Court. Contact boat operators French (not NT) (tel. 01753 851900)

🚶 Extensive programme of guided walks throughout the year. Please telephone Warden for details

🛍️ Small shop within tea-room

♿ Limited access to tea-room and meadows by prior arrangement. WC by tea-rooms. Good vehicle access to riverbank during summer months; no charge for orange badge holders. Access to memorials difficult. Riverboats admit people with disabilities. Contact Warden for information

👁️ Braille guide; contact Warden for information

☕ April to end Sept: daily 8.30–5.30; Oct to end March 1999: daily 9.30–4.30; closed 25 Dec. Coach parties welcome by prior arrangement (tel. 01784 477110)

➡️ (2: F5) On the Thames, 2ml W of Runnymede Bridge, on S side of A308 (M25, exit 13). 6ml E of Windsor *Bus:* From surrounding areas (tel. 01737 223000) *Station:* Egham 2ml

---

ST JOHN'S JERUSALEM 🏠 ✝️ ❀ *Kent*

Sutton-at-Hone, Dartford DA4 9HQ
Tel: (Regional Office) 01892 890651 Fax: 01892 890110

A large garden, moated by the River Darent. The house is attached to the former chapel of a Knights Hospitaller Commandery and is now a private residence and not open. Access to the chapel only. There are colourful spring and summer herbaceous borders and a magnificent Lebanon cedar, planted in the 17th century

Note: The property is occupied as a private residence and is administered and managed by a tenant on the Trust's behalf

🅾️ **Former chapel and garden only:** 1 April to 28 Oct: Wed only 2–6. Last admission 5.30

💷 £1, children 50p

♿ Garden only accessible

➔ (2: H5) 3ml S of Dartford at Sutton-at-Hone, on E side of A225 [177: TQSS8703] *Bus:* Kentish Bus 13–15 from 🚃 Dartford (tel. 0345 696996) *Station:* Farningham Road ¾ml

---

SANDHAM MEMORIAL CHAPEL ✝   *Hampshire*

Burghclere, nr Newbury RG15 9JT Tel: 01635 278394 Fax: 01635 278394

This red-brick chapel was built in the 1920s, specially to house the remarkable murals inside. Painted by Stanley Spencer, they cover the chapel walls in a touching and sensitive account of the everyday life of soldiers in the First World War. The chapel sits amidst beautiful and tranquil scenery, with views across to Watership Down

Note: As there is no lighting in the chapel, it is best to view the paintings on a bright day

🅾 March & Nov: Sat & Sun only 11.30–4; Apr to end Oct: Wed to Sun & BH Mon 11.30–5; (closed Wed following BH Mon); Dec to Feb by appointment only

💷 £2. No reduction for pre-booked groups. Road verge parking. Picnics on front lawn

♿ Accessible via steps; portable ramp available. Wheelchair users advised to enter through side gate

👁 Braille guide

🍴 Refreshments available 100m away at Carpenter's Arms (not NT) 11–3, tel. 01635 278251 (parties must book in advance)

🐕 On leads only

➔ (2: C5) 4ml S of Newbury, 0.5m E of A34 [174: SU463608] *Bus:* Burghfield mini coaches 123/4 from Newbury (passing close 🚃 Newbury) (tel. 01734 590719) *Station:* Newbury 4ml

---

SCOTNEY CASTLE GARDEN 🏰 ❀ 🌳 🎭   *Kent*

Lamberhurst, Tunbridge Wells TN3 8JN Tel: 01892 891081 Fax: 01892 890110

One of England's most romantic gardens, designed in the Picturesque style around the ruins of a 14th-century moated castle. There are rhododendrons and azaleas in profusion, with wisteria and roses rambling over the old ruins. Wonderful vistas and viewpoints abound, and there are beautiful woodland and estate walks

🅾 **Garden:** 1 April to 1 Nov: (**Old Castle:** May to 13 Sept) Wed to Fri 11–6; Sat & Sun 2–6, or sunset if earlier; BH Sun & BH Mon 12–6 (closed Good Fri). Last admission 1hr before closing. **Events:** tel. 01892 891001 for details

💷 £3.80, children £1.90; family ticket £9.50. Pre-booked parties £2.80 (no party reduction on Sat, Sun or BH Mon)

🖸 Shop open as garden

♿ Garden partly accessible to wheelchair users, but strong companion necessary; approach to garden and paths very steep in places. Wheelchairs available

👁 Herb garden; roses. Braille guide

🍴 In Goudhurst & Lamberhurst villages (not NT). Picnicking in car park area only

🧍 Children's quiz

🐕 On leads on estate walks only

→ (2: H6) 1ml S of Lamberhurst on A21 [188: TQ688353] *Bus:* Autopoint 256 Tunbridge Wells–Wadhurst (passing ≋ Tunbridge Wells), alight Lamberhurst Green, 1ml (tel. 0345 696996) *Station:* Wadhurst 5½ml

---

SHALFORD MILL
Surrey

Shalford, nr Guildford GU4 8BS Tel: 01483 561617

A large 18th-century water-mill on the River Tillingbourne, given in 1932 by a group of anonymous NT benefactors calling themselves 'Ferguson's Gang'

Note: Owing to fire regulations, it is not possible for visitors to go higher than the first floor

🅾 Daily 10–5

💷 Free but donations in the box (emptied daily) most welcome. No parking at property. Children must be accompanied by an adult

→ (2: F6) 1½ml S of Guildford on A281 opposite Sea Horse Inn *Bus:* Tillingbourne 21–5, 31/2 Guildford & West Surrey 273, 283 from Guildford (pass close ≋ Guildford) (tel. 01737 223000) *Station:* Shalford (U), ½ml; Guildford 1½ml

---

SHAW'S CORNER 🏠 ❖ 🛡
Hertfordshire

Ayot St Lawrence, nr Welwyn AL6 9BX Tel: 01438 820307

An Edwardian villa, the home of George Bernard Shaw from 1906 till his death in 1950. The rooms remain much as he left them, with many literary and personal effects evoking the individuality and genius of this great dramatist. The garden has richly planted borders and views over the Hertfordshire countryside

What's new in 1998: Braille guide, education programme, guided tours; new opening times

🅾 1 April to 1 Nov: daily except Mon & Tues (but closed Good Fri and open BH Mon) 1–5. Parties by written appointment only. Last admission 4.30 (but 3.30 on 19, 20, 21 June & 24, 25, 26 July). On busy days admission is by timed ticket. *Note*: No large hand luggage inside property. **Events:** for details of Shaw's birthday play and other events, please send s.a.e. to Custodian

£ £3.20; family ticket £8. No reduction for parties. Car park

🏃 Pre-booked guided tours available, Wed to Sun, mornings only; please tel. for details

♿ Access to garden and house, but some steps. Wheelchair available

👁 Braille guide to house; items to touch. Many scented plants in garden

☕ Teas available in village (not NT)

🚼 No baby back carriers in house, but front sling baby carrier available

🏫 School and adult groups welcome by prior arrangement, Wed to Sun, mornings only

🅿 In car park only

➔ (2: F3) At SW end of village, 2ml NE of Wheathampstead; approx. 2ml from B653 [166: TL194167] *Bus:* Sovereign 304 ⇌ St Albans City–Hitchin, alight Gustardwood, 1¼ml (tel. 0345 244344) *Station:* Welwyn North 4ml; Harpenden 5ml

---

SHEFFIELD PARK GARDEN ✿ 🏃 ♥   *East Sussex*

Uckfield TN22 3QX Tel: 01825 790231 Fax: 01825 791264

A magnificent landscape garden, laid out in the 18th century by 'Capability' Brown and further developed in the early years of this century by its owner, Arthur G . Soames. The centrepiece is the original four lakes, linked by cascades and waterfalls. There are dramatic shows of daffodils and bluebells in spring, and the rhododendrons, azaleas and stream garden are spectacular in early summer. Autumn brings stunning colours from the many rare trees and shrubs

What's new in 1998: Ornate iron gate on top bridge

🅾 March: Sat & Sun only 11–6; 1 April to 15 Nov: daily except Mon (but open BH Mon) 11–6 or sunset if earlier; 18 Nov to 20 Dec: daily except Mon & Tues 11–4. Last admission 1hr before closing. **Events:** for details tel. 01892 891001

£ £4.20, children £2.10; family ticket £10.50. Parties £3.20. No reduction for parties on Sat, Sun & BH Mon

🚹 Pre-booked guided tours in groups of 10 or more Tues to Fri mornings; tel. 01825 790231 for rates

🛍 Shop as garden. Also Christmas shop until 20 Dec: daily except Mon & Tues; tel. 01825 790655 for details

♿ Most parts of garden accessible with the exception of woodland path beyond lower lakes; paths mostly firm and level; four powered self-drive cars and four wheelchairs available. Recommended route map supplied. WCs. Car parking near entrance

👁 Water sounds; scented trees and shrubs (especially mid May to early June)

🍽 Restaurant (not NT) and picnic area adjoining car park; no picnics in garden

👶 Baby-changing facilities; all-terrain pushchair and two back carriers. Children's free trail guide

🐕 Dogs on leads in car park only

➔ (2: G7) Midway between East Grinstead and Lewes, 5ml NW of Uckfield, on E side of A275 (between A272 & A22), ½ml from Sheffield Park station (Bluebell Rly) [198: TQ415240] *Bus:* Brighton & Hove 21 from Lewes (Sat only); RDH 246 from Uckfield (Mon, Fri only); otherwise Stagecoach South Coast 781 Eastbourne– Haywards Heath (passing ⊠ Haywards Heath and Uckfield), alight Chailey Crossroads,1¼ml (tel. 01273 474747) *Station:* Sheffield Park (Bluebell Rly) ½ml; Uckfield 6ml; Haywards Heath 7ml

---

SISSINGHURST CASTLE GARDEN 🏠 🏠 ❀ 🏊 *Kent*

Sissinghurst, nr Cranbrook TN17 2AB
Tel: 01580 715330 Infoline 01580 712850 Fax: 01580 713911

One of the world's most celebrated gardens, the creation of Vita Sackville-West and her husband Sir Harold Nicolson. Developed around the surviving parts of an Elizabethan mansion with a central red-brick prospect tower, a series of small, enclosed compartments, intimate in scale and romantic in atmosphere, provide outstanding design and colour through the season. The study, where Vita worked, and Long Library are also open to visitors

Note: Due to the limited capacity of the garden, timed tickets are in operation and visitors may have to wait before admission. Daily visitor numbers are restricted; visitors may still visit the Oast House exhibition,woodland and lakes walks, restaurant and shop. The library and Vita Sackville-West's study close each day at 5.30. No tripods or easels in the garden. The garden is closed on Mon, including BH Mon

🅾 1 April to 15 Oct: Tues to Fri 1–6.30; Sat, Sun & Good Fri 10–5.30. Closed Mon, incl. BH. Last admission 30min before closing. Ticket office & exhibition open at 12 on weekdays. (The garden is less crowded in April, Sept & Oct, also Wed to Fri after 4 and on Sat)

£ £6. Coaches and parties by appointment only; no reduction. Contact Bookings Secretary for details (tel. 01580 715330 or fax 01580 713911)

[⌂] Shop open same days as garden. Tues to Fri 12–5.30; Sat, Sun & Good Fri 10–5.30. Christmas shop, daily except Mon & Tues 11–4; for details tel. 01580 713090

[♿] Admission restricted to two wheelchairs at any one time because of narrow and uneven paths. Limited access to visitors with powered wheelchairs – if transfer to a manual wheelchair is not possible please tel. 01580 715330 in advance. Wheelchairs available on loan. Disabled visitors may be set down at ticket office. Disabled drivers may park near ticket office. Plan of recommended wheelchair route available. Restaurant and shop accessible. WC

[◑] Braille garden plan and guide; scented plants & flowers; herb garden

[☕] Coffee, lunches, teas in Granary Restaurant (licensed – no spirits) Tues to Fri 12–5.30, Sat, Sun & Good Fri 10–5. Christmas opening, contact restaurant for details tel. 01580 713097. Picnics in car park and field in front of garden

[†] Not ideal for children. No pushchairs admitted, as paths are narrow and uneven but baby carriers available. No children's games in garden

[🐕] No dogs in garden or picnic areas, but welcome on leads in surrounding areas

[➔] (2: J6) 2ml NE of Cranbrook, 1ml E of Sissinghurst village (A262) [188: TQ8138] *Bus:* Maidstone & District 4/5 Maidstone–Hastings (passing ☒ Staplehurst), alight Sissinghurst, 1¼ml (tel. 0345 696996) *Station:* Staplehurst 5½ml

---

SMALLHYTHE PLACE 🏠 ❈ 🌳   *Kent*

Smallhythe, Tenterden TN30 7NG Tel: 01580 762334

An early 16th-century half-timbered house, home of the Victorian actress Ellen Terry from 1899 to 1928, and containing many personal and theatrical mementoes. The charming cottage grounds include her rose garden and the Barn Theatre, open most days by courtesy of the Barn Theatre Society

[◐] 1 April to 28 Oct: daily except Thur & Fri (but open Good Fri) 1–5.30, or dusk if earlier. Last admission 30min before closing. (The Barn Theatre may be closed some days at short notice)

£ £3, children £1.50; family ticket £7.50. Pre-booked parties Tues am only; no reduction. Max. 25 people in the house at any one time; garden has shelter for a further 25. No picnicking

[†] Children must be accompanied by an adult; children's quiz

[🐕] No dogs except guide dogs in garden or house

[➔] (2: J7) 2ml S of Tenterden, on E side of the Rye road (B2082) [189: TQ893300] *Bus:* Autopoint 312 ☒ Rye–Tenterden (tel. 0345 696996) *Station:* Rye 8ml; Appledore 8ml; Headcorn 10ml

SOUTH FORELAND LIGHTHOUSE 🏠 🖼 🚻 👤

Kent

St Margaret's-at-Cliffe, Dover
Tel/fax: Office 01304 202756 Tel: Lighthouse 01304 852463

A distinctive landmark on the White Cliffs of Dover, built in 1843 and used by Marconi for the first successful trials in radio navigation. There is an information room, and access to the tower and balcony around the light, from which there are magnificent views

🅾 4 April to 25 Oct: Sat, Sun & BH Mon 2–5.30. Last admission 5 (or dusk if earlier). Access on foot from NT car park at Langdon Cliffs (2ml) or from St Margaret's village only. Access to the tower is by guided tour only, for which 45mins should be allowed

💷 £1.50, children 75p. No reduction for parties, which must tel. in advance. No parking facilities or access for vehicles, but car park at Langdon Cliffs (2ml) £1.20 (NT members free)

♿ Limited parking for disabled visitors at lighthouse. Access to tower involves spiral staircase

🍽 Refreshments in village (not NT)

🧍 Model and exhibition on display

🎒 Teacher's pack

🐕 No dogs in lighthouse, on leads in grounds

➡ (2: L6) At St Margaret's-at-Cliffe [179: TR359433] *Bus:* Stagecoach East Kent 90 Folkestone–Deal (passing ⭧ Dover Priory & Walmer) (tel. 0345 696996) *Station:* Martin Mill 2½ml

SPRIVERS GARDEN 🏵

Kent

Horsmonden TN12 8DR Tel: (Regional Office) 01892 890651 Fax: 01892 890110

A small formal garden with walled and hedged compartments, herbaceous borders and a rose garden

Note: This property is administered and maintained on the Trust's behalf by the tenant

🅾 23 & 30 May, 13 June: 2–5.30. Last admission 5

💷 £1, children 50p. No parties. Parking limited; space for one coach only. No WC

➡ (2: H6) 2ml N of Lamberhurst on B2162 [188: TQ6940] *Bus:* Maidstone & District/Fuggles 297 ⭧ Tunbridge Wells–Tenterden (tel. 0345 696996) *Station:* Paddock Wood 4ml

STANDEN 🏠 🏵 ⛵ 👤 🎭

West Sussex

East Grinstead RH19 4NE Tel: 01342 323029 Fax: 01342 316424

A family house of the 1890s, designed by Philip Webb, friend of William Morris, and a showpiece of the Arts & Crafts Movement. It is decorated throughout with Morris carpets, fabric and wallpaper, complemented by Pre-Raphaelite paintings and tapestries and furniture made by Morris's company. The house retains many of its original electrical fittings. A beautiful hillside garden gives fine views and there are delightful woodland walks

What's new in 1998: Refurbished shop featuring 'Arts & Crafts' merchandise

O 25 March to 1 Nov: daily except Mon & Tues (but open BH Mon). **Garden:** 12.30–6. **House:** 12.30–4 (last admission 4). Property may close on Sun & BHols for limited periods to avoid overcrowding. 6 Nov to 20 Dec: garden only, Fri, Sat & Sun 1–4. **Events:** please send s.a.e. or tel. for information

£ House & garden £5; family ticket £12.50. Garden only £3 (£2 in Nov/Dec). Joint ticket which includes same day entry to Nymans Garden £7, available Wed to Fri. Groups £4 Wed to Fri only, if booked in advance; other times by prior booking with Property Manager. Parking 180m

✗ By special arrangement; Wed, Thur, Fri am. Extra charge for out-of-hours opening

Δ Shop open same days as house 12.30–5, plus 6 Nov to 20 Dec: Fri, Sat & Sun 1–4 (admission charge of £2 refunded for purchases over £5 during Nov & Dec)

Ⅎ Ground floor of house, restaurant, shop and part of garden accessible; some steps in house; wheelchairs available. Disabled drivers only may park adjacent to ticket office and forecourt of house as directed, but thick gravel. Steps and gravel paths in garden. WC

◉ Braille guide to house and garden; scented plants & flowers. Stewards will describe contents and indicate those that may be touched. Guided tours by appointment

◖ Licensed restaurant serving light lunches & afternoon teas. Open same days as house 12.30–5, plus refreshments 6 Nov to 20 Dec: Fri, Sat & Sun 1–4. Picnics in lower car park and picnic area. *Note:* The Barn (Restaurant) is available for non-residential private and commercial functions with limited associated use of the house. The Property Manager welcomes enquiries

♟ 2 reins, 2 baby carriers available; suitable for children aged up to 16 months; no back carriers; pushchairs not allowed in house

▦ Education groups welcome; tel. Property Manager for details

▨ In lower car park and woodland walks only (via lower car park)

→ (2: G6) 2ml S of East Grinstead, signposted from B2110 (Turners Hill road) [187: TQ389356] *Bus:* London & Country 474 ⎘ East Grinstead–Crawley (passing ⎘ Three Bridges), alight at approach road just north of Saint Hill, ½ml, or at Saint Hill, thence ½ml by footpath (tel. 0345 959099) *Station:* E Grinstead 2ml

---

STONEACRE 🏠 ✿ *Kent*

Otham, Maidstone ME15 8RS Tel: 01622 862871 Fax: 01622 862157

A half-timbered yeoman's house with a great hall and crownpost, dating from the late 15th century and surrounded by a delightful recently restored cottage garden

Note: The property is administered and largely maintained on the Trust's behalf by the tenant

O 1 April to 31 Oct: Wed & Sat 2–6. Last admission 5

💷 £2.80, children £1.25. No reduction for parties. Car park 100m; drive narrow, unsuitable for coaches

👁 Garden recommended to accompanied visually impaired visitors; herb gardens and other scented plants

🧍 Children's trail in conjunction with Kent Gardens Trust

🐕 No dogs please

➜ (2: J6) At N end of Otham village, 3ml SE of Maidstone, 1m S of A20 [188: TQ800535] *Bus:* Maidstone & District 13 Maidstone–Hollingbourne (passing close ▆ Maidstone E & W), alight Otham, ½ml (tel. 0345 696996) *Station:* Bearsted 2ml

---

STOWE LANDSCAPE GARDENS *Buckinghamshire*

Buckingham MK18 5EH Tel: 01280 822850 Fax: 01280 822437

An epic landscape garden, one of the supreme creations of the Georgian era and a miraculous survival. Adorned with buildings by Vanbrugh, Gibbs and Kent, including arches, temples, a Palladian bridge and other monuments, the sheer scale of the garden must make it Britain's largest work of art. The House (not NT) is occupied by Stowe School, but the state rooms and Marble Hall may be visited

What's new in 1998: The newly restored Chinese House will be reinstated in July (close to the Lamport Garden); Rotunda under restoration

⭕ **Gardens:** 20 March to 12 April: daily; 13 April to 5 July: Mon, Wed, Fri, Sun; 6 July to 6 Sept: daily; 7 Sept to 1 Nov: Mon, Wed, Fri, Sun; 27 Dec to 5 Jan 1999: daily 10–5 or dusk if earlier. Last admission 1hr before closing. **House:** usually open during school holidays; for details tel. 01280 813650. *Note:* Visitors should allow plenty of time as gardens are extensive. **Events:** for details please send s.a.e. to Box Office, Stowe Landscape Gardens (tel. 01280 823334/822850)

£ Gardens £4.40; family ticket £11. House (incl. NT members) £2. Party visits by prior arrangement with Property Manager (tel. 01280 822850)

𝄇 Guided tours available by prior arrangement with Property Manager

▣ Open as gardens: Mon to Fri 10–5; Sat & Sun 11.30–5.30

♿ Unsuitable for manual wheelchairs; powered self-drive two-seater cars available free (please pre-book); details from Estate Secretary. Access to tea-room. WC

◉ Braille guide and maps, also audio-cassette guides available

▆ Licensed tea-room offers morning coffee, light lunches and teas. Same days as gardens 10.30–5 (Dec & Jan 10.30–4). Picnics permitted in gardens

♀ Highchairs available

▦ School visits welcomed

▣ On leads only

➜ (2: D2) 3ml NW of Buckingham via Stowe Avenue, off A422 Buckingham–Banbury road [152: SP665366] *Bus:* Aylesbury and the Vale 66 from ≋ Aylesbury to Gardens, Sun only (May to Sept), otherwise Paynes 32, MK Metro 51/A from Milton Keynes (passing ≋ Milton Keynes Central); Aylesbury & The Vale 66 from Aylesbury (passing close ≋ Aylesbury) (tel. 0345 382000). On all (except summer Sun), alight Buckingham, thence 3ml

---

TUDOR YEOMAN'S HOUSE ▣ *Kent*

Sole Street, Cobham DA12 3AX
Tel: (Regional Office) 01892 890651 Fax: 01892 890110

A 15th-century yeoman's house of timber construction

Note: The property is administered and maintained on the Trust's behalf by the tenant

◉ Main hall only, by written application to the tenant

£ 50p. No reduction for children or parties. No WC

➜ (2: H5) 1ml SW of Cobham, on W side of B2009, just N of Sole Street Station [177: TQ657677] *Station:* Sole Street, adjacent

---

UPPARK ▣ ❀ ♨ ♀ ☻ *West Sussex*

South Harting, Petersfield GU31 5QR
Tel: Infoline (24hrs): 01730 825857 Office: 01730 825415 Fax: 01730 825873

A late 17th-century house, set high on the South Downs and with magnificent views. The elegant mid-18th-century interior has been fully restored after the disastrous 1989 fire and houses a collection of Grand Tour paintings, as well as fine ceramics, textiles and furniture rescued from the fire. There are interesting and evocative servants' rooms where H. G. Wells spent part of his youth when his mother was housekeeper. The picturesque, predominantly foliage, garden has been restored to Repton's design

O 1 April to 29 Oct: daily except Fri & Sat; **Car park**, **woodland walk**, **ticket office**, **exhibition**, **garden**, **shop & tea-room**: 11.30–5.30; House: 1–5; last admission to house 4–4.15. Print room open only on first Mon of each month. The house continues to be very popular since its 1995 opening and entry is by timed ticket (incl. NT members), so visitors may have to wait before being admitted. Tickets will be marked with an entry slot (eg 2–2.15), visitors enter the house during that period, but may stay as long as the house is open. On Sun, BH and other busy days tickets may sell out. Some tickets are bookable at least a week in advance (small charge); tel. 01730 825415 during office hours Mon to Thur. **Events**: please contact Property Manager, tel. 01730 825415

£ House, garden and exhibition: £5.50; family ticket £13.75. Groups (no reduction) weekdays only and must be pre-booked

✗ By arrangement some mornings

🛍 Open same days as house 11.30–5.30

♿ Exhibition (stairlift to upper floor), shop, garden and house accessible; lift to basement showrooms. Wheelchairs available. WC. Disabled visitors are advised to tel. before visiting

◉ Braille guide to house; material samples available to handle from stewards

◉ Light lunches and afternoon teas. Open same days as house 11.30–5.30. Picnic area near car park and in woodland. Kiosk near car park serving sandwiches, hot and cold drinks, open from 11.30 weather permitting

🚼 Front carriers available for loan at house (no back carriers please) pushchairs not practical in the house; changing facilities, highchairs. Children's guide, hands-on items in exhibition

🐕 Woodland walk and car park only, on leads please (please note: no shade in car park)

→ (2: E7) 5ml SE of Petersfield on B2146, 1½ml S of South Harting [197: SU775177] *Bus:* Stagecoach Sussex Bus 54 (not Sun) ≋ Petersfield–≋ Chichester (tel. 0345 959099) *Station:* Petersfield 5½ml

---

THE VYNE 🏠 ❀ 🚹 🛡 *Hampshire*

Sherborne St John, Basingstoke RG24 9HL
Tel: 01256 881337 Fax: 01256 881720

Built in the early 16th century for Lord Sandys, Henry VIII's Lord Chamberlain, the house acquired a classical portico in the mid-17th century (the first of its kind in England) and contains a fascinating Tudor chapel with Renaissance glass, a Palladian staircase and a wealth of old panelling and fine furniture. The attractive grounds feature herbaceous borders and a wild garden, with lawns, lakes and woodland walks

What's new in 1998: Please note new opening arrangements for house and grounds. The house will re-open after two years of internal repair work. Additional rooms to see for the first time include a bedroom, dressing room, and service corridors. New visitor route through house. Newly designed and planted summer-house garden

O **House:** 3 June to end Oct: daily except Mon & Tues 1.30–5.30. **Grounds:** 25 March to end Oct: daily except Mon & Tues 12.30–5.30. Also open Good Fri & BH Mon 11–5.30. Last admission 30min before closing. **Events:** in garden and Stone Gallery; please send s.a.e for details or tel. Regional Box Office (tel. 01372 451596)

£ House & grounds £4.50; family ticket £11.25. Grounds only £2.50. Parties £3.50 (Wed to Fri only)

& Access to grounds and ground floor of house only (wheelchair ramp). Visitors with disabilities may be driven to door by prior arrangement. Wheelchairs available. Old Brewhouse tea-room accessible. WC

💷 Refreshments in Old Brewhouse (licensed), 25 March to 2 June: Sat, Sun, Good Fri & BHMon only, light lunches 12.30–2 (opens 11 on Good Fri & BHMon), afternoon teas 2.30–5.30, last orders 5; 3 June to end Oct: daily, except Mon & Tues, light lunches 12.30–2 (opens 11 on BHMon), afternoon teas 2.30–5.30, last orders 5. Also open for pre-booked Christmas lunches. Coach parties by prior arrangement only; please tel. for details. Picnics in car park only

↟ Baby-changing facilities

🐴 In car park only

➔ (**2:** D5) 4ml N of Basingstoke between Bramley and Sherborne St John [175 & 186: SU637566]. From Basingstoke Ring Road, follow Basingstoke District Hospital signs until property signs are picked up. Follow A340 Aldermaston Rd towards Tadley. Right turn into Morgaston Rd. Right turn into Vyne Road *Bus:* Hampshire Bus 45 from Basingstoke (passing ▣ Basingstoke) (tel. 01256 464501) *Station:* Bramley 2½ml

---

WADDESDON MANOR 🏠 ✤ ♠ 🎭 *Buckinghamshire*

Waddesdon, nr Aylesbury HP18 0JH Tel: Recorded Information 01296 651211
Booking Office 01296 651226 Administration 01296 651282 Fax: 01296 651293

Designed in the style of a French Renaissance château and built in the 1870s by Baron Ferdinand de Rothschild, Waddesdon is one of England's great treasure houses. The interior is furnished with 18th-century panelling, carpets and porcelain, much of which has a royal French provenance. There are important collections of 18th-century portraits by Gainsborough and Reynolds, of Dutch 17th-century Old Masters and of Sèvres porcelain, as well as an exhibition on the Rothschild family and the celebrated Wine Cellars. The garden and grounds contain a rococo-style aviary, complete with exotic birds, a recently restored parterre, shrubberies and many magnificent trees

What's new in 1998: The Bachelors' Wing is open (on Thur) following refurbishment; audio tours of the house available; stables closed for refurbishment

O **Grounds** (**incl. gardens, aviary, restaurant & shops**): 1 March to 20 Dec: daily except Mon & Tues (but open BH Mon) 10–5. **House** (**incl. Wine Cellars**): 2 April to 1 Nov: Thur to Sun & BH Mon, plus Wed in July & Aug only 11–4; recommended last admission 3. Entry is by timed ticket, available from 10am on a first-come, first-served basis, but also bookable in advance on tel. 01296 651226 Mon to Fri 10–4; booking charge £2.50 per transaction. The number of tickets is limited, but a proportion will be retained for on-the-day allocation.

Children under 6 are not admitted to the house. Babies must be in front slings (some available). **Events**: an active programme, celebrating Baron Ferdinand's centenary, is planned for 1998; please tel. 01296 651226 for details

£ Grounds (incl. gardens, aviary, restaurant & shops): 1 March to 1 Nov £3, children £1.50; family ticket (2 adults & 2 children) £7.50; 4 Nov to 20 Dec free. House £6 (no reduction for children). Bachelors' Wing £1. In order to visit the house a grounds ticket must be purchased

✗ A variety of guided tours, workshops, courses and special events are available to individuals and groups; for details tel. 01296 651226

⌂ Gift and wine shops open 1 March to 20 Dec, Wed to Sun & BH Mon 10–5

♿ Designated parking with drop-off at house if required. Garden, ground floor, first floor (lift), restaurant and shops accessible. No wheelchair access to Wine Cellars. Most of garden easy, some deep gravel. Free garden map shows suitable route for disabled visitors. Some wheelchairs available for house and garden, but only two allowed on each floor of the house at any one time for safety reasons

◉ Braille guide to house. Guide dogs in gardens only

♨ Licensed restaurant open as shop (last orders 30min before closing). Private dining facilities available for groups by arrangement. Picnics welcome except on north lawns, terrace, parterre and aviary garden. No barbecues

♿ Baby-changing facilities. Small play area

⊁ No dogs allowed on the property, except guide dogs in the grounds only

→ (2: D3) Access via Waddesdon village [165: SP740169], 6ml NW of Aylesbury on A41; M40 (westbound) exit 6 or 7 via Thame & Long Crendon or M40 (eastbound) exit 9 via Bicester *Bus*: Aylesbury & The Vale 16/17, Classic Coaches 78, from Aylesbury (passing close ≋ Aylesbury) (tel. 0345 382000) *Station*: Aylesbury 6ml; Haddenham & Thame Parkway 9ml

---

WAKEHURST PLACE ✿ ♨   *West Sussex*

Ardingly, nr Haywards Heath RH17 6TN Tel: 01444 894066 Fax: 01444 894069

Often described as one of the most beautiful gardens in England, Wakehurst contains a series of ornamental features with many plants from across the world providing year-round colour and interest. Extensive woodlands, including an informal arboretum and secluded valley, offer delightful walks. Information about the garden and its many interesting features is available within the Elizabethan mansion. The Loder Valley nature reserve may also be visited by permit (24 hours' notice required)

Note: Wakehurst Place is administered and maintained by the Royal Botanic Gardens Kew; tel. 01444 894066 for up-to-date information

◯ All year: daily (except 25 Dec & 1 Jan). Nov to end Jan: 10–4; Feb & Oct: 10–5; March: 10–6; April to end Sept: 10–7. Last admission 30min before closing. Mansion closes 1 hr before gardens. **Events**: Aug BH weekend, Craft Fair; tel. 01444 894066 for information on this and other events throughout the year

£ Prices under review; tel. 01444 894066 for details. Discounts for pre-booked groups of 10+. Parking 400m from mansion. Exhibition in mansion.

[X] Guided tours available most Sat & Sun: tel. 01444 894004 from Tues onwards for times & availability. Pre-booked tours available on request; please write to Administrator

[icon] Books & gifts are sold in the shop located in the mansion (not NT)

[icon] Most of upper garden accessible, but steep paths elsewhere (strong companions essential). A self-service restaurant is accessible via ramps. Wheelchairs available. WC. It may be possible for visitors with disabilities to be set down by the mansion by prior arrangement with Administrator

[icon] Year-round interest

[icon] Fully licensed self-service restaurant (not NT), serving a large selection of home-made cakes, hot & cold snacks, salads and full meals. Open all year. Picnics welcome in gardens

[icon] Baby-changing room in restaurant WCs

[icon] Contact the Education Officer (tel. 01444 894094)

[icon] No dogs, except guide dogs

[→] (2: G7) 1½ml NW of Ardingly, on B2028 [187: TQ339314] *Bus:* London & Country 472 Haywards Heath–Crawley; Brighton & Hove 772 Brighton–Crawley (tel. 0345 959099). Both pass [rail] Haywards Heath & Three Bridges *Station:* Balcombe 5ml; Haywards Heath 6ml; E Grinstead 6½ml

---

WEST GREEN HOUSE GARDEN [icon] *Hampshire*

West Green, Hartley Wintney RG27 8JB Tel: 01252 844611

A delightful series of walled gardens, surrounding a charming 18th-century house. The largest features herbaceous beds with wonderful colour combinations and a superb ornamental kitchen garden. The gardens have been under restoration for several years, and the nymphaeum and lake field will re-open when work is completed. The gardens are open by kind permission of the lessee

Note: The house is privately tenanted and not open to visitors

[O] 20 May to 16 Aug: Wed only 11–4.30; last admission 4. Also open Thur to Sun and BH Mon 11–4.30, but at a charge to all visitors (incl. NT members)

[£] £3. No reduction for groups, which must book in advance

[icon] Gravel paths and steps in garden

[icon] Simple refreshments available; no picnics

[icon] No dogs allowed

[→] (2: D6) 1ml W of Hartley Wintney, 10ml NE of Basingstoke, 1ml N of A30 [175: SU745564] *Bus:* Stagecoach Hampshire Bus 200 Basingstoke–Camberley (passing [rail] Winchfield), alight Phoenix Green 1ml (tel. 01256 464501) *Station:* Winchfield 2ml

WEST WYCOMBE PARK 🏠 ❖ ♣ 🏃 *Buckinghamshire*

West Wycombe HP14 3AJ Tel: 01628 488675

A perfectly preserved rococo landscape garden, created in the mid 18th century by Sir Francis Dashwood, founder of the Dilettanti Society and the Hellfire Club. The house is among the most theatrical and Italianate in England, its façades formed as classical temples. The interior has Palmyrene ceilings and decoration, with pictures, furniture and sculpture dating from the time of Sir Francis

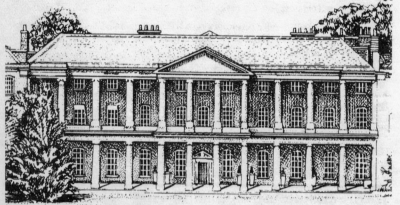

Note: The West Wycombe Caves and adjacent café are privately owned, and National Trust members are liable to admission fees

What's new in 1998: 1998 marks the tercentenary of the Dashwood family's acquisition of the estate

🅾 **Grounds only**: 1 April to end May: Sun & Wed 2–6; Easter, May & spring BH Sun & Mon 2–6. **House & grounds**: June, July & Aug: Sun to Thur 2–6. Weekday entry by timed ticket. Last admission 5.15

£ House & grounds £4.40; family ticket £11. Grounds only £2.60. Parties must book: no reductions. Parking 250m

🏃 Guided tours of house on weekdays. Guided tours of the grounds by written arrangement

♿ Some access to ground floor; designated parking approx. 150m from house; one wheelchair available - please pre-book by tel. Grounds partly accessible

👁 Braille guide; scented plants, and golden marjoram hedges in parterre

🐕 In car park only (guide dogs allowed in park)

➔ (2: E4) At W end of West Wycombe, S of the Oxford road (A40) [175: SU828947] *Bus:* Cambridge Coaches 75 Oxford–Cambridge; Classic Coaches 79 ≋ High Wycombe–Aylesbury; Chiltern Rover 290/2; Wycombe Bus 331/2, 340/1 High Wycombe–Thame (all pass close ≋ High Wycombe); (tel. 0345 382000) *Station:* High Wycombe 2½ml

WEST WYCOMBE VILLAGE AND HILL   *Buckinghamshire*

This Chilterns village comprises buildings spanning several hundred years, with particularly fine examples from the 16th to 18th centuries. The hill, with its fine views, is surmounted by an Iron Age hill-fort and is part of the original landscape design of West Wycombe Park. It is now the site of a church and the Dashwood Mausoleum

Note: The church, mausoleum and caves do not belong to the National Trust

🅾 All year. Parking available at top of hill and in village. Village architectural trail leaflet available in village store (50/51 High St) and newsagent (36/37 High St)

💷 George and Dragon, Plough, and Swan public houses. Also Bread Oven tea-room in village store (50/51 High St)

➔ (2: E4) 2ml W of High Wycombe, on both sides of A40. Public transport: as for West Wycombe Park

WHIPSNADE TREE CATHEDRAL   *Bedfordshire*

near Dunstable   Tel: (Regional Office) 01494 528051

A quiet and peaceful area with many species of trees, planted in the traditional pattern of a cathedral with grassy avenues for the nave and transepts. Nearby are Whipsnade Downs, where the Trust owns a farm and an area of botanically rich chalk grassland, to which there is unrestricted access on foot

🅾 All year. **Events:** an annual service is held at the end of June; please tel. Regional Office for details

£ Free; car-parking on Whipsnade village green or in Whipsnade Downs car park

➔ (2: F2) 2ml S of Dunstable, off B4540 [165/166:TL000190]

WILLINGTON DOVECOTE & STABLES   *Bedfordshire*

Willington, nr Bedford

A distinctive 16th-century stable and stone dovecote, lined internally with nesting boxes for 1,500 pigeons

🅾 April to end Sept: by appointment with Mrs J. Endersby, 21 Chapel Lane, Willington MK44 3QG (tel. 01234 838278)

£ £1. No reduction for parties. Car park 30m. No WC

♿ Accessible, but floors uneven

🐕 Guide dogs admitted by arrangement

➔ (2: F1) 4ml E of Bedford, just N of the Sandy road (A603) [153: TL107499] *Bus:* Stagecoach United Counties 176–8 Bedford-Biggleswade (passing ⊜ Bedford St John's & Biggleswade and close ⊜ Sandy), alight Willington crossroads, ½ml (tel. 01604 20077) *Station:* Bedford St John's (U), not Sun, 4ml; Sandy 4½ml; Bedford 5ml

147

WINCHESTER CITY MILL ⊠ ✿ *Hampshire*

Bridge Street, Winchester SO23 8EJ Tel: 01962 870057 Fax: 01962 870057

Built over the river in 1744, the mill has a delightful small island garden and an impressive mill-race. The water-wheel was restored in 1995

O March: Sat & Sun 11–4.45; 1 April to 31 Oct: Wed to Sun & BH Mon 11–4.45. Last admission 4.30

£ £1. No reduction for groups. Parking in public car park, 200m. No WC

⚥ Groups by arrangement

⌂ Shop open Sat & Sun in March; 1 April to 30 Nov: Wed to Sun & BH Mon 11–5; 1 to 24 Dec, daily 9.30–5

♿ Unsuitable for severely disabled visitors; many steps

◉ Braille guide; sound of rushing water; some tactile contents. Informal talks can be arranged

▥ Children's quiz and information sheets. School groups welcome by appointment

➔ (2: C7) At foot of High Street, beside City Bridge [185: SU487294]
Bus: From surrounding areas (tel. 01256 464501) *Station:* Winchester 1ml

WINKWORTH ARBORETUM ✿ ▦ *Surrey*

Hascombe Road, Godalming GU8 4AD Tel: 01483 208477

A hillside woodland, created this century and now containing over 1,000 different shrubs and trees, many of them rare. The most impressive displays are in spring for bluebells and azaleas, and in autumn for stunning colours. There are two lakes and wildlife in abundance

Note: The car park is reserved for visitors to the arboretum. Those who wish to use the car park but are not visiting the arboretum are asked to contact Head of Arboretum in advance

O All year: daily during daylight hours, but may be closed during bad weather (esp. high winds)

£ £2.70; family ticket £6.75 (2 adults, 2 children, additional family member £1.25). No reduction for groups. Coach parties must book in writing with Head of Arboretum to ensure parking space

⚥ All groups must book in writing to Head of Arboretum. Guided tours £2 extra per person. NT members free, but donations welcome

⌂ Shop open 1 April to 14 Nov: daily except Mon & Tues 11–5.30 or dusk if earlier. Open daily during bluebell and autumn colour times. 15 Nov to 20 Dec & 10 Jan to 21 March 1999: weekends 11–5.30 (or dusk if earlier). Open BH Mon. May be closed during bad weather

[symbol] Limited access along level paths from upper and lower car parks; viewpoint and lake from lower entrance are accessible. Adapted WC (RADAR key); tea-room and shop accessible via ramp

[symbol] Water sounds, scented trees and shrubs, songbirds

[symbol] Tea-room for light refreshments near upper car park; open as shop (tel. 01483 208265 when tea-room open). Picnickers welcome

[symbol] Baby-changing facilities

[symbol] Dogs on leads please

[symbol] (2: F6) Near Hascombe, 2ml SE of Godalming on E side of B2130 [169/170/186: SU990412] *Bus:* Tillingbourne 42/4 Godalming–Cranleigh (passing close ✆ Godalming), Surrey Hills Leisure Bus 448 from ✆ Guildford, Sun, May to Sept only (tel. 01737 223000) *Station:* Godalming 2ml

---

WITLEY COMMON INFORMATION CENTRE [symbols] *Surrey*

Witley Centre, Witley, Godalming GU8 5QA
Tel: 01428 683207 Fax: 01428 683207

A fragment of the lowland heath that used to cover much of southern England, with varied and interesting wildlife to see. An information centre explains the importance of heathland and how it is managed, and there are walks through the different habitats

[O] **Information centre**: 1 April to end Oct: Mon to Thur & BH Mon 11–4; also Sat & Sun 2–5, car park 9–6. **Common**: open at all times. **Events**: Fun Days and children's events; tel. for details

[£] Free to centre. Parking 100m from centre; all groups must pre-book

[symbol] Guided walks at intervals throughout the year; tel. for details

[symbol] Small shop offering limited souvenirs in the centre

[symbol] Ground floor of centre and 2 trails accessible but strong companions advisable. RADAR lock WC

[symbol] Braille guides to Witley and Milford Commons

[symbol] Tea, coffee and soft drinks. Picnic tables

[symbol] Educational parties by prior arrangement with West Weald Education Officer (tel. 01428 683207). Residential group accommodation available on application

[symbol] Must be kept under close control on trails; no dogs in information centre

[symbol] (2: E6) 7ml SW of Guildford between London–Portsmouth A3 and A286 roads, 1ml SW of Milford [186: SU9341] *Bus:* Stagecoach Hants & Surrey/Coastline 60 Guildford–Bognor Regis (passing close ✆ Godalming & passing ✆ Haslemere) (tel. 01737 223000) *Station:* Milford 2ml

Introduction to London

The Trust owns a surprisingly wide range of buildings in the London area, from elegant town houses like **Carlyle's House** in Chelsea to Southwark's **George Inn**, still a working pub. Equally, these span the many centuries of the area's role as a major settlement and economic centre, from the remains of the 'Roman' Bath in Strand Lane to Erno Goldfinger's seminal 1930's house in Hampstead, **2 Willow Road**.

Many of the Trust's London properties date from the time when the countryside was still within sight of the heart of the city. Large estates such as **Osterley Park** are now hemmed in by suburban housing, and **Sutton House** in Hackney, once part of a small village, is now ideally located for its role as a centre for the Trust's work in inner city schools.

Despite being one of the world's major conurbations, London still contains areas of green and relative tranquility. The Trust has played a major role in securing fragments of the city's once extensive common land, including **East Sheen Common** (not far from **Ham House**) and **Chislehurst Common**. Nearby at **Petts Wood** and **Hawkwood** there are attractive areas of heath, farm and woodland with fine walks. Interesting features of an ancient agricultural landscape can be seen at **Morden Hall Park** and there are woods and open grassland at **Selsdon Wood** near Croydon, and at **Watermeads**, managed as a nature reserve, on the River Wandle at Mitcham (key for latter may be obtained from the Warden for a small deposit and annual subscription).

HAM HOUSE

Highlights for Disabled Visitors
Particularly recommended are the accessible paths through the rose garden and along the river at **Morden Hall Park**.

...and for Families
Lots of space to run around and play at **Osterley Park**.

Further Information
NT Regional Offices:

- **Kent & East Sussex** (tel. 01892 890651) – for properties in SE London.
- **Southern** (tel. 01372 453401) – for properties in SW London.
- **Thames & Chilterns** (tel. 01494 528051) – for properties north of the Thames.

Please contact any of the above for a free copy of the NT Countryside Guide to the South East, sponsored by Barclays, which covers key countryside sites in the London area.

BLEWCOAT SCHOOL GIFT SHOP 🏠 *London (Westminster)*

23 Caxton Street, Westminster SW1H 0PY Tel: 0171 222 2877

Built in 1709 by a local brewer to provide an education for poor children and in use as a school until 1926. It is now the NT London Gift Shop and Information Centre

O All year: daily except Sat & Sun 10–5.30 (closes 7 on Thur); but open Sat 28 Nov and Sat 5, 12 & 19 Dec 11–4.30. Closed BH Mon, Good Fri, 25 Dec to 1 Jan 1999 (inclusive)

£ Free

♿ Several steps to shop, difficult for wheelchair users; then level access

➡ (3: G4) Near the junction with Buckingham Gate. Frequent local services (tel. 0171 222 1234) *Station:* Victoria ¼ml *Underground:* St James's Park, 100m

---

CARLYLE'S HOUSE 🏠 🎭 *London (Kensington & Chelsea)*

24 Cheyne Row, Chelsea SW3 5HL Tel: 0171 352 7087

Part of a terrace in a quiet backwater of old Chelsea, this Queen Anne house was the home of writer and historian Thomas Carlyle from 1834 until his death. The house, which contains original furniture and many books, portraits and relics of his day, was visited by many illustrious Victorians, including Dickens, Chopin, Tennyson and George Eliot. The restored Victorian walled garden also reflects Carlyle's life here

O 1 April to 1 Nov: daily except Mon & Tues (but open BH Mon) 11–5. Last admission 4.30. Closed Good Fri. **Events:** NT/Chelsea Society guided themed walks around Chelsea. Annual Carlyle Memorial Lecture. Evening performances of works by Chelsea writers and readings from the letters of Thomas and Jane Carlyle; for details please send s.a.e. to Custodian

£ £3.20, child £1.60

🎟 Groups welcome; introductory talk and tour can be booked in advance with Custodian

➡ (3: F4) Off Cheyne Walk, between Battersea and Albert Bridges on Chelsea Embankment, or off the King's Road and Oakley Street [176: TQ272777] *Bus:* Frequent local services (tel. 0171 222 1234) *Station:* Victoria 1½ml *Underground:* Sloane Sq 1¼ml

EASTBURY MANOR HOUSE 🏠 🛡 *London (Barking & Dagenham)*

Barking IG11 9SN Tel: 0181 507 0119 Fax: 0181 507 0118

A brick-built Elizabethan manor house with mullioned windows, now incongruously surrounded by 20th-century housing. Leased to the London Borough of Barking & Dagenham, the manor is used for a wide range of arts and heritage activities

🅾 1 Feb to 30 Nov: daily except Sat & Sun 10–5 by appointment with Administrator. Also open one Sat ('Visitor Day') every month 10–4. Tel. for details. **Events:** exhibitions, Tudor evenings and concerts; please tel. for details

£ £1.60. Group visits by prior arrangement. Rates on application

🚶 Guided tours available

♿ Wheelchair access to ground floor only

🍵 Tea-room open on 'Visitor Day'

🏫 Teachers' resource book available. School visits by prior arrangement

🐕 In garden only

➡ (3: G4) In Eastbury Square, 10min walk S from Upney station [177: TQ457838] *Bus:* LT 287, 368 ▦ Barking–Rainham/Chadwell Heath (tel. 0171 222 1234) *Station:* Barking, then one stop on Underground District line to Upney ¼ml

FENTON HOUSE 🏠 ✤ 🛡 *London (Camden)*

Windmill Hill, Hampstead NW3 6RT Tel/fax: 0171 435 3471

A late 17th-century house with an outstanding collection of porcelain and early keyboard instruments, most of which are in working order. The delightful walled garden includes fine displays of roses, an orchard and vegetable garden

Note: For permission to use the early keyboard instruments, please apply in writing one month in advance to the Keeper of Instruments, c/o Fenton House

🅾 1 to 22 March: Sat & Sun only 2–5. 1 April to 1 Nov: Sat, Sun & BH Mon 11–5; Wed, Thur & Fri 2–5; last admission 30min before closing. Parties received at other times by appointment. Short guides available in French and German. **Events:** for details of events please send s.a.e. to Custodian

£ £4; family ticket £10. No reduction for pre-booked parties. No parking facilities. No picnics in garden

🚶 Demonstration tours (max. 20) of instruments by the Keeper, first Thur in each month from April to Nov at 2, cost £9 (incl. NT members). 1½hrs duration. Please apply to Custodian in writing or by fax

♿ Access to ground floor only

🦯 Braille guide

👶 Children's quiz

■ Tape of music played on Benton Collection of Instruments available for hire (£1) during visit

🐕 No dogs

➡ (3: G4) Visitors' entrance on W side of Hampstead Grove *Bus:* Frequent local services (tel. 0171 222 1234) *Station:* Hampstead Heath 1ml; *Underground*: Hampstead 300m

---

GEORGE INN 🏠   *London (Southwark)*

The George Inn Yard, 77 Borough High St, Southwark SE1 1NH
Tel: 0171 407 2056

The last remaining galleried inn in London, famous as a coaching inn during the 17th century and mentioned by Dickens in Little Dorrit. *Now leased to Whitbread plc and still in use as a public house*

🅾 During licensing hours

🍽 Bar food daily; à la carte restaurant Mon to Fri & Sat evening; please telephone for reservations

🧒 Children admitted subject to normal licensing regulations

🐕 In courtyard only

➡ (3: G4) On E side of Borough High Street, near London Bridge Stn *Bus:* Frequent local services (tel. 0171 222 1234) *Station:* London Bridge ▣ & Underground, few mins walk

---

HAM HOUSE 🏠 ❖ 🛡   *London (Richmond-upon-Thames)*

Ham, Richmond TW10 7RS Tel: 0181 940 1950 Fax: 0181 332 6903

An outstanding Stuart house, built in 1610 and then enlarged in the 1670s, at a time when it was at the heart of Restoration court life and intrigue. Ham is famous for its lavish interiors and spectacular collections of fine furniture, textiles and paintings, as well as for the 17th-century formal gardens, currently being restored to their former glory

What's new in 1998: Ghost Guide takes you on a tour of haunted rooms; South Terrace borders now replanted in formal late 17th-century style; kitchen restored to early 18th-century original appearance. Please note that garden charges will apply from 1 April

🅾 **House**: 28 March to 1 Nov: daily except Thur & Fri 1–5; last admission 4.30. **Garden**: open daily except Thur & Fri 10.30–6 (or dusk if earlier). Closed 25/26 Dec & 1 Jan. No dogs in garden please. **Events**: Family picnic evenings in summer; garden tours throughout season; children's events in school holidays; for details contact Regional Box Office tel. 01372 451596. The Great Hall is licensed for civil weddings and the Orangery is available for private functions and receptions; call Functions Manager on tel. 0181 332 6644 for details

£ House: £5; family ticket £12.50. Garden only £1.50. Pre-booked groups of 15+ during opening hours £4, children £2. Free parking 400m (not NT)

𝗞 Guided tours and school groups of 15+, Wed mornings only. Essential to book in advance (special rates apply)

🛍 Shop open in March, Nov & Dec: weekends 11–4.30; April to Oct: daily except Thur & Fri 11–5.30

♿ Parking near house for disabled visitors. Access to house by steep ramps only suitable for assisted wheelchair users. Lift access to all showrooms on request. Grounds include mostly firm, but some deep gravel, paths. Orangery restaurant accessible via ramps. Shop accessible. Sympathetic Hearing Scheme. WC. 2 wheelchairs available

◈ Braille guide; scented plants

🍴 Licensed Orangery restaurant and tea garden open for self-service lunches 12–2; dates and times as shop. Last orders 30min before closing. Special rates for weekday group bookings; tel. 0181 940 0735. Picnics in Orangery garden

👶 Baby-changing facility. House unsuitable for back carriers or pushchairs, but reins and baby slings available. Highchairs in tea-room; children's portions available. Children's quiz from front desk and Key Stages 1 & 2-related worksheets

🎒 School pack available; tel. 0181 940 1950

🐕 No dogs except guide dogs

➡ (3: F5) On S bank of Thames, W of A307, at Petersham [176: TQ172732] *Bus:* LT 65 Ealing Broadway–Kingston; 371 Richmond–Kingston; London & Country 415 Victoria–Guildford; (all passing ⊠ Richmond & Kingston) (tel. 0171 222 1234) *Station:* Richmond ⊠ & Underground 1½ml via Thames towpath, 2ml by road; Kingston 2ml. Also foot ferry from Marble Hill House, tel. 0181 940 1950 for details

---

LINDSEY HOUSE 🏠   *London (Kensington & Chelsea)*

99/100 Cheyne Walk SW10 0DQ Tel: (Regional Office) 01494 528051

Built on the former site of Sir Thomas More's garden and now part of Cheyne Walk. The house claims one of the finest 17th-century exteriors in London

O The ground floor entrance hall and garden room, main staircase to first floor, and the front and rear gardens are open by written appointment only on the following dates: 16 Apr, 21 May, 20 June, 9 July, 19 Sept & 15 Oct 2–4. Please write to R. Bourne, 100 Cheyne Walk, London SW10

£ Free. No parking (nearest car park Battersea Park)

♿ Inaccessible

🐕 No dogs

➡ (3: G4) On Cheyne Walk, W of Battersea Bridge near junction with Milman's Street on Chelsea Embankment [176: TQ268775] *Bus:* Frequent local service (tel. 0171 222 1234) *Station:* Victoria 1¾ml; *Underground:* South Kensington 1¼ml

MORDEN HALL PARK 📷🎭   *London (Merton)*

Morden Hall Road, Morden SM4 5JD Tel: 0181 648 1845 Fax: 0181 687 0094

A green oasis in the heart of London suburbia, this former deer park has an extensive network of waterways, ancient hay meadows, an impressive avenue and an interesting collection of vernacular buildings. The old estate workshops now house local craftworkers, whose work is on show, and there is an independently managed city farm on Bunce's Meadow

What's new in 1998: Rose garden under restoration; large tree planting project starts winter 1997

O Park only open all year during daylight hours. *Note*: Car park by the café/shop and garden centre closes at 6 daily. **Events:** 2–4 May, Craft Fair (charge, incl. NT members); details from Four Seasons Events (tel. 01344 874787)

£ Free

🏃 Guided tours by arrangement; contact Property Office

📷 Daily throughout the year 10–5. Closed 25/26 Dec and 1 Jan 1999 (tel. 0181 687 0881). Shop closed 21 & 22 Jan 1998. Garden centre independently run by Capital Gardens plc as National Trust tenants (tel. 0181 646 3002)

♿ Restaurant, shop & garden centre fully accessible. (Some thick gravel in garden centre.) WC in restaurant. Access available from car park through garden centre to riverside walkways. Wheelchair path through rose garden and beside river. Two wheelchairs available on request

🔊 Flowing water sounds by mill

🍴 Licensed riverside café serving coffee, lunches (12–2) and teas daily throughout the year 10–5. Closed 25/26 Dec and 1 Jan (tel. 0181 687 0881)

🚼 Baby-changing facilities and highchairs

🏛 Snuff Mill Environmental Centre for educational groups. Contact Education Officer (tel. 0181 542 4232)

🐕 Please keep dogs under control at all times and on leads around buildings, paths & picnic area

➔ (3: G5) Off A24, and A297 S of Wimbledon, N of Sutton [176: TQ259687] *Bus:* Frequent from surrounding areas (tel. 0171 222 1234) *Station:* Morden Road, not Sun, ½ml. *Underground*: Morden 500m

OSTERLEY PARK 🏛📷🎭   *London (Hounslow)*

Isleworth, Middlesex TW7 4RB
Tel./fax 0181 560 3918; Recorded Visitor Information 0181 568 3164

Although originally a Tudor house, Osterley was transformed into what we see today by Robert Adam in 1761. The spectacular interiors contain one of Britain's most complete examples of his work and include exceptional plasterwork, carpets and furniture. The house also has an interesting kitchen. The magnificent 16th-century stables survive largely intact and are still in use. The house is set in extensive park and farmland, complete with pleasure grounds, ornamental lakes and classical garden buildings

What's new in 1998: Opening hours have changed; public transport discount for visitors arriving on public transport

🅾 **House:** 1 April to 1 Nov: daily except Mon & Tues 2–5 (but open on BH Mon and every Sun 1–5). Closed Good Fri. Last admission 4.30. **Grand Stables:** Sun afternoons in summer. **Park and pleasure grounds:** all year 9–7.30 or sunset if earlier. Park will close early before major events. Car park closed 25/26 Dec. **Events:** For details of open-air theatre, annual summer 'Big Band' concert and other events, please send s.a.e. to Box Office, P O Box 180, High Wycombe, Bucks HP14 4XT

💷 £4; family ticket £10. Parties Wed to Sat £3.50, advance booking required. Park and pleasure grounds free. Public transport discount for those arriving by train or bus with valid LT travelcard: non-members £1 off adult ticket, NT members receive £1 voucher towards guidebook or cream tea. Non-members in pre-booked coach parties receive 50p off adult ticket. Coach-parking free, otherwise car park £2

🚶 Pre-booked out-of-hours guided 'Private View' Wed to Fri mornings £6 per person (incl. NT members). Minimum charge £120

🛍 Shop in stable yard (tel. 0181 232 8188) open 1 April to 1 Nov 1–5.30, 4 Nov to 20 Dec 12–4: Wed to Sun and BH Mon (incl. Good Fri)

♿ Car park is 250m from house, tea-room and shop. Courtesy vehicle runs between car park, house, tea-room & shop during house opening hours. Tea-room, walled tea-garden and shop are accessible. WC in park. Park is level and accessible to wheelchairs. Indoor & outdoor wheelchairs available. Self-drive battery-powered vehicles are available free of charge on Wed, Thur & Sun afternoons during the summer months. Stairclimber (must be pre-booked) gives access to principal floor of house

♿ Braille guide

☕ Coffee, light lunches & teas in Stables tea-room, 1 April to 1 Nov: Wed to Sun & BH Mon (incl. Good Fri) 11.30–5; open 8 Nov to 20 Dec: Sat & Sun 12–4. Groups of 20 or more must book in advance (tel. 0181 569 7624)

👶 Baby-changing facilities in WC. House unsuitable for pushchairs or back carriers. Highchairs in tea-room

🏛 Pre-booked education groups welcome (tel. 0181 568 7714). Study base in stable block available for groups of up to 60. Teachers' resource book, quizzes, tree guides, house and park trails

[dog icon] In park only (guide dogs and hearing dogs excepted). Must be on leads unless indicated

[arrow icon] (3: F5) Follow brown tourist signs on A4 between Gillette Corner and Osterley underground station (access via Thornbury Rd & Jersey Rd); M4, Jn 3 [176: TQ146780] *Bus:* LT H91 Hounslow–Hammersmith, not Sun, to within ½ml (tel. 0171 222 1234) *Station:* Syon Lane 1½ml *Underground:* Osterley ½ml

RAINHAM HALL [icon]   *London (Havering)*

The Broadway, Rainham RM13 9YN Tel: (Regional Office) 01494 528051

An elegant Georgian house, built in 1729 to a symmetrical plan and with fine wrought iron gates, carved porch and interior panelling

[clock icon] April to end Oct: Wed & BH Mon 2–6; also Sat by written application to tenant

[£ icon] £2.10. No reduction for parties. Parking limited. No WC

[dog icon] Guide dogs by arrangement with tenant

[arrow icon] (3: H4) Just S of the church, 5ml E of Barking [177: TQ521821] *Bus:* Frequent local services (tel. 0171 222 1234) *Station:* Rainham, few metres

'ROMAN' BATH [icon]   *London (Westminster)*

5 Strand Lane WC2 Tel: 0171 641 5264

The remains of a bath, restored in the 17th century and believed by some to be Roman

Note: The Bath is administered and maintained by Westminster City Council

[clock icon] Bath visible through window from pathway all year. Otherwise May to end Sept: every Wed 1–5 by appointment only (24hrs' notice) during office hours

[£ icon] 50p. Children under 16 and OAPs 25p. No WC

[arrow icon] (3: G4) Just W of Aldwych station (Piccadilly Line now closed), approach via Surrey Street [176: TQ309809] *Bus:* Frequent local services (tel. 0171 222 1234) *Station:* Blackfriars or Charing Cross, both ½ml *Underground:* Temple, not Sun, few metres; Embankment ½ml

SUTTON HOUSE [icon] [icon]   *London (Hackney)*

2 & 4 Homerton High Street, Hackney E9 6JQ Tel: 0181 986 2264

A unique survival in London's East End, Sutton House was built in 1535 (when Hackney was an unspoilt village) by Ralph Sadleir, a rising star at the court of Henry VIII. It became home to successive merchants, Huguenot silk-weavers, Victorian schoolmistresses and Edwardian clergy, and although altered over the years, remains an essentially Tudor house. Oak-panelled rooms and carved fireplaces survive intact and an exhibition and audiovisual presentation tell the history of the house and its former occupants

🅞 4 Feb to 25 Nov & 3 Feb 1999 onwards: Wed, Sun & BHols 11.30–5.30, Sat 2–5.30. Last admission 5. Contemporary exhibitions open as café bar.
Events: 29 Nov, Craft Fair; for full programme of monthly recitals, exhibitions, fairs, lectures, family days and other events, please contact Property Manager on above number. Rooms available for private functions, rates on application. Licensed for civil marriages

£ £1.90, child 50p; family ticket £4.50. Group visits by prior arrangement, also on Thur & Fri. Rates on application. Public car park in St John's Churchyard, ¼ml. Pay-and-display parking in immediate vicinity

🎟 Guided tours and walks available. Rates on application

🏠 Open Wed to Sun & BHols 11–5.30, except 21 Dec to 12 Jan 1999

♿ Ground floor only accessible to wheelchairs. No lift. WC. Induction loop in concert hall

◉ Braille guide

▉ Café bar open Wed to Sun & BHols 11–5, except 21 Dec to 12 Jan 1999

✚ Baby-changing facilities in WC. Family trails

▉ Teachers' resource book. School visits by prior arrangement. Rates on application

➔ (3: G4) At the corner of Isabella Road and Homerton High Street [176: TQ352851] *Bus:* Frequent services from central London (tel. 0171 222 1234) *Station:* Hackney Central ¼ml; Hackney Downs ½ml

---

2 WILLOW ROAD 🏠 🎟   *London (Camden)*

2 Willow Road, Hampstead NW3 1TH Tel: 0171 435 6166

The former home of Erno Goldfinger, designed and built by him in 1939. A three-storey brick and concrete rectangle, it is one of Britain's most important examples of modernist architecture and is filled with furniture also designed by Goldfinger. The interesting art collection includes works by Henry Moore and Max Ernst

Note: Entry by timed ticket only. Difficult access for the infirm. Cinema showing introductory film

🅞 2 April to 31 Oct: Thur, Fri & Sat 12–5. Last admission 4. Guided tours every 45min (of 1hr duration; max 12 people). Organised groups to be booked in advance with Custodian

£ £4. No parking at house. Limited on-street parking. East Heath Road municipal car park (100m), open intermittently

♿ Wheelchair access to ground floor only. Filmed tour of whole house available. Cinema equipped with induction loop

◉ Braille guide

➔ (3: G4) *Bus:* Frequent local services (tel. 0171 222 1234) *Station:* Hampstead Heath ¼ml *Underground:* Hampstead or Belsize Park ½ml

Introduction to the East

The East of England is characterised by wide expanses of open countryside and sweeping views under huge skies. Here also is a remote and beautiful coastline, studded with unspoilt fishing villages, ancient historical sites and internationally renowned nature reserves.

The North Norfolk coast is one of the most scenic and evocative places in Britain, and is particularly important for its birdlife. At **Blakeney Point** and **Morston Marshes** a range of seabirds can be seen, as well as seals, whilst **Brancaster** is noted for its coastal flora and the site of the Roman fort of **Branodonum**. There are several Trust owned properties in the Sheringham area, including the highest point in Norfolk at **West Runton**, beautiful landscape and woodland at **Sheringham Park** and woods and heathland at **Beeston Regis Heath**. Spectacular views can be had from **Incleborough Hill**. Inland are the celebrated country houses and parks of **Blickling** and **Felbrigg**.

On the edge of Norfolk's famous Broads is **Horsey Mere**, where the Trust owns over 800ha (1900 acres) of marshland, marrams and farmland, as well as **Horsey Windpump**. In the past much of East Anglia was subject to regular flooding and drainage mills such as this were essential to maintain water levels. Another example can be seen at **Wicken Fen** in Cambridgeshire, a haven for rare wildlife and virtually the last remnant of the extensive fenland that once covered much of eastern England.

The remote character of the east coast led to the construction of the fascinating military research buildings at **Orford Ness** in Suffolk. The Ness is also an important site for breeding and overwintering birds. There are many interesting natural habitats in this area, including **Dunwich Heath**, a surviving fragment of the sandy heaths locally known as the Sandlings, and **Minsmere Beach**, adjacent to the famous bird reserve. Further south, there are pleasant walks and fine views at **Kyson Hill** near Woodbridge, and at **Pin Mill** on the River Orwell, where a wealth of fishing boats are usually present.

The picturesque qualities of the Essex/Suffolk border became famous through the work of John Constable, and at Bridge Cottage at **Flatford** there is an exhibition on his work and a range of other facilities. Fine walks lead into the beautiful **Dedham Vale**.

There are good birdwatching opportunities on the Essex coast, especially on the reserve of **Northey Island** in the Blackwater estuary (access by advance permit only from the Warden, Northey Cottage, Northey Island, Maldon, tel. 01621 853142). **Copt Hall Marshes**, near Little Wigborough, is another noted site, particularly for overwintering birds, and can be viewed from a waymarked circular route.

The ancient landscapes of East Anglia include **Danbury and Lingwood Commons**, a survival of the medieval manors of St Clere and Herons and a former area of common grazing, and **Blake's Wood**, an area of hornbeam and chestnut coppice, renowned in spring for its display of bluebells. **Hatfield Forest** near Bishop's Stortford offers wonderful walking and riding through ancient woodland and forest pasture. All these areas are designated SSSIs and are rich in wildlife.

The Trust is also fortunate in owning two motte-and-bailey castles: **Darrow Wood**, near Harleston in Norfolk, and **Rayleigh Mount** in Essex, recorded in the Domesday Book and offering excellent recreational space in the heart of Rayleigh town.

East Anglia's involvement in the wool trade brought it much wealth in the past, and provided the means for building the many grand churches and buildings that dot the landscape. **St George's Guildhall** at King's Lynn and **The Guildhall of Corpus Christi** at Lavenham are two splendid examples. The other chief source of wealth was land, the evidence being the magnificent estates that are spread across much of eastern England. These range from the warm and intimate red brick of **Oxburgh Hall** and **Melford Hall** to the extravagant grandeur of **Wimpole Hall** and **Belton House**. Standing proudly over the Lincolnshire Fens is the sturdy brick tower of **Tattershall Castle**. But if any property sums up the spirit of this part of England, it is the remote and enigmatic **Gunby Hall**, set in an open landscape with great vistas.

Highlights for Disabled Visitors

Many properties have powered vehicles (see individual entries); **Wicken Fen** and **Sheringham Park** both have accessible pathways; **Orford Ness** is holding a special access day, tel. Warden on 01394 450900 for details; **Ickworth** has a special scented walk.

... and for Families

All NT restaurants in East Anglia have special play areas for children; there are children's playgrounds at **Blickling, Ickworth** and **Wimpole**, and a Family Woodland Trail at **Felbrigg; Wimpole Home Farm** is a must for families with young children. There is an adventure playground at **Belton House** in Lincolnshire.

Further Information

NT Regional Offices:

- **East Anglia** (tel. 01263 733471) – for properties in Cambridgeshire, Essex, Norfolk and Suffolk.

- **East Midlands** (tel. 01909 486411) – for properties in Lincolnshire.

Walks leaflets are available at the following properties: Blickling, Dunwich Heath, Felbrigg, Hatfield Forest, Orford Ness, Sheringham Park, Wicken Fen and Wimpole Hall.

DUNWICH BEACH

ANGEL CORNER 🏠 *Suffolk*

8 Angel Hill, Bury St Edmunds IP33 1UZ
Tel: (St Edmundsbury BC) 01284 763233

A fine Queen Anne house, containing the parlour of the Mayor of St Edmundsbury

O Open by appointment only. Further details from The Mayor's Secretary, St Edmundsbury Borough Council, 8 Angel Hill, Bury St Edmunds IP33 1UZ; direct tel. 01284 737135

£ £1, which includes coffee and biscuits. No WC

& Difficult steps up to front door

P Refreshments included in admission charge

H Guide dogs only

→ (4: J7) In Bury St Edmunds [155: TL855643] *Bus:* From surrounding areas (tel. 0645 583358) *Station:* Bury St Edmunds ½ml

ANGLESEY ABBEY AND GARDEN 🏠 ✖ ✝ ❂ ❂ *Cambridgeshire*

Lode, Cambridge CB5 9EJ Tel/fax: 01223 811200

The house, dating from 1600, is built on the site of an Augustinian priory, and contains the famous Fairhaven collection of paintings and furniture. It is surrounded by an outstanding 40ha (99 acres) landscape garden and arboretum, with wonderful statues, a display of hyacinths in spring, and magnificent herbaceous borders and dahlia garden in summer. A water-mill in the grounds is in full working order (flour on sale) and may be seen working on the first Saturday of each month

What's new in 1998: New winter walk. First phase opening winter 1998/9. Open 5 Nov to 20 Dec: Thur to Sun 11–4; Jan to Mar 1999: Sat & Sun 11–4

O **House:** 21 March to 11 Oct: daily except Mon & Tues (but open BH Mon) 1–5. **Garden:** 21 March to 1 Nov: Wed to Sun & BH Mon 11–5.30; also open Mon & Tues 6 July to 13 Sept (but house closed Mon & Tues). **Lode Mill:** 21 March to 1 Nov: Wed to Sun & BH Mon 1–5. Last admission to house, garden and Lode Mill 4.30. Property closed Good Fri. *Note:* Timed tickets to the house are issued Sun & BH Mon to ease overcrowding. Visitors are advised that at BH periods the delay in gaining admission to the house may be considerable and very occasionally admission may not be possible. **Events:** please send s.a.e. for details of musical events, theatre and garden tours

£ House & garden £5.80, Sun & BH Mon £6.80; family discounts available. Parties £4.80 per person. Garden only £3.40 (parties £2.70). Lode Mill free on entry to garden. Parties please send s.a.e to Property Manager for information pack and booking form (no reductions Sun & BH Mon)

🛒 Shop & plant centre open 21 March to 1 Nov: Wed to Sun & BH Mon (daily 6 July to 13 Sept) 11–5.30. 5 Nov to 20 Dec: Thur to Sun 11–4. Jan to March 1999: Sat & Sun 11–4

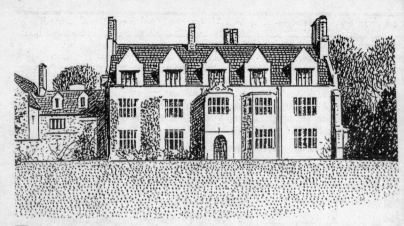

 Close car-parking arrangements: please contact Property Manager at least 24hrs in advance. Self-drive vehicles available for access to garden, shop and restaurant; house difficult (only 3 rooms accessible to wheelchair users via 4 stone steps). Ground floor of Lode Mill accessible to wheelchair users. WC

Braille guide to house only; items to touch on request in most rooms. Hyacinth garden in spring; other scented plants

Lunches and teas (full licence) in restaurant by car park, 21 March to 1 Nov: Wed to Sun & BH Mon 11–5.30; Christmas & New Year opening times as shop. Refreshments also open 6 July to 13 Sept: Mon & Tues. Picnic area. Seating:120 in restaurant, 60 in covered open-air area

Children's guide available; baby slings available. Restaurant: children's menu, baby food, highchairs, scribble sheets, children's play area

In car park only, on leads. Guide dogs only in house and garden

(4: G7) In village of Lode, 6ml NE of Cambridge on B1102 [154: TL533622] *Bus:* Stagecoach Cambus 111/122 from Cambridge (frequent services link Cambridge and bus station) (tel. 01223 423554); also 14 from Cambridge (Sun only) (tel. 01223 717740) *Station:* Cambridge 6ml

BELTON HOUSE 🏠 🏡 ✝ ✿ ● 👤 👤 👁 *Lincolnshire*

Grantham NG32 2LS Tel: 01476 566116 Fax: 01476 579071

The crowning achievement of Restoration country house architecture, Belton was built in 1685-88 and later altered by James Wyatt. The stunning interiors contain exceptionally fine plasterwork and wood-carving, as well as important collections of paintings, furniture, tapestries and silverware. There are also formal gardens, an orangery and a magnificent landscape park

What's new in 1998: Children's activity room in house

O 1 April to 1 Nov: daily except Mon & Tues (but closed Good Fri and open BH Mon) **House**: 1–5.30; please note that there is much to see and at least one hour is recommended to take full advantage. **Garden & park (incl. adventure playground)**: 11–5.30 (27 June 11–4.30; July & Aug 10–5.30); last admissions 5 (4 on 27 June). Free access to park all year, on foot only from Lion Lodge gates (this does not give admittance to house, garden or adventure playground). Park may be closed occasionally for special events. Bellmount Woods are open all year, with access from a separate car park. **Events**: 18/19 April, Belton Horse Trials; 27 June, open-air concert; 19 July, Family Fun Day. For details please send s.a.e to Property Manager

£ House & garden £5, children £2.50; family ticket £12.50. Discount for parties

Ⓚ Guided tours for parties, outside normal hours only, may be arranged

Ⓐ Shop same days as house 12–5.30. Also Nov to 20 Dec: Sat & Sun 12–4

Ⓚ House difficult; please arrange with Property Manager to visit Wed to Fri when less busy. Park, garden, restaurant, shop and refreshment kiosk accessible, but rough paths to playground, difficult in wet weather; close car parking by prior arrangement; WC; wheelchair available for use in house. Sympathetic Hearing Scheme. We recommend that people with disabilities contact property in advance

◉ Braille and audio guides

▣ Licensed restaurant open as shop, serving wide variety of home-cooked hot and cold lunches 12–2, teas 2–5 (seats 96). Open for functions and pre-booked parties throughout year; details by written application (s.a.e. please) to Property Manager

Ⓚ Extensive adventure playground, incl. under-6 'corral'; miniature train rides in summer. Children's guide; parent and baby facilities; front baby slings available on loan; children's portions in restaurant; children's activity room in house

▥ Educational visits from school parties welcomed (Education Liaison Officer, schoolrooms and teachers' pack available); also 'grounds only' arrangements available for school parties

Ⓚ In parkland only, on leads

→ (4: E4) 3ml NE of Grantham on A607 Grantham–Lincoln road, easily reached, and signposted from A1 [130: SK929395] *Bus:* Road Car 601 Grantham–Lincoln; 609 Grantham–Sleaford (both pass close ≖ Grantham) (tel. 01522 553135) *Station:* Grantham 3ml

---

BLAKENEY POINT ◪ Ⓚ Ⓚ   *Norfolk*

Warden's address: 35 The Cornfield, Langham, Holt NR25 7DQ
Tel: April to Sept: 01263 740480; Oct to March: 01328 830401 Fax: 01263 740241

One of Britain's foremost bird sanctuaries, the Point is a 3.5ml-long sand and shingle spit, noted in particular for its colonies of breeding terns and for the rare migrants that pass through in spring and autumn. Both common and grey seals can be seen, as well as an interesting range of seaside plants. An information centre at Morston Quay provides further details on the area's attractions

⭕ All year

💷 No landing fee. Access on foot from Cley Beach (3½ml) or by ferry from Morston and Blakeney (tidal). Restricted access to certain areas of the Point during the main bird breeding season (May to July). Car park at Blakeney Quay and Morston Quay £1.50, NT members free

🧒 For pre-booked school parties and special interest groups (small charge)

♿ Please give advance notice of a visit to Warden (address above). WC at Lifeboat House

🔊 Sea and bird sounds; atmosphere

🍽 Light refreshments and exhibition in the Old Lifeboat House (April to Sept); open subject to tide times

🏛 Resource book available from Warden; price £1.50 plus postage

🐕 Must be on leads. No dogs west of Old Lifeboat House on Blakeney Point, April to Sept

➡ (4: J3) Morston Quay, Blakeney [133: TG0046] and Cley are all off A149 Cromer–Hunstanton road *Bus:* Sanders Coaches, Eastern Counties Coastliner, from 🚉 Sheringham (tel. 0500 626116) *Station:* Sheringham (U) 8ml

---

BLICKLING HALL, GARDEN AND PARK
🏛 🏠 ✳ 🌳 🎎 🧒 🎭   *Norfolk*

Blickling, Norwich NR11 6NF Tel: 01263 733084 Fax: 01263 734924

Built in the early 17th century and one of England's great Jacobean houses, Blickling is famed for its spectacular long gallery, superb library and fine collections of furniture, pictures and tapestries. The gardens are full of colour throughout the year and the extensive parkland features a lake and a series of beautiful walks

What's new in 1998: Expanding events and exhibitions programme; developing countryside and educational facilities (tel. 01263 733084 for leaflet); now licensed for weddings

⭕ **House:** 4 April to end July: Wed to Sun & BH Mons 1–4.30; Aug: Tues to Sun & BH Mon 1–4.30 (guided tours on Mon 3, 10, 17 & 24 Aug); Sept to 1 Nov: Wed to Sun 1–4.30. Last admission 4.30. **Garden:** same days as house 10.30–5.30 (gates close at 6), and open daily 1–30 Aug; 2 Nov to 31 March 1999: Sun only 11–4. **Park and woods:** daily all year dawn to dusk. **Events:** wide-ranging programme; details from Property Manager

💷 House & garden £6. Garden only £3.30. Family and group discounts available. Groups please book with s.a.e. to Property Manager. Coarse fishing in lake; permits available from Warden at 1 Park Gate (tel. 01263 734181). Free access to South Front, shop, restaurant and plant centre

🧒 Private and school party guided tours of hall, garden and estate available outside normal opening hours. Evening tour with supper in hall possible. Partner programmes compiled; details from Property Office

⌂ Shop and plant centre open as garden: 4 April to 1 Nov 10.30–5.30. Also 2 Nov to 20 Dec: Thur to Sun 10.30–5.30; Jan to end March 1999: Sat & Sun only 11–4

♿ Designated parking area near house for elderly visitors and visitors with disabilities. Steep ramp at East Gate; entrance to house ramped; ground floor on one level; lift to upper floor. Garden routes available avoiding steps; two battery-operated vehicles available. Ramp to shop and restaurant. Plant centre accessible. WCs in car parks and in buildings to east of Hall. Sympathetic Hearing Scheme. *Note*: British Gas ADAPT Commendation, 1993

👁 Braille guide

🍴 Lunches & teas in restaurant (capacity 110): 4 April to 1 Nov when house and garden open 10.30–5.30; 2 Nov to 20 Dec; Thur to Sun 10.30–5.30; Jan to end March 1999: Sat & Sun only 11–4; table licence (parties by arrangement). Picnic area in orchard. Private lunch, supper & dinner parties in Hall

👶 Children's guide. Baby slings available. Baby-changing facilities. Restaurant: children's menu, baby food, highchairs, scribble sheets. Children's play area in orchard

🏫 School visits welcome, details from Property Manager

🐕 In park only, on leads. Guide dogs only in Hall, garden and orchard picnic area

➜ (4: K4) On N side of B1354, 1½ml NW of Aylsham on A140, 15ml N of Norwich, 10ml S of Cromer [133: TG178286] *Bus*: Eastern Counties 53/8, X58 Norwich–Sheringham; Sanders Coaches 40/1 (passing close ≋ Norwich), alight Aylsham, 1½ml (tel. 0500 626116) *Station*: Aylsham (Bure Valley Railway from ≋ Hoveton & Wroxham) 1¾ml, North Walsham (U) 8ml

---

BOURNE MILL ⊠ *Essex*

Bourne Road, Colchester CO2 8RT Tel: 01206 572422

The mill was originally built as fishing lodge in 1591 and features stepped 'Dutch' gables. There is a mill-pond, and much of the machinery, includng the water-wheel, is intact

○ BH Sun & BH Mon only, plus Sun & Tues in July & Aug: 2–5.30

£ £1.50. Children must be accompanied by an adult. No reduction for parties. No WC

➜ (4: J8) 1ml S of centre of Colchester, in Bourne Road, off the Mersea Road (B1025) [168: TM006238] *Bus*: Colchester Transport 8/A, Eastern National 67 from Colchester (passing ≋ Colchester) (tel. 0345 000333) *Station*: Colchester Town ¾ml; Colchester 2ml

---

BRANCASTER ⬚ ⬚ ⬚ ⬚ ⬚ ⬚ *Norfolk*

Dial House, Brancaster Staithe, King's Lynn PE31 8BW Tel: 01485 210719

An extensive area of saltmarsh, intertidal mud and sand flats, and including the site of the Roman fort of Branodunum

Note: A boat can be hired at Brancaster Staithe (weather permitting) to take visitors to the National Nature Reserve on Scolt Head Island. It is managed by English Nature (EN Warden: tel. 01485 518559). The Island is an important breeding site for four species of tern, oystercatcher and ringed plover. Nature trail. It is inadvisable to walk at low tide over the saltmarshes and sand flats

What's new in 1998: A residential Activity Centre is being developed in Dial House with funding from the Millennium Commission (opening summer 1998). Schools requiring course details should contact the Centre Manger

[O] All year. Information centre and cycle hire at Dial House are temporarily closed due to redevelopment. Cycle hire transferred meanwhile to North Shore Windsurfers, The Boatyard, Maine Road, Brancaster Staithe (opposite village green), tel. 01485 210236. **Events:** guided walks programme, leaflet from Centre Manager

[£] Golf club car park at Brancaster Beach, parking charge (incl. NT members)

[▣] Near the harbour (not NT)

[🐕] Under control at all times on the beach and not on Scolt Head Island from mid April to mid Aug. Dog-free area on Brancaster Beach, W of golf clubhouse May to Sept

[→] (4: H3) Brancaster Staithe is halfway between Wells and Hunstanton on A149 coast road [132: TF800450] *Bus:* Sanders/Dunthorne/Eastern Counties Coastliner Hunstanton–Wells, with connections from King's Lynn (passing close ▨ King's Lynn) (tel. 0500 626116)

COGGESHALL GRANGE BARN [▣] *Essex*

Grange Hill, Coggeshall, Colchester CO6 1RE Tel: 01376 562226

The oldest surviving timber-framed barn in Europe, dating from the 12th century and originally part of a Cistercian monastery. It was restored in the 1980s by the Coggeshall Barn Trust, Braintree DC and Essex CC, and contains a small collection of farm carts and wagons

[O] 29 March to 11 Oct: Tues, Thur, Sun and BH Mon 1–5

[£] £1.50. Parties £1. Joint ticket with Paycocke's £3. Car park at Grange Barn, available only during opening times

[♿] Barn accessible, parking nearby. WC next to Barn

[✋] Structure, including main aisle posts, may be touched

[▣] Refreshments available at the Clockhouse Tea-rooms (not NT) in the centre of Coggeshall (tel. 01376 563242)

[→] (4: J8) Signposted off A120 Coggeshall bypass; ½ml from centre of Coggeshall, on Grange Hill (signposted) [168: TQ848223] *Bus:* Eastern National/ Hedingham 70 Braintree–Colchester (passing close ▨ Marks Tey) (tel. 0345 000333) *Station:* Kelvedon 2½ml

EAST

DUNWICH HEATH & MINSMERE BEACH — *Suffolk*

Dunwich, Saxmundham IP17 3DJ Tel: 01728 648505/648501 Fax: 01728 648384

A remnant of the once extensive Sandlings heaths and one of Suffolk's most important nature conservation areas. There are many excellent walks, including access to the neighbouring bird reserve of Minsmere, and an observation room in the converted coastguard cottages

What's new in 1998: Field Study Centre now open

- All year: dawn to dusk. Introductory talks available for group visits. **Events:** family events programme; send s.a.e. to Property Enterprises Manager for list. Private function and events catered for
- Parking charge: season tickets £15; cars (pay-and-display) £1.50; coaches £6 (but free with 2 weeks' written notice). Members should display membership card on dashboard or obtain pass from Coastguard Cottages
- On request for groups
- Shop open as restaurant in Coastguard Cottages
- Car park viewing point and some footpaths accessible. Please contact the Warden for further information. Adapted WC at Coastguard Cottages (RADAR lock); stairlift to viewing room. Chauffeur-driven/self-drive powered vehicles available (booking essential). Shop and tea-room accessible. Holiday flat for disabled guests at the Coastguard Cottages
- Guided walks for visually impaired people; Braille guide
- Restaurant (located in Coastguard Cottages) open for morning coffee, lunch & tea: Jan to Feb & Nov to Dec: Thur to Sun; March & April: Tues to Sun; May to Oct: daily
- Restaurant: children's menu, baby food, highchairs, scribble sheets. Baby-changing facilities and children's outdoor play area
- Education Officer and Field Study Centre. Groups must book in advance
- Must be under tight control
- (4: L7) 1ml S of Dunwich, signposted from A12 [156: TM475683] *Bus:* 'The Villager' 196 from Saxmundham, alight Minsmere Junction (1ml). Eastern National 167 Colchester–Lowestoft, Sun only (tel. 0645 583358) *Station:* Darsham (U) 6ml

ELIZABETHAN HOUSE MUSEUM — *Norfolk*

4 South Quay, Great Yarmouth NR30 2QH Tel: 01493 855746

A 16th-century building with panelled rooms and 19th-century frontage. Leased to Norfolk Museums Service as a museum of domestic life

What's new in 1998: The house will be re-displayed in the winter of 1997–98 to show aspects of the lives of the families who lived there in the past. There will be special activities for children and demonstration days. Please tel. for details

167

O 6 April to 17 April: daily except Sat 10–5 (opens at 2 on Sun and closed Good Fri); 24 May to 25 Sept: daily except Sat 10–5. Please telephone in advance to confirm opening arrangements

£ Joint ticket lasting two days also gives entry to Maritime Museum for East Anglia and Tollhouse Museum and Brass Rubbing Centre. Adult £1.20, concessions 70p, children 60p; family ticket (2 adults, 4 children) £3. NT members admitted free to Elizabethan House Museum only. Prices subject to change

→ (4: L5) In Great Yarmouth [134: TG523073] *Bus:* Local services from surrounding areas (tel. 0500 626116) *Station:* Great Yarmouth ½ml

---

FELBRIGG HALL, GARDEN AND PARK

Norfolk

Felbrigg, Roughton, Norwich NR11 8PR Tel: 01263 837444 Fax: 01263 837032

One of the finest 17th-century houses in East Anglia, the Hall contains its original 18th-century furniture and Grand Tour paintings, as well as an outstanding library. The walled garden has been restored and features a dovecote and small orchard. The park is renowned for its fine trees and there are many interesting woodland and lakeside walks

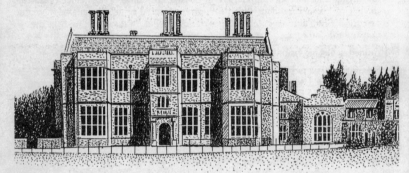

O House: 28 March to 1 Nov: daily except Thur & Fri 1–5 (but open Good Fri); BH Mon & Sun preceding BH Mon 11–5; last admission 4.30. **Garden:** same days 11–5.30. **Woodland, lakeside walks and parkland:** daily all year, dawn to dusk (closed Christmas Day). **Events:** for details of full programme please send s.a.e. to Property Manager or contact Events Box Office (tel. 01263 838297)

£ House & garden £5.40; family discounts available. Parties £4.40; please book with s.a.e. to Property Manager. Garden only £2.20

K Special guided tours of Hall outside normal opening times; details from Property Manager. Introductory tours at 12 noon most open days (charge, incl. NT members)

□ Open same days as house 11–5.30. Also 5 Nov to 20 Dec: Thur to Sun 11–4; Jan to end March 1999: Sat & Sun 11–4 (tel. 01263 837040). Secondhand book sales open as shop

♿ Parking area in main car park by information board. Wheelchairs available from visitor reception building 100m. One self-drive single-seater vehicle. Access to ground floor only, shop, restaurant, tea-room & garden; photograph album of upper floor rooms for visitors unable to climb stairs. WC. Sympathetic Hearing Scheme

👂 Braille guides for house, and walks

🍽 Park restaurant (waited service) and Turret tea-room (counter service) both licensed. 28 March to 1 Nov: same days as house 11–5.15 (occasionally only one of these facilities available). Booking advisable for Park Restaurant and Sun lunches. Private functions catered for (tel. 01263 838237). Also 5 Nov to end March 1999: same days as shop 11–3.30

👶 Baby slings available. Parent & baby room. Highchairs in restaurant. Children's menu. Scribble sheets. Free Family Woodland Trail

📖 Details of education programme from Education Officer. Teachers' resource book Key Stages 2 & 3 and teachers' pack available. 32-bed base camp available with all facilities; s.a.e to Property Manager for details

🐕 In woods under close control; in park and on farmland on leads only. Guide dogs only in house and garden

➔ (4: K4) Nr Felbrigg village, 2ml SW of Cromer; entrance off B1436, signposted from A148 and A140 [133: TG193394] *Bus:* Coastliner from Wells-next-the-Sea and ⊞ Sheringham, Sun, Tues, Wed, Thur & Fri, June–Sept only (tel. 0500 626116) *Station:* Cromer (U) or Roughton Road (U), both 2¼ml

---

FLATFORD: BRIDGE COTTAGE *Suffolk*

Flatford, East Bergholt, Colchester CO7 6OL
Tel: 01206 298260 Fax: 01206 299193

A 16th-century thatched cottage, just upstream from Flatford Mill and housing an exhibition on John Constable, several of whose paintings famously depict this property. There is a tea-garden, shop, information centre and boat hire, and access is possible on foot to Trust land in the beautiful Dedham Vale

Note: Flatford Mill, Valley Farm & Willy Lott's House are leased to the Field Studies Council which runs arts-based courses for all age groups. For further information on courses tel. 01206 298283. There is no general public access to the buildings, but the Field Studies Council will arrange tours for groups

🅾 1 March to end April: Wed to Sun 11–5.30; May to Sept: daily 10–5.30; Oct: Wed to Sun 11–5.30; Nov: Wed to Sun 11–3.30. Limited opening in Dec (telephone for details). **Events:** special evening events in tea-room (also available for private functions); details from Property Manager

£ Guided walks £1.80, accompanied children free (subject to availability). Available for school parties and coach parties, but pre-booking essential. Parking 200m; private car park, charge (NT members included). Free admission to Bridge Cottage. Audio tapes may be hired when guided walks not available

𝕏 Guided walks of the area: Easter, BHols and every afternoon May to end Sept, subject to availability

⬛ Shop open as cottage

♿ Close car-parking; 25m from cottage, or main car park, 200m. Access to tea-garden and shop. Wheelchair, powered self-drive buggy and walking aid available at Bridge Cottage

◑ Braille guide and menus. Audio commentaries accompanying raised images of Constable's 'The Haywain' and 'The Leaping Horse' available

◐ Open as cottage for morning coffee, lunches and teas (table licence)

👶 Tea-room; children's menu, baby food, highchairs, scribble sheets. Children's play table. Flatford trail on sale in cottage. Baby carriers available

📖 School visits welcome. Guided walks of sites depicted in Constable's paintings available for pre-booked educational parties; further details from Property Manager

🐕 Guide dogs only in Bridge Cottage complex

→ (4: K8) On N bank of Stour, 1ml S of East Bergholt (B1070) [168: TM077332]. Accessible on foot from East Bergholt, Dedham and Manningtree *Bus:* Eastern Counties/Eastern National 92/3, 166–8 Ipswich–Colchester (passing ⬛ Ipswich and close ⬛ Colchester Town), alight E Bergholt, ¾ml (tel. 0645 583358) *Station:* Manningtree 1¾ml by footpath, 3½ml by road

---

GRANTHAM HOUSE 🏠 ❈ ♠   *Lincolnshire*

Castlegate, Grantham NG31 6SS
Tel: (Regional Office) 01909 486411 Fax: 01909 486377

Dating from 1380, the house has been extensively altered since then and presents an attractive mixture of styles. There are delightful walled gardens running down to the river

🅾 **Ground floor only**: 1 April to end Sept: Wed 2–5 by written appointment only with the tenant, Major-General Sir Brian Wyldbore-Smith

💷 £1.50. Limited space; numbers in parties should not exceed seven. No WC

→ (4: E4) Immediately E of Grantham Church [130: SK916362] *Bus:* Road Car 601 Grantham–Lincoln, to within ¼ml (tel. 01522 553135) *Station:* Grantham 1ml

---

GUNBY HALL 🏠 🗡 🎖   *Lincolnshire*

Gunby, nr Spilsby PE23 5SS
Tel: Regional Office 01909 486411 Fax: 01909 486377

A fine red-brick house, dating from 1700 (with later extensions) and located in one of England's most remote corners. Many of the rooms are panelled and there is a beautiful oak staircase, as well as many fine paintings and items of furniture and china. The exquisite walled garden is planted with traditional English vegetables, fruit and flowers

🅾 **Ground floor & basement of house & garden**: 1 April to end Sept: Wed 2–6. Last admission 5.30. Closed BHols. Garden also open Thur 2–6. House & garden also open Tues, Thur and Fri by written appointment only with J. D. Wrisdale at above address. **Events:** occasional concerts

💷 House & garden £3.50. Garden only £2.50. No reduction for parties. Access roads unsuitable for coaches which must park in layby at gates ½ml from house

♿ Access to garden only; cobbled stableyard. Wheelchair available

🏵 Rose & herb garden

🚫 No refreshments available

🐕 In garden only, on leads

➡ (4: G3) 2½ml NW of Burgh le Marsh, 7ml W of Skegness on S side of A158 (access off roundabout) [122: TF467668] *Bus:* Road Car 6 Skegness–Lincoln (passing close ⇌ Skegness) (tel. 01522 553135) *Station:* Skegness 7ml

---

GUNBY HALL ESTATE: WHITEGATES COTTAGE 🏠 *Lincolnshire*

Mill Lane, Bratoft, nr Spilsby   Tel: 01754 890533

A small thatched cottage, built c.1770 to provide accommodation for estate workers. Notable for its mud and stud walling, it is currently being restored using traditional methods and materials

Note: Further restoration work will be carried out in 1998, but visitors are welcome to view work in progress

🔘 1 April to end Sept: Wed 2–6 by written appointment only with the tenant, Mr J. Zaremba

💷 £1.50. Numbers in parties visiting the property should not exceed six at any one time, due to the small size of rooms. WCs at Gunby Hall (above)

➡ (4: G3) 2ml W of Burgh le Marsh, 8ml W of Skegness. Approached by Gunby Lane off A158 just W of the roundabout N of Gunby Hall. Public transport: as for Gunby Hall (see above)

HATFIELD FOREST 🖼🚻🚶🛡 *Essex*

Takeley, nr Bishop's Stortford CM22 6NE Tel: 01279 870678 Fax: 01279 871938

An outstanding ancient woodland and rare surviving example of a medieval royal hunting forest. The great pollarded hornbeams and oaks support a wide variety of wildlife and there are many excellent walks and nature trails, as well as fishing in the two lakes

🔘 All year. Vehicle access restricted to entrance car park Nov to Easter. **Events:** 5/6 Sept, Wood Fair, and family events throughout the year. Please contact Property Manager for details

💷 Car park £2.70; mini-buses £5; coaches £20; school coaches £10. Parties must book in advance with Property Manager. Riding for members of Hatfield Forest Riding Association only; contact Property Manager

 ♿ Reserved car-parking; accessible paths and grassland; free self-drive powered vehicle available, please book in advance. WC

 ▣ Refreshments available near the lake

 ⚉ Baby-changing facilities

 ▣ Full education programme; details from Education Officer

 ▣ Must be kept on leads where cattle and sheep are grazing and around lake. There is a dog-free area near the lake

 ➜ (4: G9) Signposted off A120 at Takeley, E of Bishop's Stortford [167: TL547208/546199] *Bus:* Biss 317 ▣ Bishop's Stortford–▣ Elsenham, or Eastern National/Townlink 133 Bishop's Stortford–Braintree, on both alight Takeley Street (Green Man), thence ¾ml; otherwise Eastern National 33/X ▣ Bishop's Stortford–Southend or 133 Bishop's Stortford–Braintree, alight Takeley (Four Ashes), thence 1½ml (tel. 0345 000333) *Station:* Stansted Airport 3ml

---

HORSEY WINDPUMP ✕   *Norfolk*

Horsey, Great Yarmouth NR29 4EF
Tel: Regional Office 01263 733471 Fax: 01263 734924

A drainage windmill, severely damaged by lightning in 1943 and since restored

 ◉ 28 March to 30 Sept: daily 11–5

 £ £1.20. No reduction for parties. Car-parking charge for non-members, 30p per hour

 ▣ Small shop

 ▣ Light refreshments

 ▣ On leads only

 ➜ (4: L4) 2½ml NE of Potter Heigham, 11ml N of Yarmouth near B1159 [134: TG457223] *Bus:* Eastern Counties 623/6, 723/6 Great Yarmouth–Martham (passing close ▣ Yarmouth), alight W Somerton School, 1¾ml (tel. 0500 626116) *Station:* Acle (U) 10ml

---

HOUGHTON MILL ✕   ☂   *Cambridgeshire*

Houghton, nr Huntingdon PE17 2AZ Tel: 01480 301494

A large timber-built water-mill on an island in the Great Ouse, with intact machinery which is still operational. An art gallery exhibits work by local artists

What's new in 1998: NT car park and tea-room

 ◉ **Mill:** 4 April to 11 Oct: Sat, Sun & BH Mon 2–5.30; also 29 June to 9 Sept: Mon to Wed 2–5.30. Last admission 5.15. Parties and school groups at other times by arrangement with Custodian. **Art gallery:** June to end Sept: Sat & Sun 2.30–5.30

£ £2.50 (£3 on milling days); family discounts available

🕇 By prior arrangement

♿ Access to ground floor only; steep wooden stairs

Braille guide. Many items (wheat grains, wholemeal) can be enjoyed by touch

☕ Tea-room open as mill

🚼 Children's guide

Guided tours for pre-booked school parties

→ (4: F6) In village of Houghton, signposted off A1123 to Huntingdon, to St Ives [153: TL282720] *Bus:* Stagecoach United Counties 74, Whippet 1A, 4 from Huntingdon (passing close ⊠ Huntingdon) (tel. 01223 717740) *Station:* Huntingdon 3½ml

---

ICKWORTH HOUSE, PARK & GARDEN

🏠 🏛 ❀ ❦ 🚼 🕇 ♥   *Suffolk*

Ickworth, The Rotunda, Horringer, Bury St Edmunds IP29 5QE
Tel: Property Office 01284 735270/735151 Restaurant 01284 735086
Fax: 01284 735175

The eccentric Earl of Bristol created this equally eccentric house, with its central rotunda and curved corridors, in 1795 to display his collections. These include spectacular paintings by Titian, Gainsborough and Velasquez and a magnificent Georgian silver collection. The house is surrounded by an Italianate garden and set in a 'Capability' Brown park with woodland walks, deer enclosure, vineyard, Georgian summer-house, church, canal and lake

What's new in 1998: Refurbished children's play area; woodland trim trail; parent and baby room; family cycle route; vineyard walks and activities; archaeology and landscape trail; designated ball games area

🔘 **House:** 21 March to 1 Nov: daily except Mon & Thur (but open BH Mon) 1–5; last admission 4.30. **Park:** all year: daily 7–7. **Garden:** 21 March to 1 Nov: daily 10–5; 2 Nov to end March 1999: weekdays only 10–4. Garden & park closed 25 Dec. **Events:** many weekends throughout the season, including music in the house during normal opening hours. Contact the Property Office for details

£ House, garden & park £5.20, children £2.20; family discounts available. Pre-booked parties £4.20, child party rate £1.70 (no party rate Sun & BH Mon). Admission to park & garden £2, children 50p (access to shop & restaurant with park ticket)

🕇 Guided tours and pre-booked special openings of house for groups with particular interests. Also pre-booked guided tours of Italianate garden available

🛍 Shop open same days as house 12–5. Also 2 Nov to 20 Dec: Sat & Sun 11–4

♿ Disabled visitors may be driven to the house; drivers are then requested to park in the public car park. Disabled drivers are given a temporary parking permit to park outside the house. Ramp access to house. All ground-floor rooms are level. Wheelchair access to first floor by lift. Wheelchair available on all floors. Stannah lift to basement (shop and restaurant). Adapted WC on ground floor. Much of garden accessible. 1½ml woodland walk accessible to wheelchair users; powered self-drive Batricar available from house for park and garden

👁 Braille guides; scented woodland walk with tapping rail. Special guided tours if booked in advance. Handling collection planned; please enquire

🍽 Lunches & teas; table licence, open as shop. Last orders 5. 2 Nov to 20 Dec: Sat & Sun 11–4. Capacity: 60 plus overflow 50. Picnic area

🧒 Children's playground next to car park. Children's guide. Children's quiz trails during spring and summer holidays. Baby slings available. Restaurant: children's menu, baby foods, highchairs, scribble books. Parent and baby room

🏫 School groups welcome, Pre-booked tours and activities available on request

🐕 In park only, on leads. Guide dogs allowed in house

➡ (4: H7) In Horringer, 3ml SW of Bury St Edmunds on W side of A143 [155: TL8161] *Bus:* Eastern Counties 141-4 Bury St Edmunds–Haverhill; Suffolk *Bus* 757 from 🚉 Colchester (Sun only); both pass close 🚉 Bury St Edmunds (tel. 0645 583358) *Station:* Bury St Edmunds 3ml

LAVENHAM: THE GUILDHALL OF CORPUS CHRISTI

🏠 ✽ *Suffolk*

Market Place, Lavenham, Sudbury CO10 9QZ Tel: 01787 247646

This late 15th-century timber-framed building overlooks and dominates the town market place. Inside are exhibitions on local history, farming and industry, as well as the story of the medieval woollen trade. There is also an attractive walled garden with dye plants, and 19th-century lock-up and mortuary

📅 28 March to 1 Nov: daily 11–5 (closed Good Fri). The building, or parts of it, may be closed occasionally for community purposes

💷 £2.80. Accompanied children free. Parties £2.40. School parties by prior arrangement, 60p per child

🛍 Shop open as Guildhall. Also 5 Nov to 20 Dec: Thur to Sun 11–4

♿ Access to shop & tea-room only

👆 Studwork and carved wood may be touched

🍴 Tea-room for coffee, light lunches & teas, open as Guildhall, 11–5 (but closed on Mon and with reduced opening in April & Oct). Seats 43

👶 Children's guidebook. Tea-room: children's menu, highchairs, scribble sheets

➡ (4: J8) A1141 and B1071 [155: TL917494] *Bus:* Chambers Bury St Edmunds– Colchester (passing close ☒ Bury St Edmunds); Suffolk Bus 757 ☒ Colchester–Lavenham, Sun only. All pass close ☒ Sudbury (tel. 0645 583358) *Station:* Sudbury (U) 7ml

---

MELFORD HALL 🏠 ❀   *Suffolk*

Long Melford, Sudbury CO10 9AH Tel: 01787 880286

One of East Anglia's most celebrated Elizabethan houses, little changed externally since 1578 and with an original panelled banqueting hall. There is also a Regency library, Victorian bedrooms and good collections of furniture and porcelain. The small garden contains some spectacular specimen trees and a charming summer-house, and there is an attractive walk through the park

📅 April: Sat, Sun & BH Mon 2–5.30; May to end Sept: daily except Mon & Tues (but open BH Mon) 2–5.30; Oct: Sat & Sun 2–5.30. Last admission 5

💷 House, garden & park £4. Pre-arranged parties £3 per person Wed, Thur, Fri & Sat only; please book with s.a.e. to Senior Visitor Reception Assistant

♿ Disabled visitors may be driven to the Hall. Ground-floor rooms easily accessible; stairlift available to first floor. Some steps in garden. WC (by car park)

👆 Braille guide

🍴 In Long Melford (not NT)

👶 Children's guide

■ Introductory talks available

🐕 Guide dogs only

→ (4: J8) In Long Melford off A134, 14ml S of Bury St Edmunds, 3ml N of Sudbury [155: TL867462] *Bus:* Beestons/Chambers various services (but frequent) from Sudbury; Suffolk Bus 601 Colchester–Saffron Walden & 757 ▇ Colchester–Lavenham (Sun). All pass close ▇ Sudbury (tel. 0645 583358)
Station: Sudbury (U) 4ml

ORFORD NESS 🏛 🐕 🚹 🛡 *Suffolk*

Quay Office, Orford Quay, Orford, Woodbridge IP12 2NU
Tel/fax: 01394 450900

The largest vegetated shingle spit in Europe, containing a variety of habitats including shingle, salt-marsh, mud-flat, brackish lagoons and grazing marsh. An important location for breeding and passage birds as well as for the shingle flora, which includes a significant number of nationally rare species. The Ness was a secret military site from 1915 until the mid 1980s. Visitors follow a 4½ml route, which can be walked in total or in part (the full walk involves walking on shingle)

Note: The maximum number of visitors is limited to 96 per day for both conservation and safety reasons. Access on foot only. For ferry information, tel. 01394 450057

What's new in 1998: Illustrated trail guide and extended trails

🅾 9 April to 31 Oct: Thur, Fri & Sat. Access to the Ness is by ferry only from Orford Quay from 10am. A maximum stay on the Ness of 3½ hours may be imposed at busy times. **Events:** special access day for visitors with disabilities - contact Warden for details

£ Admission includes the ferry crossing; for details tel. 01394 450057. Pay-and-display car-parking in Orford town

🚹 A number of guided walks will be available in 1998; contact Warden for details

♿ Wheelchair available

🅿 In Orford town

👶 Children's 'Spy Trail'

■ Displays on natural history and history of the site. For education visits, please contact Warden in advance

🐕 Strictly no dogs allowed

→ (4: L7) Access from Orford Quay, Orford town 10ml E of A12 (B1084), 12ml NE of Woodbridge

HERRING GULL

OXBURGH HALL, GARDEN AND ESTATE 🏠 ✝ ❀ 🛉 😈 *Norfolk*

Oxborough, King's Lynn PE33 9PS Tel: 01366 328258 Fax: 01366 328066

The quintessential moated manor house, Oxburgh was built in 1482 by the Bedingfeld family, who still live here. The rooms show the development from medieval austerity to Victorian comfort, and include an outstanding display of embroidery worked by Mary, Queen of Scots during her captivity. The attractive gardens include a French parterre and there are delightful woodland walks, as well as an interesting Catholic chapel

◯ **House**: 28 March to 1 Nov: daily except Thur & Fri 1–5; BH Mon 11–5.
Garden: 7–22 March: Sat & Sun 11–4, then same days as house 11–5.30 but garden open daily in Aug. **Events**: programme of brass band concerts and garden open days; s.a.e. to Administrator for details

£ House, garden & estate £4.80; family discounts available. Pre-arranged parties £3.80 per person; please book with s.a.e. to Administrator. Garden & estate only £2.40

📷 Open as garden 11–5

♿ Parking adjoining ticket office. Access to house 200m; shallow ramp to four ground-floor rooms; difficult stairs to upper floors. WC in west wing of house. Easy access to tea-room and shop. Garden largely accessible, gravel paths; route map available; care necessary near moat. 2 shallow steps to chapel, 100m from Hall. Wheelchairs available at ticket office

👁 Braille guide; some items may be touched

🍴 Light lunches and teas in Old Kitchen, open same days as garden 11–5. Table licence. Seats 100. Private functions catered for. Pantry with open-air seating area in car park, serving light refreshments, home-made fudge and ice-cream; opening times vary according to season

👶 Baby slings available. Children's guide. Restaurant: children's menu, baby foods, highchairs, scribble sheets, toys. Baby-changing facilities

🐕 No dogs

➜ (4: H5) At Oxborough, 7ml SW of Swaffham on S side of Stoke Ferry road [143: TF742012] *Station*: Downham Market 10ml

PAYCOCKE'S 🏠 ❀

Essex

West Street, Coggeshall, Colchester CO6 1NS Tel: 01376 561305

A merchant's house, dating from c.1500 and containing unusually rich panelling and wood carving. Coggeshall was famous for its lace, examples of which are displayed inside the house, and there is also a pleasant garden

◯ 29 March to 11 Oct: Tues, Thur, Sun & BH Mon 2–5.30. Last admission 5

£ £2. Parties of 10 or more must book in advance with the tenant. No reduction for parties. Children must be accompanied by an adult. Joint ticket with Coggeshall Grange Barn £3. Parking at Grange Barn (10min walk) until 5

⟨♿⟩ Access to garden and ground floor; but one awkward step at front door. The house is small

⟨◉⟩ Braille guide

⟨→⟩ (4: J8) Signposted off A120, on S side of West Street, about 300m from centre of Coggeshall, on road to Braintree next to the Fleece Inn, 5½ml E of Braintree [168: TL848225] *Bus:* Eastern National 70 Colchester–Braintree (passing ⟨≋⟩ Marks Tey) (tel. 0345 000333) *Station:* Kelvedon 2½ml

---

PECKOVER HOUSE & GARDEN ⟨🏠⟩ ⟨🏞⟩ ⟨✿⟩ ⟨🛡⟩   *Cambridgeshire*

North Brink, Wisbech PE13 1JR Tel/fax: 01945 583463

A town house, built c.1722 and renowned for its very fine plaster and wood rococo decoration. The outstanding Victorian garden includes an orangery, summer-houses, roses, herbaceous borders, ferney, croquet lawn and reed barn

Note: The newly restored Octavia Hill Birthplace Museum is virtually opposite Peckover House. The museum charts Miss Hill's career and includes a section on her work as a founder of the National Trust. It is open the same days as Peckover House, 2–5.30, and by appointment at other times; for further details please contact the Octavia Hill Birthplace Museum Trust, 1 South Brink Place, Wisbech, PE13 1JE (tel. 01945 476358)

What's new in 1998: Special events programme; light lunches in tea-room; battery-operated vehicle in garden

⟨◯⟩ **House & garden:** 28 March to 1 Nov: Sat, Sun, Wed & BH Mon 12.30–5.30. Last admission 5. **Garden only:** Mon, Tues & Thur 12.30–5.30. Last admission 5. Parties welcome on house open days and at other times by appointment. **Events:** special programme to celebrate 50th anniversary of the Trust's acquisition of the house; please tel. for details

⟨£⟩ £3.20 (£2 on garden only days); family discounts available. Parties £2.50. *Note*: Members may, by written appointment with the tenants, view Nos. 14 and 19 North Brink

⟨🚶⟩ Out of hours tours of house and/or garden available; please contact the Property Manager for details

⟨♿⟩ Access to garden and Reed Barn only. Battery-operated vehicle available. Adapted WC at Reed Barn. Parking in courtyard by prior arrangement

⟨◉⟩ Scented flowers and plants

⟨🍴⟩ Light lunches and teas in Servants' Hall when house open. Reed Barn available for private functions

⟨🐕⟩ No dogs

⟨→⟩ (4: G5) On N bank of River Nene, in Wisbech (B1441) [143: TF458097] *Bus:* Eastern Counties X94, Stagecoach Viscount 336 from Peterborough (passing close ⟨≋⟩ Peterborough); Eastern Counties 46, X94 from King's Lynn (passing close ⟨≋⟩ King's Lynn) (tel. 01223 717740) *Station:* March 9½ml

RAMSEY ABBEY GATEHOUSE 🔲   *Cambridgeshire*

Abbey School, Ramsey, Huntingdon PE17 1DH
Tel: (Regional Office) 01263 733471 Fax: 01263 734924

The remnants of a former Benedictine monastery, built on an island in the Fens. The late 15th-century gatehouse is richly carved and contains an ornate oriel window

🅾 1 April to end Oct: daily 10–5. Other times by written application to Curator

💷 Free (but collection box for contributions). No WC

➡ (4: F6) At SE edge of Ramsey, at point where Chatteris road leaves B1096, 10ml SE of Peterborough [142: TL291851] *Bus:* Stagecoach Viscount 330/1 Huntingdon–Peterborough (passing close ⮥ Huntingdon & Peterborough) (tel. 01223 717740) *Station:* Huntingdon 10ml

RAYLEIGH MOUNT   *Essex*

Rayleigh   Tel: (Regional Office) 01263 733471 Fax: 01263 734924

The former site of the Domesday castle erected by Sweyn of Essex

🅾 All year. Summer 7am–7.30pm; winter 7am–5pm

💷 Free

➡ (4: J10) 6ml NW of Southend, path from Rayleigh station (A129) [178: TQ805909] *Bus:* From surrounding areas (tel. 0345 000333) *Station:* Rayleigh 200m

ST GEORGE'S GUILDHALL 🔲 🔲   *Norfolk*

27 King Street, King's Lynn PE30 1HA Tel: 01553 773578

The largest surviving English medieval guildhall and now converted into an arts centre, but with many interesting surviving features

🅾 All year Mon to Fri (closed Good Fri & Aug BH Mon) 10–4; Sat 10–1 & 2–3.30 (opening times may vary during July & Aug). Closed 25, 26 Dec & 1 Jan. The Guildhall is not usually open on the days when performances are taking place in the theatre (please refer to current King's Lynn Arts Centre brochure for details). **Events:** July, King's Lynn Festival. Performances, workshops and art exhibitions throughout the year; for details write to address above or tel. 01553 773578

💷 Free

🛍 Crafts. Christmas shop (open from mid Nov)

♿ Access to galleries; please telephone for advice before a visit

🍽 Light lunches & teas from Crofters Coffee Bar. Also, restaurant open for lunch and dinner Mon to Sat

➔ (4: H5) On W side of King Street close to the Tuesday Market Place [132: TF616202] *Bus:* From surrounding areas (tel. 0500 626116) *Station:* King's Lynn ¾ml

---

SHERINGHAM PARK ♣ ⛴ 🏛 🚶   *Norfolk*

Warden: Gardener's Cottage, Sheringham Park, Upper Sheringham NR26 8TB
Tel: 01263 823778

One of Humphry Repton's most outstanding achievements, the landscape park contains fine mature woodlands, and the large woodland garden is particularly famous for its spectacular show of rhododendrons and azaleas (flowering mid May to June). There are stunning views of the coast and countryside from the viewing towers and many delightful waymarked walks, including a route to North Norfolk Railway Station (a private full-gauge steam railway)

What's new in 1998: Steam-powered sawmill operating on selected weekends (see local events listings or tel. for dates)

🅾 **Park**: all year, dawn to dusk. Numerous waymarked walks through woodland, parkland and to the coast; guide on sale in car park. Sheringham Hall is privately occupied. Limited access is available to selected rooms only, April to Sept, by written appointment with the leaseholder

£ £2.50 per car, incl. all passengers. Coaches £7.50; please book in advance for May/June visits with Warden. Pay-and-display car park. Coaches display 3 valid tickets. Members display membership card or pass (available when staff on duty)

🚶 Morning/afternoon tours during rhododendron season (subject to guide availability)

♿ Raised walkway from car park to park viewpoints. Self-drive powered vehicle & wheelchair on request when car park staff present, Easter to end Sept (no pre-booking). WC

☕ Light refreshments available Easter to end Sept

🐕 On leads in park

➔ (4: K4) 2ml SW of Sheringham, access for cars off A148 Cromer–Holt road; 5ml W of Cromer; 6ml E of Holt [133: TG135420] *Bus:* Sanders Coaches Norwich–Holt (passes ▣ Sheringham) (tel. 0500 626116) *Station:* Sheringham (U) 2ml

---

TATTERSHALL CASTLE 🏰 🏠 🛡   *Lincolnshire*

Tattershall, Lincoln LN4 4LR Tel: 01526 342543

A vast fortified tower, built c.1440 for Ralph Cromwell, Lord Treasurer of England. The building was rescued from becoming derelict by Lord Curzon 1911-14 and contains four great chambers with Gothic fireplaces and brick vaulting. There are spectacular views from the battlements

What's new in 1998: New full-colour guide book

🅾 1 April to 1 Nov: daily except Thur & Fri 10.30–5.30. Nov to 20 Dec: Sat & Sun only 12–4. Last admissions 30min before closing. Ground floor of castle may occasionally be closed for functions or events. Please contact the Custodian for dates. **Events:** details from Custodian

£ £2.70, children £1.30; family ticket £6.50. Children free during July & Aug. Discount for parties; contact Custodian. Advance booking essential for coach parties

Shop open same times as castle

Access via three steps to ground floor of castle, museum not accessible; easy access to shop and grounds (gravel paths). WC. Special parking area nearer the castle – please contact Custodian for details

Limited service of drinks and ice-reams available from shop. Picnicking welcome in grounds

WC with baby-changing facility; child back carriers allowed; family guidebook

Castle is particularly suitable for school groups

In car park only, on leads. No shade in car park; hooks are provided in shade by entrance to grounds, where dogs may be left

→ (4: F3) On S side of A153, 15ml NE of Sleaford; 10ml SW of Horncastle [122: TF209575] *Bus:* Brylaine Boston–Woodhall Spa (passing close ⊒ Boston) (tel. 01205 364087) *Station:* Ruskington (U) 10ml

---

THEATRE ROYAL 🏠 🛡   *Suffolk*

Westgate Street, Bury St Edmunds IP33 1QR
Tel: 01284 755127 Fax: 01284 706035

A rare surviving example of a late Georgian playhouse, built in 1819 and still in use, presenting a year-round programme of professional drama, comedy, dance, mime, pantomime and amateur works. It boasts a national reputation and attracts the best touring companies in the country

O All year: Mon to Fri 10.30–3.30 (closed every BH except for performances). No access to theatre when theatrical activity is in progress. Please check in advance that theatre is open (tel. 01284 769505). **Events:** For 1998 events programme please send large s.a.e. (tel. 01284 769505)

£ Free. Ticket prices for performances in brochures. Limited parking in Westgate Street. No parking in front of the theatre

Organised guided tours and talks are available by prior arrangement. To book tel. 01284 755127

Induction loop system available. Signed performances. Limited wheelchair access and adapted WCs. For full details tel. 01284 769505

Guide dogs admitted

Meals; licensed bar in theatre for all performances. For reservations tel. 01284 769505

For details of education initiatives tel. 01284 755127

Guide dogs only

→ (4: J7) On Westgate Street on S side of A134 from Sudbury (one-way system)
[155: TL855637] *Bus:* From surrounding areas (tel. 0645 583358)
Station: Bury St Edmunds ¾ml

THORINGTON HALL   *Suffolk*

Stoke by Nayland, Colchester CO6 4SS

An oak-framed, plastered and gabled house, built c.1600 and later extended

 By written appointment with the tenant

→ (4: J8) 2ml SE of Stoke by Nayland [155: TM013355] *Bus:* Hedingham 84,
Carters 755 Colchester–East Bergholt (passing ≋ Colchester), thence 1¾ml
(tel. 0645 583358) *Station:* Colchester 7ml

WICKEN FEN NATIONAL NATURE RESERVE
⊠ 🐾 🚶 🛡   *Cambridgeshire*

Lode Lane, Wicken, Ely CB7 5XP Tel/fax: 01353 720274

---

*Britain's oldest nature reserve and a unique fragment of the wilderness that once covered East
Anglia. A haven for birds, plants and mammals alike, the Fen can be explored by the
traditional wide droves and lush green paths, and there is a boardwalk nature trail giving
access to several hides. The William Thorpe Visitor Centre provides a range of facilities and
further information about this fascinating place*

O **Fen:** all year: daily except Christmas
Day, dawn to dusk. Some paths
will be closed in very wet weather.
Visitor centre: daily 9–5 (but
occasionally closed in winter). **Fen
Cottage:** April to Oct: Sun & BH
Mon 2–5 (plus some other days in
summer). **Fen Cottage Garden:**
open as Fen. **Windpump:** in
operation occasionally. **Events:**
expert-led guided walks,
children's activities and many
other events throughout the
year; please tel. for details

£ Fen & Cottage £3.50. Cottage
only £1.50. Pre-booked parties
£2.80, special rates for
school/educational groups; contact
the Education Officer or write
enclosing s.a.e

[X] Guided tours by special arrangement

[X] New bookshop and giftshop in visitor centre

[X] Raised boardwalk; adapted bird hides; close parking by arrangement. Visitor centre fully accessible. WC in car park. Access to Fen Cottage by prior arrangement

[X] Hot and cold drinks, sweets and ice-creams from visitor centre

[X] Children's activities in visitor centre. Family events throughout the year

[X] Full-time Education Officer. Science, geography and history activities for school or educational groups at all levels. Simple self-catering accommodation for groups of up to 28 people available

[X] Welcome if kept on lead at all times. No dogs allowed in Fen Cottage

[X] (4: G7) S of A1123, 3ml W of Soham (A142), 9ml S of Ely, 17ml NE of Cambridge via A10 [154: TL563705] *Bus:* Stagecoach Cambus 122 Cambridge–Ely; Stagecoach Cambus 19 Cambridge–Ely (Sun only); Greys 117 from Ely (Thur, Sat only); otherwise Stagecoach Cambus 116, 122 from Cambridge, Ely & Newmarket, alight Soham Downfields 3ml, or 109 Cambridge–Ely, alight Stretham 3½ml (tel. 01223 717740). All pass [rail] Ely *Station:* Ely 9ml

---

WIMPOLE HALL [icons]   *Cambridgeshire*

Arrington, Royston SG8 0BW Tel: 01223 207257 Fax: 01223 207838

This magnificent 18th-century house, the biggest in Cambridgeshire and set in grand style in an extensive wooded park, has an extraordinary pedigree. The interior features work by Gibbs, Flitcroft and Soane, and the park - complete with grand folly, Chinese bridge and lakes - was landscaped by Bridgeman, Brown and Repton. There are a series of spectacular avenues and extensive walks through the delightful grounds. The garden has colourful parterres in July and August, as well as a collection of winter-flowering pansies

[O] **Hall**: 14 March to 1 Nov: daily except Mon & Fri 1–5 (but open Good Fri 1–5, BH Sun & BH Mon 11–5). Additional opening every Fri in Aug 1–5. **Garden**: open as Hall. **Park**: open daily throughout the year from sunrise to sunset, but closes at 5 on concert nights. **Events:** 18/19 July, open-air concerts with fireworks; 22/23 Aug, garden concerts with fireworks. For bookings tel. 01223 207001

[£] Hall & garden £5.50, child £2.25. Adult party rate (12+ in group) £4.50, child party rate £1.75. Adult joint ticket with Home Farm £7.50, child £3.50. Garden only £2. Car park 200m

[X] By special arrangement outside normal opening hours

[X] Shop open same days as Hall 11–5.30, including Fri in Aug. Also Nov to March 1999: daily except Mon & Fri 11–4 (closed 25–27 Dec, but open 1 Jan)

[X] Parking near stable block. Disabled visitors may be set down near Hall. Stairlift usually available to ground-floor rooms, which are fully accessible. WC open 10.30–5.30 at stable block; 12–5.30 at Hall. 1 self-drive vehicle available; please book in advance. New restaurant fully accessible. Garden accessible from south-west garden gate; gravel paths

♿ Braille guide; some items may be touched if advance notice given

🍴 Full lunches and teas in new restaurant, open same days as Hall 11–5 (lunches 12–2). Also 4 Nov to 23 Dec Tues to Thur & Sat & Sun 11–4; Jan to mid March 1999 11–4. Table licence. Stable block: light refreshments same days as Hall 10.30–5, also open Sun Nov to March 1999 11–4. Picnic area.

🧒 Children's guide. Parent & baby room in stable block; baby slings available. Restaurant: children's menu, baby food, highchairs, scribble sheets

📖 Full education programme; details from Education Officer (tel. 01223 207801)

🐕 In park only, on leads

➔ (4: G7) 8ml SW of Cambridge (A603), 6ml N of Royston (A1198) [154: TL336510] *Bus:* Whippet 175, Stagecoach Cambus 14 Cambridge–Biggleswade (passing close ⛧ Biggleswade & Cambridge) (tel: 01223 717740) *Station:* Shepreth 5ml

---

WIMPOLE HOME FARM 🏠 ♣ 📷 🛡   *Cambridgeshire*

As Wimpole Hall

A model farm, built by Soane in 1794 and now home to a fascinating range of rare animal breeds, including sheep, goats, cattle, pigs and horses. The vast Great Barn houses a collection of farm machinery dating back 200 years

🔘 14 March to 1 Nov: daily except Mon & Fri (but open Good Fri & BH Mons) 10.30–5. Additional opening every Fri in July & Aug 10.30–5. Nov to March 1999: Wed, Sat & Sun 11–4 (closed 25–27 Dec but open 1 Jan). Also open Feb half-term week. **Events:** 13/14, 20/21, 27/28 March, lambing weekends; 5/6 Sept, heavy horse show; please tel. for details

💷 NT members £2.20, children £1.10. Non-members £4.20. Children (over 3) £2.50. Adult party rate (12+ in group) £3.20, child party rate £1.70, please

book with s.a.e. to Property Manager, Wimpole Hall. Joint ticket for hall & farm £7.50, child £3.50. School parties especially welcome (Education Group members £1.10 per child). Parking 400m from farm

K By special arrangement

◻ Shop open same days as farm 11–5

& Ask for directions and parking at stable block. Level access throughout farm and ramps to most farm buildings. Light refreshments in stableyard. Shop accessible. WC at farm. Wheelchairs available. Battery-operated vehicle available at stable block; please book in advance

◉ Braille guide; animal sounds and smells; some animals may be patted and stroked

▶ Warm indoor seating overlooking children's play area; light refreshments available 11–5 same days as farm. Children's birthday parties catered for

† Baby-changing room. Special area set aside as a children's corner; woodland adventure playground; children's publications. Special events for children April, May and during Aug

▦ Full education programme; details from Education Officer (tel. 01223 207801)

✕ No dogs allowed

→ (4: G7) As Wimpole Hall, above *Bus:* As Wimpole Hall, above

---

WOOLSTHORPE MANOR **▦**   *Lincolnshire*

23 Newton Way, Woolsthorpe-by-Colsterworth, nr Grantham NG33 5NR
Tel/fax: 01476 860338

A small 17th-century manor house, the birthplace and family home of Sir Isaac Newton, who formulated some of his major works here during the Plague years (1665–66). An early edition of one - Principia Mathematica *- is on display. The orchard includes a descendant of the famous apple tree*

O 1 April to 1 Nov: Wed to Sun plus BH Mon (closed Good Fri) 1–5.30. Last admission 5. *Note*: in the interests of preservation, numbers of visitors admitted to rooms at any one time may be limited, particularly at peak weekends and BH

£ £2.60, children £1.30; family ticket £6.50. No reduction for parties, which must book in advance with Custodian as parking for coaches is limited to one at a time

K For all parties

& Limited access to ground floor only (assistance required); album of photographs of upper floor rooms. No wheelchairs available

◉ Braille guides for adults and children

✕ In car park only, on leads

→ (4: E4) 7ml S of Grantham, ½ml NW of Colsterworth, 1ml W of A1 (not to be confused with Woolsthorpe near Belvoir). Leave A1 at Colsterworth roundabout via B676, at second crossroads turn right following NT signs [130: SK924244] *Bus:* Road Car 606–8 Grantham–South Witham (passing close ⊠ Grantham) (tel. 01522 553135) *Station:* Grantham 7ml

Introduction to Central

The heart of England is an intriguing mix of urban areas and delightful unspoilt countryside of much variety and charm. There are surprisingly extensive tracts of open moorland and hills, as well as picturesque villages, grand country houses and some notable gardens.

The Trust manages over 12% of the Peak District National Park, grouped into three estates: **High Peak, Longshaw** and **South Peak**. High Peak includes the **Hope Woodlands**, less wood than wild and dramatic Pennine moorland, adjoining the impressive 600 mile-high **Kinder Scout** and with superb views. Nearby are the stunning valley of **Edale** and landmark of **Mam Tor**, next to the spectacular limestone gorge of **Winnats Pass**. Within the Longshaw Estate is the notorious village of Eyam, visited by the Plague in 1665. Three quarters of its inhabitants perished and the Trust cares for the meadow containing the famous **Riley Graves**.

The South Peak Estate straddles the Derbyshire/Staffordshire border and includes **Dovedale**, famous for its ashwoods and geological features, as well as the former **Manifold and Hamps Light Railway**, now a surfaced track leading through dramatic limestone scenery. Nearby **Ilam Park** has a range of visitor facilities and local information and there is an information shelter at **Milldale**. Not far from the Peak District are four of the Trust's most celebrated country houses, all in Derbyshire – **Calke Abbey**, **Hardwick Hall**, **Kedleston Hall** and **Sudbury Hall**, as well as the extensive parkland and woods of **Clumber Park** in Nottinghamshire. Just beyond the western fringe of the Park is **Biddulph Grange**, one of England's most extraordinary gardens.

ST BERTRAM'S BRIDGE, ILAM

The area's other key upland properties are to the south west – the **Clent Hills** in Worcestershire, splendid country for walkers and with breathtaking views in all directions, and Shropshire's **Long Mynd**. The Mynd is an area of upland heath and a Site of Special Scientific Interest. Excellent access is possible via the **Carding Mill Valley**. The Trust owns 7 miles of nearby **Wenlock Edge**, a geologically interesting wooded escarpment running from Craven Arms to Ironbridge and famous for its flora and dramatic views. Elegant **Attingham Park** and the Elizabethan **Wilderhope Manor** lie not far away.

Further south, the Cotswolds offer excellent walking, superb views and some of the most charming villages to be found anywhere in England. The natural limestone amphitheatre at **Dover's Hill** is the venue for the annual Cotswold 'Olympick Games' and at the other end of the escarpment **Haresfield Beacon**, the site of a prehistoric hill-fort, offers magnificent views across to Wales. The **Ebworth Estate** near Painswick has many delightful waymarked walks through beechwoods rich in wildlife, and just south of Stroud are **Minchinhampton and**

Rodborough Commons, where the open grassland and woodland form a steep-sided plateau particularly important for the wild flowers it harbours.

The **Sherborne Park Estate** at Northleach offers attractive waymarked walks and watermeadows. Gloucestershire is also home to two notable Trust gardens – celebrated **Hidcote**, at the northern end of the county, and in the west, on the banks of the Severn, the delightful 17th-century water garden at **Westbury Court**. The borderland of England and Wales runs northwards from near here into the green rolling countryside of Herefordshire, where excellent walking is possible at the Iron Age hillfort of Croft Ambrey, part of the **Croft Castle Estate**. This site is particularly famous for its wildlife, including the rare hawfinch and polecats, which have ventured here from their stronghold across the Welsh border.

The central conurbation of Birmingham lies within easy distance of many Trust properties, including the beautiful medieval manor of **Baddesley Clinton** and **Packwood House**. A little further away is **Charlecote Park**, rich in associations with William Shakespeare. In the far south of the area, the **Buscot and Coleshill Estates** offer a wide expanse of unspoilt countryside, including **Badbury Hill**, from which there are splendid views over the upper Thames valley. Buscot and Coleshill are both attractive villages built of Cotswold stone, and there is a popular picnic area at **Buscot Weir**. Not far from here is **White Horse Hill**, with its famous landmark of a horse cut into the chalk. The hill is crowned by the Bronze Age hillfort of **Uffington Castle** and nearby is **Dragon Hill**, where St George allegedly slew the beast. The Ridgeway Path gives good access to these sites. To the east, on the Chiltern escarpment and on the very edge of this area, is **Watlington Hill**, 210m high and celebrated for its chalk-loving flora and fine yew forest.

Highlights for Disabled Visitors
Particularly recommended are **Clumber Park**, with excellent pathways and visitor facilities; all interesting parts of **Dovedale** are wheelchair accessible, as are parts of the **Brockhampton Estate** and the viewpoint at **Dover's Hill**.

... and for Families
The Museum of Childhood at **Sudbury Hall** is of special interest; there is cycle hire available at **Clumber Park**.

Further Information
NT Regional Offices:

- **East Midlands** (tel. 01909 486411) – for properties in Derbyshire (including all of the Peak District), Leicestershire, Northamptonshire and Nottinghamshire.
- **Mercia** (tel. 01743 709343) – for properties in Shropshire, Staffordshire and north & west of the Birmingham area.
- **Severn** (tel. 01684 850051) – for properties in Gloucestershire, Herefordshire, Warwickshire, Worcestershire and part of the West Midlands.
- **Thames & Chilterns** (tel. 01494 528051) – for properties in Oxfordshire.

Please contact the offices for East Midlands or Severn for a free copy of the NT Countryside Guide to the Midlands, sponsored by Barclays, which gives full details of a range of Trust countryside properties.

ASHDOWN HOUSE 🏠 ❀ ♿ 𝕀 *Oxfordshire*

Lambourn, Newbury RG16 7RE Tel: 01488 72584

An extraordinary Dutch-style 17th-century house, perched on the Berkshire Downs and famous for its association with Elizabeth of Bohemia ('The Winter Queen'), Charles I's sister, to whom the house was 'consecrated'. The interior has an impressive great staircase rising from hall to attic, and important paintings contemporary with the house. There are spectacular views from the roof over the formal parterre, lawns and surrounding countryside, as well as beautiful walks in neighbouring **Ashdown Woods.** *Nearby* **Weathercock Hill** *and* **Alfred's Castle**, *an Iron Age hill-fort where King Alfred is rumoured to have defeated the Danes, also offer fine walking (there is a car park 250m from the house, but please note the estate is closed on Fri)*

🅾️ **Hall, stairway, roof and grounds only:** April to end Oct: Wed & Sat 2–5. Guided tours only; at 2.15, 3.15 & 4.15 from front door. Closed Easter weekend & every BHol. Last admission to house 4.15. **Woodland:** all year: Sat to Thur, dawn to dusk

💷 Grounds, hall, stairway & roof £2.10. No reduction for parties, which should book in writing. Woodland free. Car park 250m. No WC or refreshments available. Picnic area in car park

♿ Access to grounds only; house not accessible to wheelchair users

🐕 In woodland only (not in house or grounds)

➔ **(5: J10)** 2½ml S of Ashbury, 3½ml N of Lambourn, on W side of B4000 [174: SU282820] *Bus:* Thamesdown 47 Swindon–Lambourn, with connections from Newbury (passing close ≋ Swindon & Newbury) (tel. 0345 090899)

ASHLEWORTH TITHE BARN 🏠 *Gloucestershire*

Ashleworth   **Tel: (Regional Office) 01684 850051**

A 15th-century tithe barn, picturesquely located on the banks of the Severn and with an immense stone-tiled roof

🅾️ April to 1 Nov: daily 9–6 or sunset if earlier. Closed Good Fri. Other times by prior appointment only (please tel. 01684 850051)

💷 60p

➔ **(5: G9)** 6ml N of Gloucester, 1¼ml E of Hartpury (A417), on W bank of Severn, SE of Ashleworth [162: SO818252] *Bus:* Swanbrook Transport Gloucester– Tewkesbury (passing close ≋ Gloucester), alight Ashleworth ¼ml (tel. 01242 574444) *Station:* Gloucester 7ml

ATTINGHAM PARK 🏚 🌳 👤 🎭

Shropshire

Shrewsbury SY4 4TP Tel: 01743 709203 Fax: 01743 709352

One of the jewels of the Midlands. An elegant mansion of the late 18th century, with magnificent Regency interiors and exceptional collections of silver, neo-classical furniture and paintings. The park was landscaped by Repton and there are attractive walks along the river

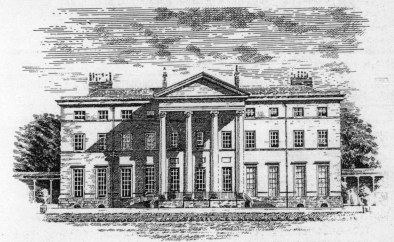

House: 28 March to 1 Nov: Sat to Wed (and Good Fri)1.30–5; BH Mon 11–5. Last admission to house 4.30. **Deer park & grounds**: March to Oct: daily 8–9; Nov to Feb 1999 daily 8–5 (closed Christmas Day). **Events**: please send s.a.e. to Property Manager

House & park £4; family ticket £10. Park & grounds only £1.50. Pre-booked parties £3

Tours for pre-booked parties at 11 and 4.30; £5 per head (NT members £3). Evening visits by special arrangement with the Property Manager

Shop open same days as house 12.30–5; BH Mon 11–5; daily in Aug 12.30–5. Also Nov to 21 Dec: Sat & Sun 12.30–4

Prior notice of visit appreciated as access to house is by rear lift with staff help; then rooms easily accessible; disabled visitors may be driven to side of tea-room or outer courtyard on request. Self-drive powered vehicle available for use in grounds; park easily accessible. Tea-room access difficult; some outside tables accessible. WC at brewhouse. Sympathetic Hearing Scheme

Braille and large-print guides at house

Light lunches and refreshments in tea-room same days as house 12.30–5, lunches 12.30–2.30; BH Mon 11–5; daily in Aug 12.30–5. Also Nov to 21 Dec: Sat & Sun 12.30–4. March 1999: Sat & Sun 2–4. Licensed. Lunches & suppers at other times for pre-booked parties. Separate tea-room available. Picnic sites along Mile Walk

[icon] Baby-changing facilities. Highchairs available in tea-room

[icon] Environmental education resource pack; park exhibition in Bothy. Education room available for pre-booked parties (max. 30 children)

[icon] No dogs in deer park, on leads in immediate vicinity of house

[icon] **(5: F5)** 4ml SE of Shrewsbury, on N side of B4380 in Atcham village [126: SJ550099] *Bus:* Williamsons 96, X96, Midland Red 81/2/4, 481 Shrewsbury–Telford/Wellington (all passing close ⊠ Shrewsbury & Telford Central (tel. 0345 056785) *Station:* Shrewsbury 5ml

---

BADDESLEY CLINTON [icons] *Warwickshire*

Rising Lane, Baddesley Clinton Village, Knowle, Solihull B93 0DQ
Tel: 01564 783294 Fax: 01564 782706

A romantic and atmospheric moated manor house, dating from the 15th century and little-changed since 1634. The interiors reflect the house's heyday in the Elizabethan era, when it was a haven for persecuted Catholics - there are no fewer than three priest-holes. There is a delightful garden, ponds and lake walk

[icon] 4 March to 1 Nov: daily except Mon & Tues (but closed Good Fri and open BH Mon); March, April, Oct & 1 Nov 1.30–5; May to end Sept 1.30–5.30 (grounds, shop and restaurant open from 12). March 1999: daily except Mon & Tues 1.30–5. Last admission to house 30min before closing. **Events:** for details please send s.a.e to Property Manager or tel. 01564 783294

[icon] £4.80; family ticket £12. Grounds, restaurant & shop only, £2.40. Parties of 15+ and coaches are welcome by prior written arrangement. Free parking. Admission to the house is by timed ticket which does not restrict the amount of time visitors may spend in the house

[icon] Wed/Thur evenings by appointment. Supper can be included

[icon] Shop open 4 March to 13 Dec: daily except Mon & Tues (but closed Good Fri and open BH Mon); March, April & Oct 12–5; May to end Sept 12–5.30; 4 Nov to 13 Dec 12–4.30

[icon] Access to ground floor, photo album shows upstairs rooms and contents; most of garden and grounds, lakeside walk, restaurant & shop accessible; some thick gravel. Parking by visitor reception area. Wheelchairs available. WC near shop. Sympathetic Hearing Scheme

[icon] Braille guide; please enquire about items to touch

[icon] Licensed restaurant open 4 March to 13 Dec: daily except Mon & Tues (but closed Good Fri and open BH Mon); lunches 12–2; teas 2.30–5.30 (March, April & Oct closes 5). 4 Nov to 13 Dec 12–4.30. Freshly prepared home-cooked food. Party lunches and dinners arranged. Picnic tables at car park (no picnicking in garden)

[icon] No prams, back carriers or pushchairs in house. Baby-changing facilities. Children's guide. Restaurant offers children's menu and high chairs

[icon] School parties by appointment: Wed, Thur & Fri mornings. Schools base and resource book available

🐾 In car park only. Reasonable walks available outside property

➜ (5: H7) ¾ml W of A4141 Warwick–Birmingham road, at Chadwick End, 7½ml NW of Warwick, 6ml S of M42 exit 5; 15ml SE of central Birmingham
[139: SP199715] *Station:* Lapworth (U), 2ml; Birmingham International 9ml

---

BANTOCK HOUSE MUSEUM   *Wolverhampton*

Bantock Park, Bradmore Road, Wolverhampton WV3 9LQ Tel: 01902 312132

The museum (not NT) houses Thomas Balston's collection of Victorian Staffordshire miniature figures, given to the Trust in 1960, as well as important collections of 18th-century enamels, Georgian and Victorian japanned tin and papier-mâché, Worcester porcelain, dolls and toys

What's new in 1998: The Museum will close for major redevelopment between June 1998 and Easter 1999. The new facilities will include a tea-room, education and community-use rooms in the courtyard buildings, new retail and orientation point and the installation of a lift and full access for visitors with disabilities

🅾 Jan to May: Tues to Sat 10–5; Sun 2–5 (closed daily between 1–2). Closed Mon. **Closed for major alterations between June 1998 and Easter 1999**

💷 Free. Car & coach parking 300m, access via Finchfield Road

🏃 Group parties (25 max.) and guided tours by arrangement with the Museum Assistant

♿ Access for wheelchair users. Ground floor only, includes Balston Collection; cars may draw up to the front door, access via Bradmore Road

🍽 Morning coffee and afternoon teas available; also for group parties by prior arrangement

🏛 Education pack and children's worksheet available

🐾 In park only, on leads

➜ (5: G5) SW of Wolverhampton town centre on B4161; access via Bradmore Road
Bus: Travel West Midlands 513/4, 585–7 from 🚆 Wolverhampton
(tel. 0121 200 2700) *Station:* Wolverhampton 2ml

BENTHALL HALL 🏛 ✚ ❋ 🛡   *Shropshire*

Broseley TF12 5RX Tel: 01952 882159

Situated on a plateau above the gorge of the Severn, this 16th-century stone house has mullioned and transomed windows and a stunning interior with carved oak staircase, decorated plaster ceilings and oak panelling. There is an intimate and carefully restored plantsman's garden, old kitchen garden and interesting Restoration church

🅾 5 April to 30 Sept: Wed, Sun & BH Mon 1.30–5.30. Last admission 5.
House and/or garden for parties at other times by arrangement: Tues & Wed am.
Events: church services most Suns 3.15; visitors welcome

191

£ £3, children £1. Reduced rates for booked parties. Garden only £2. Parking 150m. Coaches by appointment

& Access to ground floor and parts of garden. WC. No wheelchairs available

Braille and large-print guides

Catering for groups (Wed only) by arrangement at Dudmaston. No picnics

→ (5: F5) 1ml NW of Broseley (B4375), 4ml NE of Much Wenlock, 1ml SW of Ironbridge [127: SJ658025] *Bus:* Midland Red 9 & 99 Telford/Wellington–Bridgnorth, alight Broseley, 1ml (pass close ⊞ Telford Central) (tel. 0345 056785) *Station:* Telford Central 7½ml

BERRINGTON HALL 🏠 ❖ 🛡️   *Herefordshire*

nr Leominster HR6 0DW Tel: 01568 615721 Fax: 01568 613263

Beautifully set above a wide valley with sweeping views to the Brecon Beacons, this elegant Henry Holland house was built in the late 18th century and is set in parkland designed by 'Capability' Brown. The rather austere external appearance belies a surprisingly delicate interior, with beautifully decorated ceilings and a spectacular staircase hall. There are good collections of furniture and paintings, as well as a nursery, Victorian laundry, Georgian dairy and an attractive garden

What's new in 1998: Children's play area; children's orienteering course

O April: Fri, Sat & Sun (open BH Mon but closed Good Fri) 1.30–5.30. May, June & Sept: daily except Mon & Tues (but open BH Mon) 1.30–5.30. July & Aug: daily 1.30–5.30. Oct to 1 Nov: Fri, Sat & Sun 1.30–4.30. Last admission 30min before closing. Garden from 12.30–6 (Oct 5.30). Park walk open July, Aug, Sept & Oct same days and times as house. **Events:** August horse trials; for details of this and other events please contact the Property Manager

£ £4; family ticket £10. Grounds only £1.80. Parties of 15 or more by prior written arrangement only. Free car and coach park

𝆑 By prior arrangement with Property Manager

🛍 Shop open same days as house 1–5.30. Also 7 Nov to 13 Dec: Sat & Sun 1–4.30. Tel. 01568 610134

♿ Access to house via 12 steps; thereafter ground floor level; advisable to avoid peak visiting times. Two wheelchairs, stairclimber and powered self-drive buggy (please book in advance). WC. Access to garden; firm gravel paths. No wheelchair access to restaurant (5 steps) but a table can be set up in the courtyard in good weather on request. Parking: please enquire at ticket office

👁 Braille guide; staircase balustrades are interesting to touch

🍽 Licensed restaurant in Servants' Hall open same days as house: light refreshments 12.30–5.30. Edwardian tea-room open BH weekends and for pre-booked groups. Last orders 30min before closing. Oct: 12.30–4.30. Also open as shop Nov & Dec 12.30–4.30. Picnic tables near car park. Tel. 01568 610134

🚶 Children's outdoor and indoor quizzes. Baby-changing facilities. Play area in walled garden. Garden orienteering course

🐕 No dogs in house, garden or on parkland

→ (5: F7) 3ml N of Leominster, 7ml S of Ludlow on W side of A49 [137: SO510637] *Bus:* Midland Red West/Go Whittle 192, 292 Birmingham–Hereford (passing close ✉ Ludlow & Leominster), alight Luston, 2ml (tel. 0345 125436) *Station:* Leominster (U) 4ml

---

BIDDULPH GRANGE GARDEN ⍒ 🛡   *Staffordshire*

Biddulph Grange, Biddulph, Stoke-on-Trent ST8 7SD Tel: 01782 517999

One of Britain's most exciting and unusual gardens. A series of connected 'compartments', designed in the mid 19th century by James Bateman to display specimens from his extensive and wide-ranging plant collection. Visitors are taken on a miniature tour of the world, featuring the Egyptian Court and imitation of the Great Wall of China, as well as a pinetum, fernery and rock gardens

What's new in 1998: Mrs Bateman's secret garden on the top terrace has been replanted with herbaceous plants. There is also an intriguing mosaic parterre

🕑 1 April to 1 Nov: Wed to Fri 12–6, Sat, Sun & BH Mon 11–6 (closed Good Fri). Last admission 5.30 or dusk if earlier. Also open 7 Nov to 20 Dec: Sat & Sun 12–4 or dusk if earlier. **Events:** for details please send s.a.e. to Property Manager

£ 1 April to 1 Nov: £4; family ticket £10. Pre-booked parties £3 per person. Joint ticket with Little Moreton Hall £6; family ticket £15. 7 Nov to 20 Dec: Sat & Sun, £2; family £5. Free car park 50m. Coach party organisers must book in advance

✉ Pre-booked guided tours in groups of 10 or more, at 10 on Wed, Thur & Fri; £5 per person (NT members incl.)

🏢 Shop open as garden

♿ Access for visitors with impaired mobility extremely difficult; unsuitable for wheelchairs but access possible to tea-room & terrace with views over garden. Please contact Garden Office for details. WC

👁 Suitable for accompanied visually impaired visitors, with care. Braille & large-print guides

⬛ Tea-room serving coffee, teas and light refreshments open as garden. Light lunches 12–2 (waited service). Seating for 50. Last admission 5.30. Picnics in car park only

⬛ 2 highchairs in tea-room

⬛ School visits by arrangement

⬛ No dogs in garden, car park only

➡ (5: G3) ½ml N of Biddulph, 3½ml SE of Congleton, 7ml N of Stoke-on-Trent. Access from A527 (Tunstall–Congleton road). Entrance on Grange Road [118:SJ895591]. *Bus:* Bakers/Stevensons 86–8 from Congleton (passing ✆ Congleton) (tel. 01785 223344) *Station:* Congleton 2½ml

BREDON BARN 🏠 *Worcestershire*

Bredon, nr Tewkesbury   Tel: (Regional Office) 01684 850051

A 14th-century barn, beautifully constructed of local Cotswold stone and noted for its dramatic aisled interior and unusual stone chimney cowling

🅾 April to 29 Nov: Wed, Thur, Sat & Sun 10–6 or sunset if earlier. Dec to Feb: by prior appointment only (tel. 01684 850051)

£ 60p

➡ (5: G8) 3ml NE of Tewkesbury, just N of B4080 [150: SO919369] *Bus:* Boomerang 540/5 Evesham–Cheltenham (passing ✆ Evesham) (tel. 0345 125436) *Station:* Pershore (U) 8½ml

BUSCOT OLD PARSONAGE 🏠 ✿ *Oxfordshire*

Buscot, Faringdon SN7 8DQ Tel: (Coleshill Estate Office) 01793 762209

An early 18th-century house of Cotswold stone, set on the banks of the Thames and with a small garden

🅾 April to end Oct: Wed only 2–6 by appointment in writing with tenant

£ £1.10. Not suitable for parties. No WC

➡ (5: H10) 2ml from Lechlade, 4ml from Faringdon on A417 [163: SU231973] *Bus:* Thames Transit 64 Swindon–Carterton, or Stagecoach Swindon and District 77 Swindon–Cirencester (both passing close ✆ Swindon). On both, alight Lechlade, 1½ml (tel. 0345 090899)

BUSCOT PARK 🏠 ✿ ♣ *Oxfordshire*

Faringdon SN7 8BU Tel: 01367 240786 Fax: 01367 241794

The late 18th-century neo-classical house contains the Faringdon Collection of paintings and furniture. The park features a water garden, designed in the early 20th century by Harold Peto

Note: This property is administered on behalf of the National Trust by Lord Faringdon, and the contents of the house are owned by The Faringdon Collection Trust

⊙ **House & grounds**: 1 April to end Sept: Wed to Fri 2–6 (incl. Good Fri and also open Easter Sat & Sun). Also open every second & fourth Sat and immediately following Sun 2–6 (i.e. April 11 & 12, 25 & 26; May 9 & 10, 23 & 24; June 13 & 14, 27 & 28; July 11 & 12, 25 & 26; Aug 8 & 9, 22 & 23; Sept 12 & 13, 26 & 27). Timed entry to house may be imposed if crowding occurs. Last admission to house 5.30. **Grounds only**: 1 April to end Sept: open as house but also Mon (but not BH Mon) & Tues 2–6

£ House & grounds £4.40. Grounds only £3.30. Children half price. No reduction for parties which must book in writing or by fax to the Estate Office stating numbers and time of arrival

♿ Unsuitable for wheelchair users due to gradients, gravel paths throughout grounds and steep flight of steps to house

☕ Tea-room open same days as house, 2.30–5.30

🐕 No dogs allowed

➔ (**5**: H10) Between Lechlade and Faringdon, on A417 [163:SU239973]
Bus: Thamesdown 67 Swindon–Faringdon (Fri only); otherwise as for Buscot Old Parsonage (see above) but 2¾ml walk from Lechlade

---

CALKE ABBEY 🏛 🏠 ✝ 🎛 🍀 🔊 🛈 😀 *Derbyshire*

Ticknall, Derby DE73 1LE Tel: 01332 863822 Fax: 01332 865272

This baroque mansion, built 1701-3 and set in a stunning landscape park, has become famous as a graphic illustration of the English country house in decline. Little restored, the house contains the spectacular natural history collection of the Harpur Crewe family, as well as a magnificent 18th-century state bed and interiors that are essentially unchanged since the 1880s. The attractive grounds include a beautiful walled garden and newly restored orangery

Note: One-way system operates in the Park; access only via Ticknall entrance. Entry to the house is by timed ticket (incl. NT members). Waiting time may be spent in the park, garden, church, stables, restaurant or shop; visitors are advised that at BH periods the delay in gaining admission to the house may be considerable, and very occasionally admission may not be possible. The house, church and garden are closed on Sat 15 Aug for a classical concert

What's new in 1998: Alternative exit from house along tunnel to brewhouse; display of family silver and jewellery

⊙ **House, garden & church**: 1 April to 1 Nov: daily except Thur & Fri, incl. BH Mon (closed Good Fri). **House & church**: 12.45–5.30; last admission 4.45.
Garden: 11–5.30; last admission 5. **Ticket office**: 11–5. Last admission 5. Admission to house for all visitors (incl. NT members) is by timed ticket, obtained on arrival. This gives the time of entry to the house, but does not restrict the time visitors may spend on their tour. **Park**: open during daylight hours all year; April to Oct closed 9pm (or dusk if earlier); Nov to March closes at dusk.
Events: 15 August, outdoor classical concert, plus other events throughout the season; details from Property Manager (s.a.e. please)

£ All sites: £4.90, children £2.45; family ticket £12.25. Garden only: £2.20. Discount for parties. Vehicle charge £2 (refundable on entry to the house when open)

🏃 Guided tours for parties may be arranged for mornings (but not Sat or BH weekends). Tours last approx 1hr 20min (extra charge incl. NT members); evening meals are also available with house tours. Parties must book through Calke office (tel. 01332 863822)

🛍 Shop open same days as house 11–5.30. Also Nov to 20 Dec: Sat & Sun 12–4

♿ Access above ground floor difficult; advisable to avoid peak visiting times. Moderate access to garden, park and church (some steps), good access to stables and all visitor facilities. WC at stable block. 4-seater volunteer-driven buggy (ask at ticket office). Sympathetic Hearing Scheme

👁 Braille guide

🍴 Licensed restaurant open same days as house 11–5, serving wide variety of home-cooked hot and cold lunches 12–2 and teas 2–5 (Nov to 20 Dec: Sat & Sun 12–4). Seats 126. Booked meals available for large groups. Kiosk serving snacks and ice-creams on busy afternoons

👶 Parent & baby facilities; highchairs available; children's portions of selected dishes

🏫 Curriculum-related tours and other activities for school groups. Teachers must book (tel. 01332 863822)

🐕 In park only, on leads (not in garden, house or church, except guide dogs). No shaded areas in car parks

→ (5: J4) 10ml S of Derby, on A514 at Ticknall between Swadlincote and Melbourne. Access from M42/A42 Jn 13 [128: SK356239] *Bus:* Derby Integrated 69B from Swadlincote (passing ≋ Derby)(Sun, May–Sept only), to hall; otherwise City Rider 68/9, Derby–Swadlincote (passing close ≋ Derby), alight Ticknall, thence 1¼ml walk through park to house (tel. 01332 292200)
Station: Derby 10ml; Burton-on-Trent 10ml

CANONS ASHBY HOUSE 🏠 ✝ ❄ ♠ 🛡 *Northamptonshire*

Canons Ashby, Daventry NN11 3SD Tel: 01327 860044 Fax: 01327 860168

The home of the Dryden family since its construction, this Elizabethan manor house has survived more or less unaltered since c.1710. The intimate and atmospheric interior contains wall-paintings and Jacobean plasterwork of the highest quality. There is also a formal garden, an orchard featuring varieties of fruit trees from the 16th century, and a surprisingly grand church - all that remains of the Augustinian priory from which the house takes its name

What's new in 1998: Property opening delayed until Sat 11 April due to important building work. Please contact Property Manager for information

🅾 **House:** 11 April to 1 Nov: Sat to Wed incl. BH Mon (closed Good Fri) 1–5.30 or dusk if earlier. Last admission 5. **Park, gardens & church:** same days as house 12–5.30, access through garden. **Events:** details from Property Manager (s.a.e. please)

💷 £3.60; children £1.80; family ticket £8.90. Discount for parties; contact Property Manager. Donation box for church. Parking 200m; coaches and parties should pre-book in writing with the Property Manager.

📷 Shop open 12.30–5

♿ Disabled visitors may park close to house, by prior arrangement. Access to garden via 3 steps. House access via 7 steps. WC. Guidebook for hearing-impaired visitors. Sympathetic Hearing Scheme. Wheelchairs available

👁 Braille and taped guides

🍽 Light lunches 12–2 and afternoon teas 2–5 in Brewhouse; same days as house. Party bookings by prior arrangement. 36 seats

🎒 Teachers' pack available; contact Property Manager

🐕 On leads, in Home Paddock only

➔ (5: K7) Easy access from either M40, exit 11 or M1, exit 16. From M1, take A45 (Daventry) and at Weedon crossroads turn left onto A5; 2ml S turn right onto unclassified road through Litchborough. From M40 at Banbury, take A422 (Buckingham) and after 3ml turn left onto B4525; after 3ml turn left onto unclassified road signposted to property [152: SP577506] *Bus:* Occasional Sun services from Northampton (tel. 01604 236712) *Station:* Banbury 10ml

CARDING MILL VALLEY & LONG MYND 🏞 *Shropshire*

Chalet Pavilion, Carding Mill Valley, Church Stretton SY6 6JG
Tel: 01694 722631 Fax: 01694 723068

An extensive area of historic upland heath, part of the Long Mynd and with stunning views across the Shropshire and Cheshire plains and Black Mountains. This is excellent walking country with much of interest to the naturalist; the Chalet Pavilion in Carding Mill Valley offers further information about the area, as well as a tea-room and shop

O Heathland: all year. **Chalet Pavilion (tea-room, shop & information centre):**
28 March to 2 Oct: daily 11–5; 3 Oct to 20 Dec & Jan to March 1999: weekends
only 11–4 (or dusk if earlier); also open 28–30 Dec 11–4

£ Car park charge: £1.70, motorcycle 50p, minibus £2.50, minicoach £3.50,
coach £5. Education coaches £5 if pre-booked, £10 if unbooked

Ⓚ Guided walks in summer

Ⓒ See above for opening times

Ⓖ Tea-room, shop & information centre accessible. Parking immediately outside
building. WC

Ⓟ Light lunches & teas at the Chalet Pavilion. Seating capacity 80

Ⓜ Highchairs available; baby-changing facilities

Ⓢ School parties must pre-book visits (tel: 01694 724536). Environmental
education programme available

Ⓓ Must be kept under control on moorland; not admitted to the Chalet Pavilion

→ (5: E6) 15ml S of Shrewsbury, W of Church Stretton valley and A49; approached
from Church Stretton and, on W side, from Ratlinghope or Asterton
[137: SO443945] *Bus:* Midland Red 435 Shrewsbury–Ludlow, alight Church
Stretton, ½ml (tel. 0345 056785) *Station:* Church Stretton (U) 1m

---

CHARLECOTE PARK 🏛 ✿ ♠ 🍴 Ⓚ 🎭   *Warwickshire*

Warwick CV35 9ER Tel: 01789 470277 Fax: 01789 470544

*The home of the Lucy family for over 700 years, the mellow brickwork and great chimneys of
Charlecote seem to sum up the very essence of Tudor England. There are strong associations
with both Queen Elizabeth and Shakespeare, who knew the house well - he is alleged to have
been caught poaching the estate deer. The rich early Victorian interior contains many
important objects from Beckford's Fonthill Abbey and outside, the balustraded formal garden
gives onto a fine deer park landscaped by 'Capability' Brown*

O 3 April to 1 Nov: daily except Weds & Thur 12–5 (but closed Good Fri). Grounds
12–6. **Events:** details from Property Manager (please note NT members are
charged for events)

£ £4.80; family ticket £12. Parties (max. 60) by prior arrangement. Group rate
and introductory talk available, weekdays only. Car and coach park 300m. Video
film of life at Charlecote Park in the Victorian period

Ⓚ Evening guided tours for pre-booked parties May to Sept: Tues 7.30–9.30 (£5.50,
incl. NT members; minimum charge £137.50 for party)

Ⓒ Shop & Victorian kitchens open as property 12–5.30

Ⓖ Access to all open rooms, except the gatehouse museum. Wheelchairs available.
Restaurant accessible. Shop & Victorian kitchens have alternative access
avoiding steps. WCs behind orangery and near gatehouse. Arrangements should
be made at the kiosk for disabled visitors' parking. Video can be viewed in the
gatehouse. Sympathetic Hearing Scheme

👁 Braille guide available at gatehouse; arrangements can be made to enhance a visit

☕ Morning coffee, lunches, afternoon teas in the orangery restaurant (licensed); open as property 12–5. Picnicking in deer park only

🚼 Changing and feeding room

🏫 School parties by arrangement: schools' base and resource book available

🐕 In car park only. Reasonable walks available outside park

➡ (5: H7) 1ml W of Wellesbourne, 5ml E of Stratford-upon-Avon, 6ml S of Warwick on N side of B4086 [151: SP263564] *Bus:* Stagecoach Midland Red 18, X18 Coventry–Stratford-upon-Avon (passing ⮕ Leamington Spa) (tel. 01788 535555) *Station:* Stratford-upon-Avon, 5½ml; Warwick 6ml; Leamington Spa 8ml

---

CHASTLETON HOUSE 🏚 ❊ *Oxfordshire*

Chastleton, Moreton-in-Marsh GL56 0SU Tel: 01608 674355

Chastleton is one of England's finest and most complete Jacobean houses. It is filled not only with a mixture of rare and everyday objects, furniture and textiles collected since its completion in 1612, but also with the atmosphere of four hundred years of continuous occupation by one family. The gardens have a typical Elizabethan and Jacobean layout with a ring of fascinating topiary at their heart and it was here in 1865 that the rules of modern croquet were codified. Since acquiring the property, the Trust has concentrated on conserving rather than restoring it to a pristine state

Note: Chastleton House opened in 1997 after six years of conservation. The overriding concern is the protection of the house and its contents and so the number of visitors will be restricted. All entry is by pre-booked timed ticket only. Due to narrow access roads, the largest vehicles that can be accommodated are minibuses (25-seater, 7.5m long). There are WCs, but no shop or tea-room

⊙ 1 April to end Oct: Wed to Sat 12–4. Last admission 3.30 or dusk if earlier. Admission for all visitors (incl. NT members) by pre-booked timed ticket only; bookings can be made by letter (do not include payment) to the ticket office or tel. 01608 674284, Mon to Fri 2–5 from 3 Feb 1998

£ £4.80, children £2.40; family ticket £12. Groups (min. 11, max. 25) by prior written arrangement only. No access for coaches. Car park on hill 270m from house; return walk includes a short but steep hill

⚡ Out-of-hours guided 'Private View' Wed to Fri mornings £7 (incl. NT members); must be booked in advance on tel. 01608 674284

♿ House unsuitable for wheelchairs; please tel. for further information on access for disabled visitors

👁 Braille guide available

🛍 No shop or tea-room. Picnic area in car park

🐕 Guide dogs only

➔ (5: H8) 6ml from Stow-on-the-Wold. Approach only from A436 between the A44 (west of Chipping Norton) and Stow [163: SP248291] *Station:* Moreton-in-Marsh 4½ml; Kingham 5ml

---

CHEDWORTH ROMAN VILLA 🏛 ⛨   *Gloucestershire*

Yanworth, nr Cheltenham GL54 3LJ Tel: 01242 890256 Fax: 01242 890544

The remains of Romano-British villa, first excavated in 1864 and beautifully set in a wooded valley. Exquisite mosaics and two elaborate bath complexes indicate the life of ease and luxury led by wealthy families. A museum displays a range of local finds

What's new in 1998: Audio tour (CD) £1.20 (adult/child versions); activity room for pre-booked school parties

⊙ 3 Feb to 27 Feb: Tues to Fri 10–4 site open for pre-booked parties; 28 Feb to 29 Nov: daily except Mon (but open BH Mon) 10–5 (closes 4 from 27 Oct onwards). Open Good Fri. Also 5/6 Dec: 10–4. **Events:** 11/12/13 April, Easter Egg Hunt; 30/31 May, Archaeology Activity Weekend; late July, Jazz Picnic (outdoor concert); Aug, children's holiday activity days; mid-Sept, National Archaeology Days. There is a charge for all events, incl. NT members

£ £3.20; family ticket £8. School and other parties are given an introduction to the site, but must be booked in advance. No reduction for parties. Free coach and car park

⚡ For pre-booked parties only; £7.50 for schools, £15 for non-school parties. Maximum of 30 people per guide

🛍 Shop open as villa

♿ Ramps to reception building and site. Access to villa features is limited - some ability to climb steps is required to view whole site

👁 Braille guide

➜ **(5: H9)** 3ml NW of Fossebridge on Cirencester–Northleach road (A429), approach from A429 via Yanworth or from A436 via Withington (coaches must approach from Fossebridge) [163: SP053135] *Station:* Cheltenham Spa 9ml

---

CLUMBER PARK 🏠 ✝ 🧺 🌳 👤 🛡 *Nottinghamshire*

The Estate Office, Clumber Park, Worksop S80 3AZ
Tel: 01909 476592 Fax: 01909 500721

A wide expanse of parkland, farmland and woodland, part of Nottinghamshire's famed 'Dukeries' and with a superb serpentine lake at its heart. There are many interesting features across the estate, including a classical bridge, temples, lodges and gate piers. The walled garden contains a working apiary and vineries. Clumber House was demolished in 1938, but the fine Gothic Revival chapel survives

Note: Enquiries to Estate Office (tel. 01909 476592). Guided walks may be booked for parties throughout the summer. Information room open April to Oct, afternoons (tel. 01909 484977). 166-berth caravan site run by Caravan Club; open to non-members. NT & Caravan Club members have priority (tel. 01909 484758). Camp site run by Camping & Caravanning Club of Great Britain (booking advisable due to limited spaces): April to end Sept (tel. 01909 482303). Clumber Conservation Centre for school and other groups (book with Head Warden): open weekends April to end Sept and other times by arrangement

🅾 **Park:** open all year during daylight hours. **Walled garden, Victorian apiary, fig house, vineries, orchard & garden tools exhibition:** 4 April to end Sept: Sat, Sun & BH Mon 11–5 (no dogs please). Last admission 4.30. **Conservation Centre:** 4 April to 27 Sept: Sat, Sun & BH Mon 1–5. **Chapel:** please tel. Estate Office for opening times. **Events:** full programme; please ring 01909 476592 for events leaflet

💷 Pedestrians free. Cars, motorbikes & caravanettes £3 (exemption for NT members only); cars with caravans & mini coaches £4.30; coaches midweek £7, weekends and BH £14. Parking 100m from visitor facilities. Bicycle hire (identification essential): £3 per 2hr session, child carriers. buggies and tandems also available (midweek party bookings for min. 20 cycles); book through Estate Office. Orienteering by arrangement (orienteering packs £1.50). Horse riding by permit. Coarse fishing: 16 June to 14 March; 7am to dusk; day ticket £3 (senior citizen £1.50); season ticket £50 (senior citizen £20). Day tickets available on the bank from fishing bailiff. Walled garden, Victorian apiary, vineries & garden tools exhibition 70p

🚶 Guided walks may be booked for parties throughout the summer. Details from Estate Office

▣ Clocktower shop (tel. 01909 474468) open daily, Jan to 28 March: 10.30–4; 29 March to 24 Oct: 10.30–6; 25 Oct to 24 Dec: 10.30–4 (closed 25/26 Dec); 27 Dec to end March 1999: 10.30–4. Plant sales centre: open daily 29 March to 24 Oct 10.30–6

♿ 13ml of tarmac roads, most areas accessible; walled garden, Victorian apiary, fig house, kitchen garden, vineries & garden tools exhibition fully accessible. Restaurant & shop accessible. Wheelchairs (incl. child size) available (identification required) from cycle hire. Access across grass for special events (see below). WCs. WC at cricket ground (RADAR lock). Visitors with special needs please contact Estate Office. Powered self-drive vehicle available free of charge weekdays – booking essential from Estate Office (identification required)

👁 Nature trails recommended to accompanied visually impaired visitors; map and guide available

▣ Self-service cafeteria: daily Jan to 28 March: 10.30–4; 29 March to 24 Oct: 10.30–6; 25 Oct to 24 Dec: 10.30–4; 27 Dec to end March 1999: 10.30–4. Restaurant open daily 12–2 (closed 25/26 Dec and very occasionally for private functions). Open for functions and booked parties throughout the year. Bookings and enquiries tel. 01909 484122. Seats 150

👪 Parent & baby facilities; highchairs and children's portions in restaurant; cycles with child carriers or buggies; open parkland ideal for family activities

▣ Conservation Centre available for school parties; educational exhibitions; please contact Warden, Estate Office

→ (5: K2) 4½ml SE of Worksop, 6½ml SW of Retford, 1ml from A1/A57, 11ml from M1 exit 30 [120: SK645774 or 120: SK626746] *Bus:* Stagecoach E Midland 136 251/2 from Retford and Hucknall, Sun only; otherwise 33 Worksop–Nottingham (passing close ⚏ Worksop), alight Carburton, 1¾ml (tel. 0115 9240000) *Station:* Worksop 4½ml; Retford 6½ml

---

COUGHTON COURT ▣ ✚ ❀ ▣　　　　　　　　　　*Warwickshire*

nr Alcester B49 5JA
Tel: Office: 01789 400777 Visitor Information: 01789 762435 Fax: 01789 765544

One of the great Tudor houses, Coughton has been the home of the Throckmorton family since 1409. It has important associations with the Gunpowder plot and saw much activity during the Civil War. The impressive central gatehouse and half-timbered courtyard are particularly noteworthy and inside there are fine collections of furniture, porcelain and paintings. Two churches, a lake, riverside walk and new formal walled garden provide additional interest

Note: Coughton Court is lived in, opened and managed by the Throckmorton family

◎ 14 March to end April: Sat & Sun 11.30–5. Easter Mon to Wed 11.30–5 (closed Good Fri). May to end Sept: daily except Thur & Fri 11.30–5; but every Fri in July & Aug 11.30–5. 3 to 18 Oct: Sat & Sun 11.30–5. Grounds open 11–5.30 (Oct closes 5). Last admission to house and grounds 30min before closing. The house may occasionally close on Sat afternoons; the gardens and grounds will remain open (tel. visitor information line to check). On busy days entry to the house is by timed ticket. **Events:** concerts & other events; please tel for details

£ £5.90; family ticket £18.50. Parties of 15 or more by prior arrangement (not BH). Grounds only £3.90. New walled garden (created by the family) £2 (incl. NT members)

⚡ Evening guided tours for pre-booked parties Mon to Wed. Garden tours by appointment. No party rate or membership concessions for out of hours visits

🛍 Shop & plant sales centre open as grounds (managed by family)

♿ Access to three rooms on ground floor, restaurant and shop. Wheelchairs available. WC. Grounds, garden & riverside path suitable for wheelchairs. Disabled drivers please contact Admissions for advice on parking

👁 Braille guides

🍴 Restaurant managed by family, open for morning coffee, lunches & teas same days as house 11–5.30. Picnics in car park picnic area

🏫 School visits by arrangement

🐕 Dogs on leads in car park only

➔ (5: H7) 2ml N of Alcester on A435 [150: SP080604] *Bus:* Midland Red West 146, Birmingham–Evesham; Stagecoach Midland Red 228 Redditch–Stratford-upon-Avon (passing ≋ Redditch & close ≋ Evesham) (tel. 0345 125436) *Station:* Redditch 6ml

---

CROFT CASTLE 🏰 ✝ ✳ ● 🏛 🚹   *Herefordshire*

nr Leominster HR6 9PW Tel: 01568 780246

One of the area's most fascinating houses, Croft illustrates the turbulent history of this part of England. The essentially defensive exterior contrasts with the comfortable and decorative state rooms inside. Most date from the 18th century and there are fine plasterwork ceilings, rare furniture and family portraits. The park contains a superb avenue of 350-year-old Spanish chestnuts

⭘ April & Oct to 1 Nov: Sat & Sun 1.30–4.30 (closed Good Fri). May to end Sept: daily except Mon & Tues (but open BH Mon) 1.30–5.30. Last admission to house 30min before closing. Car park, parkland and Croft Ambrey open all year

£ House & grounds: £3.30; family ticket £8.30. Grounds only: car park charge £1.50 per car; £10 per coach. Parties of 15 or more by prior written arrangement. Picnics in the car park only

♿ Access to all rooms (one ramped step), garden (gravelled terrace difficult) and part of grounds; parking near castle

👁 Braille guide

🚹 Children's quiz

🐕 In parkland only, on leads

➔ (5: E7) 5ml NW of Leominster, 9ml SW of Ludlow; approach from B4362, turning N at Cock Gate between Bircher and Mortimer's Cross; signposted from Ludlow–Leominster road (A49) and from A4110 at Mortimer's Cross [137: SO455655] *Bus:* Primrose 493/4 from ≋ Leominster to Castle, Sat only;

otherwise Midland Red West/Go Whittle 192, 292 Birmingham–Hereford
(passing close ≋ Ludlow & Leominster), alight Gorbett Bank, 2¼ml
(tel. 0345 125436) *Station:* Leominster (U) 7ml

CROOME LANDSCAPE PARK ❁ ♣ *Worcestershire*

The National Trust Estate Office, Builder's Yard, High Green,
Severn Stoke WR8 9JS

---

*Croome was 'Capability' Brown's first significant landscape, making his reputation and
proving highly influential in park design. The exquisite park buildings and other structures
are mostly by Robert Adam and James Wyatt. The Trust acquired a large area of the park in
1996 with substantial grant aid from the Heritage Lottery Fund*

Note: The Trust has embarked on a 10-year restoration plan, including dredging the
water features, extensive tree planting in the park and woodland and the provision of
facilities for visitors. The Royal & SunAlliance Insurance Group plc is making a major
financial contribution towards the cost of this restoration

What's new in 1998: Major restoration work will continue on the Lake Garden which
will be open only to pre-booked guided tours; booking is by written application only
to: The National Trust Estate Office, Builder's Yard, High Green, Severn Stoke WR8 9JS

🅾 4 April to 1 Nov: Sat, Sun & BH Mon 10.30–6 (dusk if earlier). The focus of
visitor access will be the church, which is open in association with the Churches
Conservation Trust, and where information is available. The new pay-and-
display car park links directly with 6ml of footpaths and is open daily. Car park
charge £1 (incl. NT members)

£ By pre-booked guided tour only, £2 (incl. NT members)

♿ Wheelchair access to Lake Garden on pre-booked guided tours

🐕 Dogs are welcome, but must be kept on leads

➜ (5: G8) 8ml S of Worcester and E of A38 and M5 [150: SO878448]
Bus: Midland Red West 372–4 Worcester–Gloucester, alight Severn Stoke,
thence 2ml (tel. 0345 125436) *Station:* Pershore 7ml

CWMMAU FARMHOUSE 🏠 🛈 *Herefordshire*

Brilley, Whitney-on-Wye HR3 6JP Tel: 01497 831251

An early 17th-century timber-framed and stone-tiled farmhouse

🅾 May to Aug inclusive: Wed only, 2–5.30

£ £2.50. Not suitable for coaches

🛈 Viewing by guided tours only

☕ Tea-room (managed by tenant)

➜ (5: E8) 4ml SW of Kington between A4111 & A438; approach by a narrow lane
leading S from Kington–Brilley road at Brilley Mountain [148: SO267514]

DUDMASTON 🏛 ❖ ♨ 🛡 *Shropshire*

Quatt, nr Bridgnorth WV15 6QN Tel: 01746 780866 Fax: 01746 780744

A late 17th-century house with intimate family rooms containing fine furniture and Dutch flower paintings, as well as interesting contemporary paintings and sculpture. The delightful gardens are a mass of colour in spring and include a walk in the Dingle, a wooded valley. There are also estate walks starting from Hampton Loade

O 1 April to 30 Sept: Wed & Sun only 2–5.30. Last admission 5. Special opening for pre-booked parties only, Thur 2–5.30. **Events**: please send s.a.e. to Administrator

£ House & garden £3.50, children £2; family ticket £8. Garden only £2.50. Parking 100m

🏃 For pre-booked parties

🛍 Shop open as house

♿ Ramp to entrance; access to main and inner halls, Library, Oak Room, No 1 & Darby galleries and Old Kitchen. Tea-room accessible. Shop accessible via ramp. For access arrangements apply to Administrator; wheelchairs and self-drive powered vehicle available; signed route in garden (some steep slopes) and through Gerard's Wood. WC by car park. Sympathetic Hearing Scheme

👁 Braille & large-print guides for house and woodland; taped guide for house with cassette players. Scented plants in garden

🍽 Light lunches 1–2.15. Home-made teas 2.15–5.30. Light lunches for booked parties by arrangement on Wed and Thur. (Please note that the tea-room is open to the general public and not restricted to those visiting the house or garden)

👶 Highchairs in tea-room. Baby slings available. Baby-changing facilities

🐕 In the Dingle and on estate only, on leads

➡ (5: F6) 4ml SE of Bridgnorth on A442 [138: SO746887] *Bus:* Shropshire Bus 297 Bridgnorth–Kidderminster (passing close ⊞ Kidderminster) (tel. 0345 056785) *Station:* Hampton Loade (Severn Valley Rly) 1½ml; Kidderminster 10ml

FARNBOROUGH HALL 🏛 ❖ ♣ *Warwickshire*

Banbury OX17 1DU Tel: 01295 690002

A beautiful honey-coloured stone house, built in the mid 18th century and the home of the Holbech family for over 300 years. The interior plasterwork is quite outstanding and the charming grounds contain 18th-century temples, terrace walk and obelisk

Note: Farnborough Hall is occupied and administered by Mr & Mrs Holbech

O **House, grounds & terrace walk**: April to end Sept: Wed & Sat 2–6: also 3 & 4 May 2–6. **Terrace walk only**: Thur & Fri 2–6. Last admission to the house 5.30

£ House, grounds & terrace walk £2.90. Garden & terrace walk £1.50. Terrace walk only (Thur & Fri) £1. Parties by written arrangement only, no reduction. Coach and car park. Strong shoes advisable for terrace

[♿] Ground floor of house and garden accessible (terrace walk is very steep)

[🐕] Welcome, on leads in grounds only

[➜] (5: J8) 6ml N of Banbury, ½ml W of A423 [151: SP430490]

THE FLEECE INN [🏠]   *Worcestershire*

Bretforton, nr Evesham WR11 5JE Tel: 01386 831173

A black and white half-timbered medieval farmhouse, largely unaltered since first becoming a licensed house in 1848

Note: The Inn is managed by a commercial tenant

[🅞] During normal public house licensing hours

[£] Car-parking in village square. Coaches by written appointment only

[🍴] Lunchtime snacks

[➜] (5: H8) 4ml E of Evesham, on B4035 [150: SP093437] *Bus:* Barry's/Cresswell/
Spring & Son/Midland Red West 554 from Evesham (tel. 0345 125436)
Station: Evesham 3ml

GREAT COXWELL BARN [🏠]   *Oxfordshire*

Great Coxwell, Faringdon   Tel: (Coleshill Estate Office) 01793 762209

A 13th-century monastic barn, stone-built with a stone-tiled roof and interesting timber structure

[🅞] All year: daily at reasonable hours

[£] 50p. No WC

[🐕] On leads only

[➜] (5: H10) 2ml SW of Faringdon between A420 and B4019 [163: SU269940]
Bus: Stagecoach Swindon & District 66 Swindon–Oxford (passing close
[🚆] Swindon & passing [🚆] Oxford), alight Great Coxwell Turn, ¾ml
(tel. 0345 090899) *Station:* Swindon 10ml

THE GREYFRIARS [🏠] [✿] [🛡]   *Worcestershire*

Friar Street, Worcester WR1 2LZ Tel: 01905 23571

A fine timber-framed town house, built in 1480 but with later additions. Rescued from demolition and now carefully restored, the panelled interior contains interesting textiles and furnishings. An archway leads through to the delightful garden

[🅞] 13 April to end Oct: Wed, Thur & BH Mon 2–5. **Events:** 3,4 & 5 Dec, Street Fayre

£ £2.40; family ticket £6. Parties of 15 or more by written appointment. No
reductions. Not suitable for large parties of children. Public car park in Friar
Street. No WC

→ (5: G7) In centre of Worcester [150: SO852546] *Bus:* From surrounding areas
(tel. 0345 125436) *Station:* Worcester Foregate Street ½ml

GREYS COURT 🏠 🏘 ✿ 🛡 *Oxfordshire*

Rotherfield Greys, Henley-on-Thames RG9 4PG Tel: 01491 628529

*A picturesque and intriguing house, originally 14th century but much added to later, with a
beautiful courtyard and one surviving tower dating from 1347. The house has an interesting
history and was involved in Jacobean court intrigue. Inside, the intimate rooms contain some
outstanding 18th-century plasterwork. The outbuildings include a Tudor wheelhouse and the
beautiful walled gardens are full of old-fashioned roses and wisteria*

O **House** (**part of ground floor only**): 1 April to end Sept: Mon, Wed & Fri 2–6.
(closed Good Fri). **Garden:** daily except Thur & Sun 2–6 (closed Good Fri).
Last admission 5.30. **Events:** for details please send s.a.e. to the Box Office,
PO Box 180, High Wycombe, Bucks HP14 4XT

£ House & garden £4.40; family ticket £11. Garden only £3.20; family ticket £8.
Parking 220m. No picnicking in grounds. No reduction for coach parties, which
must book in advance with the Custodian

♿ Garden only, in part accessible; WC

🍽 Teas in Cromwellian stables: 1 April to end Sept: Mon, Wed, Fri & Sat 2.30–5.15

🐾 In car park only

→ (5: K10) 3ml W of Henley-on-Thames; from Henley town centre take A4130
towards Oxford and at Nettlebed mini roundabout take B481 - the property is
signed on the left after Highmoor [175: SU725834] *Bus:* Yellow Bus M1 from
🚉 Reading, alight Greys Green, ½ml (tel. 01296 613831); otherwise Reading
Buses 137 from Reading (passing close 🚉 Reading), alight Peppard Common, 2ml
(tel. 0118 959 4000) *Station:* Henley-on-Thames 3ml

HAILES ABBEY ✝ 🛡 *Gloucestershire*

nr Winchcombe, Cheltenham GL54 5PB Tel: 01242 602398

*Founded in 1246 and once a celebrated pilgrimage site, this Cistercian abbey now lies in
ruins. Remains of the dramatic cloister arches survive and there is a small museum*

Note: Hailes Abbey is in the guardianship of English Heritage. For further information
contact EH Regional Office (tel. 0117 9750700)

O **Site & Museum:** 1 April to end Oct: daily 10–6 (or dusk if earlier in Oct); Nov to
end March 1999: Sat & Sun 10–4 (closed 24 to 26 Dec). **Events:** programme to
be confirmed – some events may be subject to an additional charge for all
attending (incl. NT members)

£ £2.50; OAP/student/UB40 holder £1.90; children £1.30 (incl. of tape guide)

Small English Heritage shop in museum

Access to most of site and museum. WC. Loop system for hearing-impaired visitors

Braille guide. Some touch prints available; taped guides, including basic tape for people with learning disabilities

Ice-creams and soft drinks available

Baby-changing facilities available

Teachers' handbook available. Free admission for pre-booked school parties; for information contact the property

On leads only in abbey grounds, but not in museum

(5: H8) 2ml NE of Winchcombe, 1ml E of Broadway road (B4632, originally A46) [150: SP050300] *Bus:* Castleways from Cheltenham (passing close Cheltenham) alight Didbrook, 1½ml, or more frequent to Greet, 1¼ml by footpath (tel. 01242 602949) *Station:* Cheltenham 10ml

HANBURY HALL   *Worcestershire*

Droitwich WR9 7EA Tel: 01527 821214 Fax: 01527 821251

A William & Mary-style red-brick house, famed for its beautiful painted ceilings and staircase by Thornhill, but with other, more unusual, features. These include a detached long gallery and Moorish gazebos at each corner of the forecourt. There is also a formal 18th-century garden and handsome orangery

29 March to 28 Oct: Sun to Wed 2–6. Last admission 5.30 (dusk if earlier). **Events**: varied programme through the year: for details and inclusion on mailing list please send s.a.e. to the property

£ House & garden £4.30; family ticket £10.50. Garden only £2.50. House is available for private and commercial functions and civil wedding ceremonies; please contact Property Manager. Free car- and coach-parking

𝟖 Evening guided tours for pre-booked parties, May to Sept, £4.30 (incl. NT members), minimum charge £86

Shop open as house

Wheelchair access to ground floor, tea-room; easy access to garden; disabled visitors may be driven to front door. Self-drive powered vehicle. WC

Braille guide

Cream teas in tea-room in house, open as house. Picnic area in car park

No dogs in garden, but allowed on leads in park on footpaths only

→ (5: G7) 4½ml E of Droitwich, 1ml N of B4090, 6ml S of Bromsgrove, 1½ml W of B4091 [150: SO943637] *Bus:* Midland Red West 142/4 Worcester–Birmingham (passing close ≷ Droitwich Spa), alight Wychbold, 2½ml (tel. 0345 125436) *Station:* Droitwich Spa 4ml

---

HARDWICK HALL 🏠 ✥ ♣ 🏠 𝟖 😈   *Derbyshire*

Doe Lea, Chesterfield S44 5QJ Tel: 01246 850430 Fax: 01246 854200

One of Britain's foremost Elizabethan houses and a magnificent statement of the wealth and authority of its builder, Bess of Hardwick. Like a huge glass lantern, the house dominates the surrounding area and contains outstanding collections of 16th-century furniture, tapestries and needlework. Walled courtyards enclose fine gardens, orchards and herb garden, and the surrounding country park contains rare breeds of cattle and sheep

Note: Due to limited light in the Hall's ancient rooms, visitors wishing to make a close study of tapestries and textiles should avoid dull days early and late in the season. To avoid congestion, access to the house may be limited at peak periods. The remains of Hardwick Old Hall in the grounds are in the guardianship of English Heritage

What's new in 1998: Three newly restored statues now on display in the garden; the Eglantine table restored and returned to the High Great Chamber; four Jordaens' tapestries rehung after conservation. During 1998 exterior building works will be in progress and these may affect the visitor route

O **Hall:** 1 April to 1 Nov: Wed, Thur, Sat, Sun & BH Mon 12.30–5 (closed Good Fri). Last admission to hall 4.30. **Garden:** 1 April to 1 Nov: daily 12–5.30. No picnics in garden; only in car park & parkland. Car park gates close 6. Parkland open daily throughout the year, 7am to 7pm. **Old Hall** (EH): 1 April to 1 Nov: Wed to Sun & BH Mon (but closed Good Fri) 10–6. **Events:** details from Property Manager

£ Hall & garden £6, child £3; family ticket £15. Garden only £2.70, child £1; family £6.50. Parties of 10+ (no reduction) only by written arrangement with Property Manager; please send s.a.e. Vehicle charge £2 (refundable on purchase of house and garden ticket; NT members free). Car park charge for country park to non-members 50p. Joint ticket available for Hall (NT) and Old Hall (EH): adult £7.70, child £4.20. Children under 15 must be accompanied by an adult. For information on Stainsby Mill, please see p.222

[📱] By special written arrangement with Property Manager

[🛍] Shop open as restaurant (shop/restaurant tel. 01246 854088)

[♿] Access to garden and some parts of park and ponds. Great Kitchen and shop accessible by ramp. Access to house limited to ground floor via ramp to main entrance. WC. Wheelchair available (please pre-book)

[👁] Herb & flower garden particularly recommended for visually impaired visitors (pre-booking advised); herbs (and some objects in house) may be touched. Braille guide to hall, park, garden, children's guide, tactile maps of garden and park walks; large-print introductory guides

[🍴] Lunches 12–2 & teas 2–4.45 (closes 5.15) in licensed restaurant in the Great Kitchen, on days hall is open. Party bookings by written application only (s.a.e. please). Limited seating of 60 in Great Kitchen and 30 in Still Room

[👶] Parent & baby facilities, accessible from car park; highchair, children's portions and baby carriers available

[🏫] School parties Wed and Thur only; pre-booking essential (s.a.e. please). Schools resource pack and environmental education facility available

[🐕] In park only, on leads; not in garden

[➜] (5: J3) *Note*: All visitors please note that a one-way traffic system operates in the Park; access only via Stainsby Mill entrance (leave M1, exit 29, follow brown signs), exit only via Hardwick Inn. Park gates closed at night (7 in summer, 5.30 in winter) 6½ml W of Mansfield, 9½ml SE of Chesterfield; approach from M1 (exit 29) via A6175 [120: SK463638] *Bus:* Cosy Coaches C1 from Workshop to Hall (Sun, June–Aug only); otherwise Stagecoach E Midland 737, 747 Sheffield/Chesterfield–Nottingham, 48 Chesterfield-Bolsover (local buses link with Chesterfield [🚆] station), alight Glapwell 'Young Vanish', 1½ml (tel. 01332 292200) *Station:* Chesterfield 8ml

---

HAWFORD DOVECOTE [🏠]   *Worcestershire*

Hawford   Tel: (Regional Office) 01684 850051

A 16th-century half-timbered dovecote, the remnant of a former monastic grange

[⭕] April to 1 Nov: daily 9–6 or sunset if earlier. Closed Good Fri. Other times by prior appointment only with Severn Regional Office. Visitors should please note that access is on foot only via the entrance drive to the adjoining house

[£] 60p

[➜] (5: G7) 3ml N of Worcester, ½ml E of A449 [150: SO846607] *Bus:* Midland Red West 303 Worcester–Kidderminster (passing [🚆] Worcester Foregate Street & Kidderminster), alight Hawford Lodge, ½ml (tel. 0345 125436) *Station:* Worcester Foregate Street 3ml; Worcester Shrub Hill 3½ml

HIDCOTE MANOR GARDEN 🏵 🛡 *Gloucestershire*

Hidcote Bartrim, nr Chipping Campden GL55 6LR
Tel: 01386 438333 Restaurant 01386 438703 Fax: 01386 438817

One of England's great gardens, an 'Arts & Crafts' masterpiece created by the horticulturist Major Lawrence Johnston. A series of outdoor rooms, each with a different character and separated by walls and hedges of many different species, the garden is famous for its rare shrubs and trees, outstanding herbaceous borders and unusual plant species from all over the world. Careful planting has ensured a spectacular display of art and colour throughout the season

What's new in 1998: Autumn lecture programme

⭕ 1 April to end Sept: daily except Tues & Fri 11–7 (closed Good Fri). Also open Tues in June & July only 11–7. Oct & 1 Nov: daily except Tues & Fri 11–6. Last admission 1 hr before closing or dusk if earlier. **Events:** autumn lecture series and Christmas lunches/dinners; please contact Property Catering Manager for details

💷 £5.50; family ticket £13.80. Coaches & parties by appointment only (tel. 01386 438333); no party concessions. No picnicking and no games in garden. Free car park 100m. Liable to overcrowding on BH Mon and fine Suns. Number of parties limited per day; *party leaders should therefore check with the property before booking transport*

🛍 Shop open as garden; also open 7 Nov to 13 Dec: Sat & Sun 12–4. Plant sales centre open same days as garden to end Sept: 10.30–5.45

♿ Gravelled car park; disabled visitors may be set down at garden entrance. Access limited for wheelchair users due to the nature of some informal stone paved paths and some steps. Wheelchair users requiring refreshments contact Restaurant Manager; level access can be arranged. Tea bar accessible. WC in plant sales centre adjacent to car park. Neck loop for use with hearing aids with T position

👁 Scented plants; Braille and tape guides (deposit required for tape)

🍴 The Garden Restaurant offers licensed, waitress service, open same days as garden for coffee/full lunch menu 11–2, teas 2.30–5. Also open 7 Nov to 13 Dec at weekends only 12–4. Booking essential in Nov/Dec. Parties of 10+ are advised to book in advance with Property Catering Manager. Tea bar, adjacent to plant centre, provides open courtyard setting with covered area and serves light refreshments; open April to end Sept, same days as garden, 10.30–5.45 (but times may vary according to weather). Further details from Property Catering Manager

➔ (5: H8) 4ml NE of Chipping Campden, 1ml E of B4632 (originally A46), off B4081 [151: SP176429] *Bus:* Stagecoach Midland Red 215/6 from Stratford-upon-Avon (tel. 01242 425543); Castleways ⊞ Moreton-in-Marsh–⊞ Evesham, June to Sept only (tel. 01242 602949) *Station:* Honeybourne (U) 4½ml

ILAM PARK ✚ ● ❖ ⧍ *Staffordshire*

Ilam, Ashbourne DE6 2AZ Tel: 01335 350245

A beautiful area of open park and woodland, running on both banks of the River Manifold and with spectacular views towards Dovedale

○ **Grounds and Park:** all year, daily. Hall is let to YHA and is not open. *Note:* small caravan site run by NT (basic facilities) open to Caravan Club/NT members; Easter to Oct (tel. 01335 350310)

£ Free. Pay-and-display car park (NT members free)

⧍ Guided walks around the estate may be booked by groups; contact Property Manager (tel. 01335 350503)

⌂ Shop and information centre with an exhibition on Ilam and the South Peak Estate: 3 Jan to 28 March: Sat & Sun 11–4; 29 March to 24 Oct: daily 11–5; 25 Oct to 20 Dec: Sat & Sun 11–4; Jan to end March 1999: Sat & Sun 11–4

♿ Access to information centre and shop only; limited access in grounds near Hall. WC. Wheelchair available

☕ Manifold tea-room open for selection of light refreshments & teas: 3 Jan to 28 March: Sat & Sun 11–4; 29 March to 17 May: Sat & Sun 11–5; 18 May to end Sept: Fri to Tues 11–5; Oct to 20 Dec: Sat & Sun 11–4; Jan to end March 1999: Sat & Sun 11–4. Seats 58

⧍ Children's portions available in tea-room

▦ School visit room, resource material, teachers' resource book for Dovedale, illustrated talks and guided walks available for educational groups. Further details from the Education Coordinator, South Peak Estate Office, Home Farm (tel. 01335 350503)

🐾 On leads only

→ (5: H3) 4½ml NW of Ashbourne [119:SK132507] *Bus:* Warrington 443 from Ashbourne, Thur & Sat only, with connections from Derby; also various services from ▆ Buxton and Derby, summer Sun only; otherwise Stagecoach Manchester 201 Derby–Manchester (passing close ▆ Derby & Macclesfield), alight Ilam Cross Roads, 2ml (tel. 01332 292200)

KEDLESTON HALL ▦ ✚ ❖ ● ▣ *Derbyshire*

Derby DE22 5JH Tel: 01332 842191 Fax: 01332 841972

A classical Palladian mansion, built 1759-65 for the Curzon family, who have lived in the area since the 12th century. The house boasts the most complete and least-altered sequence of Robert Adam interiors in England, with the magnificent state rooms retaining their great collections of paintings and original furniture. The Indian Museum houses a fascinating range of objects collected by Lord Curzon when Viceroy of India (1899-1905)

What's new in 1998: Lake island restored to 18th-century appearance; electric stairclimber to assist disabled visitors

House: 28 March to 1 Nov: daily except Thur & Fri (closed Good Fri) 1–5.30 (11–5.30 on BH weekends). Last admissions to house 5 (4 from 18 Oct). **Garden:** same days as house 11–6. **Park:** 1 April to 1 Nov: daily 11–6; Nov to 20 Dec: Sat & Sun only 12–4. **Events:** concerts and theatre events; August BH, Working Crafts Show; details from Property Manager

£4.70, children £2.40; family ticket £11.50. £1 reduction for pre-booked parties of 15+. Park & garden only: £2 per adult, £1 per child (refundable against tickets for house); Thur & Fri vehicle charge of £2 for park only (other facilities closed).

Guided walks around the park and/or gardens may be booked (tel. 01332 842393/842338)

Shop open as house. Also Nov to 20 Dec: Sat & Sun only 12–4

Access to house via electric stairclimber for wheelchairs. Wheelchairs and self-drive vehicle available for garden and limited use in park. Garden accessible. WC. Access to restaurant and shop. Sympathetic Hearing Scheme

Braille guide. Many items may be touched

Licensed restaurant same days as house serving a full range of home-cooked fare 11–5. Nov to 20 Dec: light lunches and teas only, Sat & Sun 12–4. Party bookings by written application (s.a.e. please). Seats 50

WC with baby-changing facility; children's guide and quiz; children's portions available in restaurant

Teachers' leaflets available, please contact Education Coordinator

In park only, on leads. No dogs on Long Walk or in gardens

(5: J4) 5ml NW of Derby, entrance off Kedleston road and signposted from roundabout where A38 crosses A52 close to Markeaton Park [SK312403] *Bus:* Derby Integrated 69B from ⊠ Derby to Hall (Sun only); otherwise Dunn Line 109 Derby–Ashbourne, alight the Smithy (1ml); Trent R51/2 from Derby to Askerfield Avenue, thence 2ml. All pass close ⊠ Derby (tel. 01332 292200) *Station:* Duffield (U) 3½ml; Derby 5½ml

KINVER EDGE 🖼 🔟 *Staffordshire*

The Warden's Lodge, The Compa, Kinver, nr Stourbridge DY7 6HU
Tel: 01384 872418

A sandstone ridge, covered in woodland and heath and from which there are dramatic views across surrounding counties. There are several famous rock-houses, which were inhabited until the 1950s

What's new in 1998: Improvement work was carried out to the lower rock houses in 1997 and included reinstatement of external doors and windows

O Kinver Edge open all year. Lower rock house grounds open: April to Sept: daily 9–7; Oct to March: daily 9–4. Access to upper terrace, April to Sept: Wed, Sat & Sun 2–5; Oct to March 1999: Wed, Sat & Sun 2–4: prior confirmation with Custodian advisable (tel. 01384 872553)

£ Free

& Route to lower caves at Holy Austin Rock is suitable for wheelchair users; limited access onto escarpment from east side. Roadside parking

🐕 On leads within grounds of rock houses

➔ (5: F6) 5ml W of Stourbridge, 6ml N of Kidderminster. 2½ml off A458 [138:SO836836] *Bus:* Travel West Midlands/Midland Red West 242 **🚌** Stourbridge–Kinver (tel. 01785 223344) *Station:* Stourbridge Town 5ml

KINWARTON DOVECOTE 🏠 *Warwickshire*

Kinwarton, nr Alcester   Tel: (Regional Office) 01684 850051

A circular 14th-century dovecote, still housing doves and retaining its potence, an unusual pivoted ladder from which access is possible to the nesting boxes

O April to 1 Nov: daily 9–6 or sunset if earlier. Closed Good Fri. Other times by prior appointment only with Regional Office. Key obtainable from Glebe Farm next door

£ 60p

➔ (5: H7) 1½ml NE of Alcester, just S of B4089 [150: SP106585] *Bus:* As Coughton Court, but alight Alcester, 1½ml except on the 228 which passes the Dovecote *Station:* Wilmcote (U), 5ml; Wootton Wawen (U), not Sun, 5ml

LITTLE FLEECE BOOKSHOP 🏠 *Gloucestershire*

Bisley Street, Painswick GL6 6QQ Tel: 01452 812103

A 17th-century building, originally part of a former inn and restored in an exemplary 'Arts & Crafts' fashion in 1935. Now open as a bookshop, with the ground-floor room only on view

O 1 April to 31 Oct: daily except Sun & Mon 10–1 & 2–5. Closed Good Fri. Nov & Dec: Sat only 10–1 & 2–5

➡ (5: G9) 3ml N of Stroud A46, 6ml SE of Gloucester B4073. Off main High Street, Painswick [162: SO868098] *Bus:* Stagecoach Stroud Valleys 46 Stroud–Cheltenham Spa (passes close ♿ Stroud) (tel. 01242 522021) *Station:* Stroud 4ml

---

LONGSHAW ESTATE ♣ 🦀 🔠 👤 🚶 🏃 🛡 *Derbyshire*

Sheffield S11 7TZ Tel: Visitor Centre 01433 631708
Wardens' Office 01433 631757 Fax: 01433 631757

A wide expanse of open moorland, woodland and farms within the Peak District National Park, with dramatic views and excellent walking

🅾 **Estate:** open at all times. Lodge is converted into flats and is not open.
Visitor centre (café, shop and information centre): 3 Jan to March, Nov & Dec: Sat & Sun only; April, May & Oct: daily except Mon & Tues (but open BH Mon) 11–5 (or sunset if earlier); June, July, Aug & Sept: daily 11–5. Booked parties at other times by arrangement. **Events:** 3–5 Sept, Longshaw Sheepdog Trials

💷 Car park 200m from visitor centre [SK266800]; access difficult for coaches; no coaches at weekends or BH. Car parks for estate at Haywood [110/119: SK256778] and Wooden Pole [110/119: SK267790]. Riding permits available. Longshaw Walks & Family leaflets from visitor centre

🏃 Guided walks around the estate may be booked by groups: contact Wardens' office (tel. 01433 631757)

🛍 Shop open as visitor centre

♿ WC. Limited access to the estate. One car-parking space available at visitor centre – please book in advance with Visitor Centre Manager

🍴 Selection of home-made light lunches and teas at visitor centre. Seats 40

👶 Baby-changing facilities. Highchairs in café

🐕 On leads only; no dogs in visitor centre

➡ (5: H2) 7½ml from Sheffield, next to A625 Sheffield–Hathersage road; Woodcroft car park is off B6055, 200m S of junction with A625 [110/119: SK266802] *Bus:* Mainline 240 Sheffield–Bakewell (passing ♿ Grindleford); Mainline 272 Sheffield–Castleton (passing ♿ Hathersage). All pass close ♿ Sheffield (tel. 01332 292200) *Station:* Grindleford (U) 2ml

---

LOWER BROCKHAMPTON 🏠 🏃 *Herefordshire*

Bringsty WR6 5UH Tel: 01885 488099

A late 14th-century moated manor house, with a beautiful timber-framed gatehouse and interesting ruined chapel

What's new in 1998: New car park for cars and coaches, with information panels and facilities; woodland walks, including 'access for all' and 'sculpture' trails

🅾 Medieval hall, parlour, minstrels gallery & chapel open 1 April to end Sept: Wed to Sun & BH Mon 10–5 (closed Good Fri). Oct to 1 Nov: Wed to Sun 10–4

£ £2; family ticket £5. Car park £1.50

📷 Small selection of NT goods, local artists' pictures, greetings cards, bookmarks and postcards

♿ Access to most parts. Gatehouse & upper floor not accessible

👁 Braille guide; timber-framing and oak furniture may be touched

➡ (5: F7) 2ml E of Bromyard on Worcester road (A44); reached by a narrow road through 1½ml of woods and farmland [149: SO682546] *Bus:* Midland Red West 419/20 Worcester–Hereford (passing ⬛ Worcester Foregate Street & close ⬛ Hereford) (tel. 0345 125436)

LYVEDEN NEW BIELD 🏠 ✝ 🛡 *Northamptonshire*

nr Oundle, Peterborough PE8 5AT Tel/fax: 01832 205358

An incomplete lodge or garden house, begun c.1595 by Sir Thomas Tresham and now an intriguing and roofless shell. Designed in the shape of a cross, with interesting exterior friezework

🅾 All year: daily. Parties by arrangement with the Custodian, Lyveden New Bield Cottage, Oundle, Peterborough PE8 5AT. Elizabethan water gardens open selected Sun during July. **Events:** details from Custodian

£ £1.70. Limited roadside parking; access on foot ½ml along farm track; no parking for coaches which may drop and return to pick up passengers. No WC

🚶 Tours of the remains of the late Elizabethan water gardens by prior arrangement with the Custodian

🐕 On leads only

➡ (5: M6) 4ml SW of Oundle via A427, 3ml E of Brigstock, off Harley Way [141: SP983853] *Bus:* Stagecoach United Counties X65 Northampton–Peterborough (passing close ⬛ Peterborough); alight Lower Benefield, 2ml by bridlepath; Stagecoach United Counties/Blands 8 Kettering Corby, alight Brigstock, 2½ml. Both pass close ⬛ Kettering (tel. 01604 20077) *Station:* Kettering 10ml

MIDDLE LITTLETON TITHE BARN 🏠 🔧 *Worcestershire*

Middle Littleton, Evesham

One of the largest and finest tithe barns in the country, dating from the 13th century and still in use as a farmbuilding

🅾 April to 1 Nov: daily 2–5

£ 60p

➡ (5: H8) 3ml NE of Evesham, E of B4085 [150: SP080471] *Bus:* Midland Red West 146, Evesham–Birmingham (passing close ⬛ Evesham), alight Middle Littleton School Lane, ½ml (tel. 0345 125436) *Station:* Honeybourne (U) 3½ml; Evesham 4½ml

MORVILLE HALL 🏠 ❀ 🏊 *Shropshire*

nr Bridgnorth WV16 5BN

An Elizabethan house of mellow stone, converted in the 18th century and set in attractive gardens

🅾 By written appointment only with the tenants, Dr & Mrs C. Douglas

🎫 For pre-booked parties

♿ Ground floor and most of garden accessible

➡ (5: F6) [138: SO668940] *Bus:* People Express 436/7 Shrewsbury–Kidderminster (passing close ⬛ Shrewsbury & Severn Valley Rly Bridgnorth) (tel. 0345 056785) *Station:* Bridgnorth (Severn Valley Rly) 3½ml

MOSELEY OLD HALL 🏠 ❀ 🛡 *Staffordshire*

Moseley Old Hall Lane, Fordhouses, Wolverhampton WV10 7HY
Tel/fax: 01902 782808

An Elizabethan house, altered in the 19th century and famous for its association with Charles II, who hid here after the Battle of Worcester (1651). The story of his escape is recounted in an exhibition in the barn, and there is an interesting garden full of 17th-century plants

🅾 28 March to 13 Dec; March to May: Sat & Sun, BH Mon and following Tues (except Tues 5 May) 1.30–5.30 (BH Mon 11–5); June to Oct: Wed, Sat, Sun, BH Mon and following Tues; also Tues in July & Aug 1.30–5.30 (BH Mon 11–5); Nov & Dec: Sun 1.30–4.30 (guided tours only, last tour at 4). Pre-booked parties at other times incl. evening tours. **Events:** summer events and concerts; for programme please send s.a.e. to Property Manager

💷 £3.60; family ticket £9

🎫 Optional free guided tours

🛍 Shop open as house. Christmas shop

⌖ Access to ground floor (3 rooms) and garden only. Two tables for wheelchair users on ground floor of tea-room. WC in garden. Wheelchair available

◉ Braille and large-print guides; some items, including fabric samples, may be touched

◖ Tea-room in 18th-century barn. Teas, as house, 1.30–5.30. Light lunches BH Mon, also Sun July & Aug, from 1. Christmas shop & tea-room open 2 Nov to 21 Dec: Sun 1.30–4.30. Other times for parties by prior arrangement. Licensed. Seating for 54

⌁ Highchair available in tea-room

▨ Education programme includes living history

➔ (5: G5) 4ml N of Wolverhampton; S of M54 between A449 and A460; traffic from N on M6 leave motorway at exit 11, then A460; traffic from S on M6 & M54 take exit 1; coaches must approach via A460 to avoid low bridge [127: SJ932044] *Bus:* Midland Red 870–2 Wolverhampton–Cannock, alight Bognop Road, ¾ml; Travel West Midlands 613 from Wolverhampton, thence ¾ml (all pass close ⌦ Wolverhampton) (tel. 0121 200 2700) *Station:* Wolverhampton 4ml

---

NEWARK PARK ▥ ⛶   *Gloucestershire*

Ozleworth, Wotton-under-Edge GL12 7PZ Tel: 01453 842644

A Tudor hunting lodge, converted into a castellated country house by James Wyatt and of specialist architectural interest

Note: The property is let and the tenant, Mr M. Claydon, is responsible for the showing arrangements

◯ House open in April, May, Aug & Sept: Wed & Thur 2–5

£ £2. No reduction for parties. Car park. Not suitable for coaches. No WC

➔ (5: G10) 1½ml E of Wotton-under-Edge, 1¾ml S of junction of A4135 & B4058 [172: ST786934] *Bus:* Badgerline 309 Bristol–Dursley, alight Wotton-under-Edge, 1¾ml. Frequent services link ⌦ Bristol Temple Meads with the bus station (tel. 0117 955 3231) *Station:* Stroud 10ml

---

THE OLD MANOR ▥ ▤ ✚ ✿   *Derbyshire*

Norbury, Ashbourne DE6 2ED

A stone-built hall, dating from the 13th to 15th centuries and of specialist architectural interest only. The adjacent church (not NT) is also worth visiting

◯ Medieval hall by written appointment only with the tenant, Mr C. Wright. 1 April to end Sept: Tues, Wed & Sat

£ £1.50

➔ (5: H4) *Bus:* Stevensons 409 Uttoxeter–Ashbourne (passing close ⌦ Uttoxeter), alight Ellastone, ¾ml (tel. 01332 292200) *Station:* Uttoxeter (U) 7½ml

PACKWOOD HOUSE 🏠 ❖ 🚶 ❤️   *Warwickshire*

Lapworth, Solihull B94 6AT Tel: 01564 782024

The house, originally 16th-century, is a fascinating 20th-century evocation of domestic Tudor architecture. Created by Graham Baron Ash, its interiors reflect the period between the world wars and contain a fine collection of 16th-century textiles and furniture. The gardens have renowned herbaceous borders and a famous collection of yews

🅾️ 1 March to 22 March: car park only, Sat & Sun 12–4; 25 March to end Sept: daily except Mon & Tues (but closed Good Fri and open BH Mon) car park opens 12, garden 1.30–6, house 2–6. Oct & 1 Nov: daily except Mon & Tues 12.30–4.30, car park opens 12. Last admission 30min before closing. **Events:** 7 June, Teddy Bears' Picnic; July, 1920s Summer Follies; tel. bookings from 1 April. For full summer events leaflet please send s.a.e. to Property Manager

💷 £4.20; family ticket £10.30. Garden only £2.10. Car park £2, refunded on entry to house & garden. Walks available through parkland and woodland. Picnic site in avenue opposite main gates. Timed tickets may be in operation at busy times

🛍️ Shop open as house

♿ Access to ground floor (except great hall which can be seen from door) and part of garden.Wheelchairs available. WC (in car park) with handrails, otherwise unadapted. Shop inaccessible to wheelchair users. Visitors with disabilities are invited to contact the property before a visit to make special arrangements

👁️ Braille guide. Tactile tour. Yew trees and hedges may be touched

🏫 School parties by appointment Wed, Thur & Fri mornings

➡️ (**5:** H7) 2ml E of Hockley Heath (on A3400), 11ml SE of central Birmingham [139: SP174722] *Bus:* Stagecoach Midland Red X20 Birmingham–Stratford-upon-Avon, alight Hockley Heath, 1½ml (tel. 0121 200 2700) *Station:* Lapworth (U), 1½ml; Birmingham International 8ml

PRIEST'S HOUSE 🏠   *Northamptonshire*

Easton on the Hill, nr Stamford

A pre-Reformation priest's lodge, of special architectural interest and containing a small museum of village bygones

🅾️ By appointment only. Please tel. Regional Office 01909 486411

💷 Donation of 50p requested. Unsuitable for coaches

♿ Ground-floor room only

➡️ (**5:** M5) Approx. 2ml SW of Stamford off A43 [141: TF011045] *Bus:* Road Car 180, Blands, First Choice Travel from Stamford (passing close ≋ Stamford), alight Easton, ½ml (tel. 01522 553135) *Station:* Stamford 2ml

PRIORY COTTAGES 🏠 *Oxfordshire*

1 Mill Street, Steventon, Abingdon OX13 6SP
Tel: (Coleshill Estate Office) 01793 762209

Former monastic buildings, now converted into two houses. South Cottage contains the Great Hall of the original priory

O **The Great Hall in South Cottage only:** April to end Sept: Wed 2–6; by written appointment with tenant

£ £1. No reduction for parties. No WC. Unsuitable for coach parties

➔ (5: J10) 4ml S of Abingdon, on B4017 off A34 at Abingdon West or Milton interchange on corner of The Causeway and Mill Street, entrance in Mill Street [164: SU466914] *Bus:* Thames Transit 32/A, Cityline 35A Oxford–🚇 Didcot Parkway (passing close 🚇 Oxford) (tel. 01865 772250)
Station: Didcot Parkway 5ml

SHUGBOROUGH ESTATE 🏠 🏡 🍽 ✿ ♠ 🔭 🐾 *Staffordshire*

Milford, nr Stafford ST17 0XB Tel: 01889 881388 Fax: 01889 881323

The magnificent seat of the Earls of Lichfield, now being restored as a 19th-century working estate. The late 17th-century house was enlarged c.1750 and again at the turn of the 19th century, and contains interesting collections of china, silver, paintings and furniture. The stable block houses the original kitchens and there is a working farm museum and formal terraced gardens

Note: Shugborough is financed and administered by Staffordshire County Council. NT members are entitled to free entry to the House, reduced rate to County Museum & Farm but must pay site admission charge per vehicle and any special event charge which may be in operation. Admission charges and opening arrangements may vary when special events are held. Tel. property for details of 1998 events programme

O **House, County Museum, Farm & Gardens:** 28 March to 25 Oct: daily 11–5 until 27 Sept; Suns only in Oct. Open daily all year from 10.30 for booked parties. (County Museum, Farm, Gardens and tours of house: tel. property for details). **Events:** a wide range of events, incl. open-air concerts, theatre and themed activities, Christmas evenings and craft festivals take place from Easter to Dec; civil wedding ceremonies can be arranged; please tel. for details

£ Parkland £1.50 per vehicle (NT members incl.), coaches free, giving access to parkland, gardens, picnic area and walks and trails. Free car park at Farm for Farm visitors. House £3.50 (NT members free), concessions £2.50; Farm £3.50 (NT members and concessions £2.50); County Museum £3.50 (NT members and concessions £2.50); all sites £8 (concessions £6). *Note:* concessions apply to children, OAPs, registered unemployed and parties. Guided walks and trails for booked parties throughout the year £3 per head. Evening visits for booked parties: prices on request. Guided tours available for school parties at £2 per head per site (2 sites for £3); working demonstrations available from Oct to Easter £2.50–£5; schools must book in advance

K Available throughout year; evening guided tours and garden tours also available. Range of connoisseur talks and tours designed for special-interest groups

🛍 NT shop at main site (tel. 01889 882122). Open 28 March to 27 Sept: daily 11–5. NT shop also open 28 Sept to 23 Dec: daily (except Sat) 11–4

♿ County Museum and Farm accessible (reduced admission charge); access can be arranged to ground floor of house for wheelchairs using stepclimber. WC. Some staff have been trained in basic sign language. Tours and demonstrations can be adapted to your special needs. Self-drive powered vehicles and wheelchairs available for park and garden; accessible picnic tables

👁 Braille, taped and large-print guides; rose garden

🍽 Lunches, high teas and snacks in Lady Walk Restaurant on main site; dinners available to pre-booked parties (min. 15). Tea-room at farm for light refreshments open as house. Picnic sites by main and farm car parks. Main site car park picnic area features special picnic tables for wheelchair users

👶 Farm gives children chance to see and touch domestic and rare breeds of animal and poultry. Games gallery in corn mill. Children's play area. Extensive puppet collection in County Museum. Highchairs; baby-changing facilities

🏫 Extensive schools and adult demonstration programme. Education rooms can be booked at each of the three sites

🐕 On leads in parkland only. Guide dogs admitted to house and County Museum

→ (5: G4) Signposted from M6 exit 13; 6ml E of Stafford on A513; entrance at Milford. Pedestrian access from E, from the canal/Little Haywood side of the Estate [127: SJ992225] *Bus:* Midland Red 825 ⭤ Stafford–Tamworth (passing close ⭤ Lichfield City) (tel. 01785 223344) *Station:* Stafford 6ml

SNOWSHILL MANOR 🏠 ❋ 🛡 *Gloucestershire*

Snowshill, nr Broadway WR12 7JU Tel: 01386 852410

A Cotswold Tudor manor house, best known for Charles Paget Wade's extraordinary collections of craftmanship and design, including musical instruments, clocks, toys, bicycles, weavers' and spinners' tools and Japanese armour. His own cottage and charming garden can also be visited

Note: The manor is a 10min walk (500m) along an undulating country path; a buggy is available to assist the elderly and visitors with disabilities

🅾 1 April to 1 Nov: daily except Tues 1–5 (but closed Good Fri). **Grounds & visitor facilities** open at 12. **Grounds & shop** open till 5.30 May to Sept. Last admission to house 45min before closing. Timed tickets will be issued for the house. **Events:** please tel. for details

£ £5.50; family ticket £13.80. Grounds, restaurant & shop £2.50. Coach and school parties by prior written appointment only. Photography only by prior written arrangement with Curator

🛍 Shop open same days as house 12–5 (to 5.30 May to Sept). Also 7 Nov to 13 Dec: Sat & Sun 12.30–4.30

♿ Access to visitor facilities but house and grounds unsuitable (see note above regarding buggy). WC

⚑ Braille guide for house and description of garden; audiotape

⌨ Restaurant open for coffees, lunches & teas on same days as house 12–5. Also Nov & Dec as shop. No picnics. Tel. 01386 858685

⚖ No pushchairs or back carriers allowed in house. Parent & baby room

→ (5: H8) 2½ml SW of Broadway, approach only from turning off the A44 by Broadway Green [150: SP096339] *Bus:* Thames Trains buslink ⚭ Moreton-in-Marsh–⚭ Evesham (June–Sept) (tel. 0345 484950); otherwise Castleways ⚭ Evesham–Broadway, thence 2½ml (tel. 01242 602949)
Station: Moreton-in-Marsh 7ml

STAINSBY MILL: HARDWICK ESTATE ⚙   *Derbyshire*

Doe Lea, Chesterfield S44 5QJ Tel: 01246 850430 Fax: 01246 854200

A remarkably complete water-powered flour mill, with newly reconstructed 1849-50 machinery and still in good working order

What's new in 1998: Tail race wall repaired

◎ 1 April to 1 Nov: Wed, Thurs, Sat, Sun & BH Mon 11–4.30; June, July, Aug & Sept also open Fri 11–4.30. Last admission 4. **Events:** 10 May, National Mills Day

£ £1.50, children 70p; family ticket £3.70. Children under 15 must be accompanied by an adult. Parties (no reduction) by prior arrangement only with Property Manager, Hardwick Hall. *Note:* No WC at mill, but available at Hardwick Hall car park

⚙ On request at the mill. Private out-of-hours tours available, please contact Property Manager

☂ Available at Hardwick Hall

♿ Limited access to ground floor only; no wheelchairs available

⚑ Panelling and millstones on display may be touched. Braille guide

⌨ Refreshments available at Hardwick Hall

■ School parties Wed & Thurs only, plus Fri in June to Sept. Please send s.a.e. to Property Manager at Hardwick Hall for further information

🐾 In park only, on leads. Not in Mill

→ (5: J2) From M1 exit 29 take A6175 signposted to Clay Cross then first left and left again to Stainsby Mill *Bus:* As for Hardwick Hall, but, except for the C1, alight Heath, thence 1ml (1½ml on X2) *Station:* Chesterfield 7ml

STAUNTON HAROLD CHURCH ✠ ♠   *Leicestershire*

Staunton Harold, Ashby-de-la-Zouch Tel: 01332 863822 Fax: 01332 865272

One of the very few churches built during the Commonwealth, set in attractive parkland. The interior retains its original 17th-century cushions and has fine panelling and painted ceilings

Note: A voluntary vehicle charge may be requested on busy summer Sundays and Bank Holidays, at which times a one-way system will be in operation on the estate. No coaches allowed due to limited parking

O 1 April to end Sept: Sat to Wed & BH Mon (closed Good Fri) 1–5 or sunset if earlier; Oct: Sat & Sun only 1–5

£ Donations of £1 requested, collection box. WCs (not NT) 300m

♿ Church and park largely accessible; no wheelchair available

▣ Light refreshments available at Hall (Sue Ryder Foundation)

➔ (**5:** J4) 5ml NE of Ashby-de-la-Zouch, W of B587. Access from M42/A42, jct13 [128: SK379208] *Bus:* City Rider 68/9; Derby Integrated 69B Derby–Swadlincote (passing close ⭍ Derby), alight Melbourne, 3½ml or Ticknall via Calke Park, 3ml (tel. 01332 292200)

MR STRAW'S HOUSE 🏠 ♥   *Nottinghamshire*

7 Blyth Grove, Worksop S81 0JG Tel: 01909 482380

This modest semi-detached Edwardian house provides a fascinating insight into everyday life in the early part of the 20th century. The interior has remained unaltered since the 1930s and features contemporary wallpaper, Victorian furniture and household objects. There are also displays of family memorabilia and a typical suburban garden

Note: Blyth Grove is a private road; there is no access without booking in advance. There is a car park with picnic area opposite the house for visitors with timed tickets. On arrival please go to reception at 5 Blyth Grove

O 1 April to 1 Nov: daily except Sun & Mon (but closed Good Fri) 11–4.30. Last admission 4. Admission for all visitors (incl. NT members) by pre-booked timed ticket only. All bookings by telephone or letter (s.a.e. please) to Custodian. **Events:** please contact Custodian

£ £3.50, children £1.70; family ticket £8.70. *Note:* Guided tours for groups (max. 16) may be arranged on Wed & Fri mornings only (£15 extra per group, incl. NT members)

♿ Wheelchair access not possible

👁 Access advisable outside peak viewing times, as house is small and quickly becomes congested; please telephone in advance. Braille guide; audio cassette; some items may be touched

➔ (**5:** K2) In Worksop, follow signs to Bassetlaw General Hospital. House signposted from Blyth Road (B6045) [120: SK590802] *Bus:* From surrounding areas (tel. 0115 9240000) *Station:* Worksop ½ml

223

SUDBURY HALL 🏠 ❖ 🛡 *Derbyshire*

Sudbury, Ashbourne DE6 5HT Tel: 01283 585305 Fax: 01283 585139

One of the most individual of late 17th-century houses, with rich interior decoration including wood carving by Gibbons, superb plasterwork, and mythological decorative ceilings by Laguerre. The Great Staircase is one of the finest of its kind in an English house

Note: Owing to low light levels, visitors wishing to study the Hall's plasterwork or paintings in detail should avoid dull days and late afternoons towards end of season

🅾 1 April to 1 Nov: daily except Mon & Tues, but open BH Mon (closed Good Fri) 1–5.30 or sunset if earlier. Opening times change to 12.30–5 on Sat & Sun and on all open days during July & Aug; last admission 30min before closing. Grounds open 12.30–6. Note: New visitor car park 400m from Hall (please do not park in road). No WC in car park. **Events**: details of concerts and special events from the Administrator (s.a.e. please)

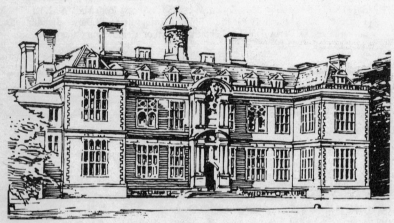

💷 Hall £3.50, children £1.60; family ticket £8.60; joint individual ticket for Hall & Museum £5.50, child £2.70; joint family ticket £13.70. All party bookings by prior arrangement with the Bookings Secretary

🧍 Guided and specialist tours available; contact Administrator

🏬 Shop open as Hall. Also Nov to 20 Dec: Sat & Sun only 12–4

♿ Parking in visitor car park. Multi-seater volunteer-driven buggy. Hall and garden difficult. Lake, tea-room and shop accessible; one wheelchair available for inside use only; for entrance arrangements, please contact Administrator. WC in Stable Block (see following entry); Sympathetic Hearing Scheme

👁 Braille guide

🍴 Coach House tea-room open same days as house 12.30–5.30 (last orders 5); also Nov to 20 Dec: Sat & Sun 12–4. Seats 68. Coaches by appointment only, booking form by written application (s.a.e. please)

224

🚼 Changing facilities in Stable Block; children's portions available in tea-room

▣ Special facilities linked to National Curriculum for pre-booked school parties, by arrangement with Education Officer (tel. 01283 585022)

♿ In visitor car park only

➔ (5: H4) 6ml E of Uttoxeter at jct of A50 Derby–Stoke and A515 Ashbourne [128: SK160323] *Bus:* Stevensons 401 Burton-on-Trent–Uttoxeter (passing ⊞ Tutbury & Hatton and close ⊞ Burton-on-Trent (tel. 01332 292200) *Station:* Tutbury & Hatton (U) 5ml

---

SUDBURY HALL – THE NATIONAL TRUST MUSEUM OF CHILDHOOD 🏛 𝘟 🛡 *Derbyshire*

As Sudbury Hall

Housed in the 19th-century service wing of Sudbury Hall, the Museum contains fascinating and innovative displays about children from the 18th century onwards. There are chimney climbs for the adventurous 'sweep-sized' youngster, and Betty Cadbury's fine collection of toys and dolls is on show

🔘 1 April to 1 Nov: daily except Mon & Tues, but open BH Mon (closed Good Fri) 1–5.30 or sunset if earlier; opening times change to 12.30–5 on Sat & Sun and on all open days during July & Aug. Also open Nov to 20 Dec: Sat & Sun 12–4. Last admission 30min before closing. **Events:** special events and activities for children; details from Education Officer (s.a.e. please)

💷 Museum & Garden £3.50, children £1.60; family ticket £8.60. Joint individual ticket for Hall & Museum £5.50, child £2.70; joint family ticket £13.70. Party bookings by arrangement with the Bookings Secretary

𝘟 Guided tours available; contact Administrator

🛍 Shop open as Hall; also Nov to 20 Dec, Sat & Sun 12–4

♿ Most of Museum accessible. Wheelchair available for inside use only. WC in Stable Block

👆 Museum items, such as toys, glove puppets, games and puzzles, may be touched

🍽 Coach House tea-room open same days as Museum 12.30–5.30 (last orders 5); also Nov to 20 Dec, Sat & Sun 12–4. Coaches by appointment only, by written application (s.a.e. please). Seats 68

🚼 Baby-changing facilities; baby back carriers accepted; pushchairs difficult

▣ Educational materials available. Special facilities for schools as for Sudbury Hall

♿ In car park only

➔ (5: H4) 6ml E of Uttoxeter at jct of A50 Derby–Stoke and A515 Ashbourne road [128:SK160323] *Bus:* Stevensons 401 Burton-on-Trent–Uttoxeter (passing ⊞ Tutbury & Hatton and close ⊞ Burton-on-Trent) (tel. 01332 292200) *Station:* Tutbury & Hatton (U) 5ml

TOWN WALLS TOWER 🏠 *Shropshire*

Shrewsbury SY1 1TN Tel: (Regional Office) 01743 709343

Shrewsbury's last remaining watchtower, built in the 14th century and overlooking the River Severn

🅾 By written appointment only with the tenant, Mr A. A. Hector, Tower House, 26a Town Walls, Shrewsbury SY1 1TN

➔ (5: F5) A few mins walk from town centre, on S of Town Walls *Bus:* From surrounding areas (tel. 0345 056785) *Station:* Shrewsbury ½ml

ULVERSCROFT NATURE RESERVE 🐦 *Leicestershire*

nr Loughborough   Tel: (Regional Office) 01909 486411 Fax: 01909 486377

Part of the ancient forest of Charnwood, especially beautiful in spring during the bluebell season

🅾 Access by permit only, from The Secretary, Leicestershire & Rutland Trust for Nature Conservation, Leicester LE1 6UU

➔ (5: K5) *Bus:* Midland Fox 109, 117–9, 217/8 Leicester–Swadlincote (passing close ≊ Leicester) (tel. 0116 251 1411) *Station:* Barrow upon Soar 7ml, Loughborough 7½ml

UPTON HOUSE 🏠 ❊ 🛡 *Warwickshire*

Banbury OX15 6HT Tel: 01295 670266

The house, built in 1695 of mellow local stone, contains an outstanding collection of English and Continental Old Masters, tapestries, procelain, Chelsea figures and 18th-century furniture. The garden is also very fine, with terraces, herbaceous borders, kitchen garden, ornamental pools and an interesting 1930's water garden.

Note: Entry to house by timed tickets at peak times on Sun & BHols, when delays are possible

🅾 4 April to 1 Nov: daily except Thur & Fri (incl. BH Mon) 2–6. Closed Good Fri. Last admission 5.30 (5 after 25 Oct). **Events:** fine arts study tours, jazz concert and other events; please send s.a.e. or tel. for details

💷 £5; family ticket £12.50. Garden only £2.50. Parties of 15+ by written arrangement. Free parking

🎭 Evening guided tours by written arrangement

🛍 Shop open as house. Plant and garden produce on sale (when available) by admission kiosk

♿ Access to ground-floor rooms via ramped side door, tea-room and part of garden. Access to lower floor (avoiding stairs) can be provided by prior arrangement. Wheelchair available for use in house. WC. Parking near house for disabled drivers. Motorised buggy with driver available for access to/from lower garden

⬛ Braille guide

⬛ Tea-room in house. Last teas 5.30; 5 on weekdays in April & Oct

⬛ Parent & baby room

➜ **(5: J8)** On A422, 7ml NW of Banbury, 12ml SE of Stratford-upon-Avon [151: SP371461] *Bus:* Midland Red X70, 270 from Banbury (tel. 01788 535555) *Station:* Banbury 7ml

WALL ROMAN SITE (LETOCETUM BATHS & MUSEUM)
🏛️ 🛡️ *Staffordshire*

Watling Street, Wall, nr Lichfield WS14 0AW Tel: 01543 480768

The excavated bathhouse of a Roman posting station on Watling Street, and the most complete example of its kind. An interesting museum displays local finds

Note: Letocetum is in the guardianship of English Heritage

⬛ 1 April to 31 Oct: daily 10–6 or dusk if earlier (closed for lunch 1–2). Closed in winter. **Events:** send s.a.e. to property for details

£ Museum & site £1.75, children 90p. OAPs and UB40 holders £1.30 (all prices provisional). Parties of 11 or more 15% discount. School bookings (tel. 01604 730325)

⬛ Informal talk given in museum for small parties only, on prior request

⬛ Open same times as property

♿ Access to museum only. Site on uneven ground

⬛ Audiotape available at small extra charge

⬛ Free entry for education groups who book 14 days in advance

🐕 On leads only

➜ **(5: H5)** 2ml SW of Lichfield, on N side of A5 [139: SK099067] *Station:* Shenstone 1½ml

THE WEIR 🏵️
Herefordshire

Swainshill, nr Hereford HR4 8BS

A delightful riverside garden, particularly spectacular in early spring and with fine views over the River Wye and Black Mountains

⬛ 14 Feb to 1 Nov: Wed to Sun (incl. Good Fri) & BH Mon 11–6

£ £1.80; free car park (unsuitable for coaches). No WC

♿ Not advisable for wheelchair users

🐕 In car park only (no shade or water)

→ **(5: E8)** 5ml W of Hereford on A438 [149: SO435421] *Bus:* Yeoman's Canyon 446 from Hereford; otherwise Midland Red West 101 Hereford–Credenhill (both passing close ⇌ Hereford), thence 1½ml (tel. 0345 125436) *Station:* Hereford 5ml

WESTBURY COURT GARDEN ✿ ☻   *Gloucestershire*

Westbury-on-Severn GL14 1PD Tel: 01452 760461

A rare and beautiful survival: a formal water garden, laid out 1696-1705 and the earliest of its kind remaining in England. It was restored in 1971 and is planted with species dating from before 1700

◉ 1 April to 1 Nov: daily except Mon & Tues (but open BH Mon and closed Good Fri) 11–6. Other months by appointment only. **Events:** Pillowell Silver Band concert; please contact property for details

£ £2.70. Free car park. Parties of 15 or more by written arrangement. Picnic area

♿ Most parts of garden accessible; wheelchair available. WC

❀ Scented plants; Braille guide

🐕 Strictly no dogs except guide dogs

→ **(5: F9)** 9ml SW of Gloucester on A48 [162: SO718138] *Bus:* Stagecoach Red & White 73 ⇌ Gloucester–Newport (passing close ⇌ Newport); 31 ⇌ Gloucester–Coleford (tel. 01633 266336) *Station:* Gloucester 9ml

WICHENFORD DOVECOTE ⌂   *Worcestershire*

Wichenford

A 17th-century half-timbered black and white dovecote

◉ April to 1 Nov: daily 9–6 or sunset if earlier. Closed Good Fri. Other times by prior appointment only with Regional Office (tel. 01684 850051)

£ 60p

→ **(5: G7)** 5½ml NW of Worcester, N of B4204 [150: SO788598] *Bus:* Midland Red West 310/2/3 from Worcester (passing close ⇌ Worcester Foregate Street), alight Wichenford, ½ml (tel. 0345 125436) *Station:* Worcester Foregate Street 7ml; Worcester Shrub Hill 7½ml

WIGHTWICK MANOR 🏠 ❈ 🚹 🎭   *Wolverhampton*

Wightwick Bank, Wolverhampton WV6 8EE
Tel: 01902 761108 Fax: 01902 764663

One of only a few surviving examples of a house built and furnished under the influence of the Arts and Crafts Movement. The many original William Morris wallpapers and fabrics, Pre-Raphaelite paintings, Kempe glass and de Morgan ware help conjure up the spirit of the time. An attractive garden reflects the style and character of the house

O **House:** 1 March to 31 Dec and March 1999: Thur & Sat 2.30–5.30. Also open BH Sat, Sun & Mon 2.30–5.30 (ground floor only, no guided tours). Open for pre-booked parties Wed & Thur and special evening tours. Admission to house by timed ticket, issued from 2 at front door. Owing to the fragile nature of contents and the requirements of conservation, some rooms cannot always be shown; tours will therefore vary during the year. School visits on Wed & Thur, contact Property Manager for details. **Garden:** Wed & Thur 11–6; Sat, BH Sun & BH Mon 1–6. Other days by appointment. **Events:** details from Property Manager; please send s.a.e.

£ £5.20. Students £2.60. Garden only £2.40. Parking: only room for one coach in lay-by outside main gate; car park (120m) at bottom of Wightwick Bank (please do **not** park in Elmsdale opposite the property)

🚹 Except BHols

🛍 William Morris Arts & Crafts shop open Wed and Thur 11–5.30; Sat, BH Sun & BH Mon 1–5.30. Pottery (not NT) open as shop. *Note:* the William Morris shop, tea-room and pottery are open to the general public, independent of visiting the house and garden

♿ Access (via steps to ground floor) to 5 rooms & garden (but site slopes; strong companions necessary). No wheelchairs available. Ring for parking advice

◉ Braille guides to house and Pre-Raphaelite collection

☕ Tea-room open as shop

🖼 Pre-booked school visits; details from Property Manager

🐕 In garden only, on leads

➔ (5: G5) 3ml W of Wolverhampton, up Wightwick Bank (off A454 beside the Mermaid Inn) [139: SO869985] *Bus:* Midland Red 890 Wolverhampton–Bridgnorth; 516 Wolverhampton–Pattingham (both pass close 🚉 Wolverhampton) (tel. 0121 200 2700) *Station:* Wolverhampton 3ml

WILDERHOPE MANOR 🏠 ⛵ 🚹   *Shropshire*

Longville, Much Wenlock TF13 6EG Tel: 01694 771363

A gabled and unspoilt manor house, dating from 1586 and with fine views. Although unfurnished, the interior is of interest for its remarkable wooden spiral staircase and fine plaster ceilings. There is a circular walk through farmland and woods

⊙ April to end Sept: Wed & Sat 2–4.30. Oct to end March 1999: Sat only 2–4.30

£ £1. No reduction for parties

🛍 YHA shop

♿ Access to house via steep section of path (strong companion needed) then ground floor accessible. Shop (not NT) accessible

☕ Tea and coffee available

🏛 Field Study Centre run by YHA

🐕 On leads in area around Manor

➔ (5: F6) 7ml SW of Much Wenlock, 7ml E of Church Stretton, ½ml S of B4371 [138: SO545929] *Station:* Church Stretton (U) 8ml

---

WINSTER MARKET HOUSE 🏠 *Derbyshire*

nr Matlock | Tel: 01335 350245

A market house of the late 17th or early 18th century, now restored and housing a NT information room

⊙ 29 March to end Oct: open daily

£ Free. Public WC in side street near house

➔ (5: H3) 4ml W of Matlock on S side of B5057 in main street of Winster [119: SK241606] *Bus:* Hulley's 170/2 Matlock–Bakewell (passing close ⊞ Matlock) (tel. 01332 292200) *Station:* Matlock (U) 4ml

---

WOODCHESTER PARK 🌳 ♿ 🚶 *Gloucestershire*

The Warden's Office, Old Ebworth Centre, Ebworth Estate, The Camp, Stroud GL6 7ES Tel: 01452 814213

This secret wooded valley, formerly an 18th-century park with five lakes, was first opened to the public in 1996. There are waymarked trails (steep and strenuous in places) through delightful scenery with spectacular views

Note: Woodchester Mansion is not NT; for details, please contact the Woodchester Mansion Trust, tel. 01453 860661

⊙ Park open daily; March & April: 9–5; May to Sept: 9–8; Oct to March 1999: 9–5

£ Car park £1 (NT members free). Last admission to car park 1hr before closing

🐕 Dogs are welcome on leads

➔ (5: G10) 4ml SW of Stroud off B4066 Stroud–Dursley road; NT car park accessible from Nympsfield road, 300m from the junction with B4066 [162:SO797012] *Station:* Stroud 5ml

Introduction to the North West

The North West of England contains some of Britain's most impressive scenery. The dramatic grandeur of the Lake District offers unparalleled opportunites for walking in virtually pristine landscapes. In the south of the area, the urban centres of Manchester and Liverpool have good access to unspoilt countryside and splendid country houses, as well as to interesting reminders of the area's industrial heritage.

The Trust is responsible for the conservation and management of approximately one quarter of the Lake District National Park, including England's highest mountain, Scafell Pike, her deepest lake, Wastwater, and over 90 farms. Almost all of the central fell area and major valley heads are owned or held on lease by the Trust, and six of the main lakes and much of their shoreline are also fully protected. These 50,000ha (123,500 acres) constitute almost one quarter of the Trust's entire holding across England, Wales and Northern Ireland.

In addition to the main Lake District properties, all detailed within this Handbook, the Trust also cares for many other sites across the area. These include the prehistoric site of **Castlerigg Stone Circle**, a free-standing megalithic circle of thirty-eight stones near Keswick, and the medieval **Keld Chapel** near Shap. There are delightful walks through **Wetheral Woods**, along the River Eden near Carlisle, and in the south near Barrow is **Sandscale Haws**. This expanse of dunes and marshes is an internationally renowned nature reserve harbouring the rare natterjack toad and over 500 species of wild flower. A further stretch of important coastline is the **Solway Commons** in the far north west, offering magnificent views across the Solway Firth to Scotland.

The Trust also owns key properties along the Lancashire coast, including **Heysham Head** and **Jack Scout**, clifftop land on the fringe of Morecambe Bay. **Arnside Knott**, just inside Cumbria, is renowned for its butterflies, and the Silverdale properties of **Eaves and Waterslack Woods**, where there is a 2 mile self-guided walk through beautiful woodland, and **Lambert's Meadow**, wet meadowland rich in plants and invertebrates, offer much of interest. In east Lancashire the **Stubbins Estate** and **Holcombe Moor** serve as an important green lung to the North Manchester conurbation and are noted for their numerous bird species. Equally important for wildlife are the sand dunes and pinewoods at **Formby**, and the ancient woodland of **Stocktons Wood**, part of the historic landscape surrounding the magnificent **Speke Hall**.

Across the Mersey, the Wirral peninsula has a 12 mile-long country park, several parts of which are owned by the Trust. **Caldy Hill** gives spectacular views across the mouth of the River Dee, home to a wide variety of wildfowl and waders, some of which congregate here in huge numbers. At **Thurstaston Common** there is a rare surviving fragment of acid heathland, rich in insect life. To the south east lies **Helsby Hill**, from the summit of which there are breathtaking views over the Mersey and the mountains of North Wales.

Several of the Trust's beauty spots in the south of the area are very near the great industrial conurbations of Liverpool and Manchester. The wooded sandstone escarpment of **Alderley Edge** gives fine views over the Cheshire Plain. A path from here links up with neighbouring **Hare Hill Garden**. Nearby **Styal Country Park** offers both pleasant riverside walks and much historic interest at **Quarry Bank Mill** and the factory colony village of Styal. There is another interesting watermill at **Nether Alderley**. Some of the area's most impressive country houses are also to be found on the fringes of Manchester, including **Lyme Park**, **Tatton Park** and **Dunham Massey**.

The south of the area runs towards the Welsh border and comprises beautiful mixed woodland, heathland and fields, with excellent walking opportunities. **Bickerton Hill** lies at the southern tip of the Peckforton Hills, a wooded ridge crossed by a 30 mile-long footpath, the Sandstone Trail, which passes a variety of dwellings from black-and-white cottages to prehistoric hill-forts.

Highlights for Disabled Visitors

Both **Tarn Hows** and **Borrowdale** have accessible routes; at Restharrow on the shores of **Windermere** there is a holiday cottage which has been adapted for disabled visitors (tel. 01225 791133 for details).

... and for Families

Particularly recommended are **Fell Foot Park and Garden** and the steam yacht *Gondola* on Coniston Water.

Further Information

NT Regional Offices:

- **North West** (tel. 015394 35599) – for properties in Cumbria and Lancashire.
- **Mercia** (tel. 01743 709343) – for properties in Cheshire and Liverpool/ Manchester area.

Please contact the North West office for a free copy of the NT Countryside Guide to the North West, sponsored by Barclays, which gives full details of a range of Trust countryside properties in Cumbria and Lancashire (please send s.a.e.).

A leaflet detailing boat and fishing opportunities on Trust-managed waters in the Lake District is available from local NT information centres or the North West Regional Office, as is information detailing cycle routes in the Borrowdale area; another leaflet lists car parks where NT members can park free (please send s.a.e.).

From April to October the Trust organises Landscape Tours by minibus, half day excursions designed to introduce visitors to the landscape of the Lake District and to the Trust's work in protecting this landscape. Please contact the North West Regional Office for details.

SIZERGH CASTLE

ACORN BANK GARDEN AND WATER-MILL ❊ ♥ *Cumbria*

Temple Sowerby, nr Penrith CA10 1SP Tel: 017683 61893

Ancient oaks and the high enclosing walls of this delightful 17th-century garden keep out the worst of the Cumbrian climate, resulting in a spectacular display of shrubs, roses and herbaceous borders. Sheltered orchards contain a variety of traditional fruit trees and the famous herb garden is the largest collection of medicinal and culinary plants in the North. A circular woodland walk runs along Crowdundle Beck to Acorn Bank water-mill, which although under restoration, is open to visitors. The house is not open to the public

O 28 March to 1 Nov: daily 10–5.30. Last admission 5.
Events: 28 May, newt-watching; 18 Oct, Apple Day

£ £2.20, children £1.10; family ticket £5.80. Pre-arranged parties £1.60 per person. Car-parking

🛍 Small shop and plants for sale, open 28 March to 30 Sept, same times as garden. From 1 Oct to 1 Nov: daily 12–4

♿ Access to herb garden, herbaceous borders, greenhouse & shop; to water-mill via level path from car park, suitable for wheelchair users with strong companions. Upper information room accessible. Wheelchair available. WC

◉ Herbs, sounds of water from beck. Braille guide

🚼 Baby-changing facilities, children's quiz sheet

🐕 Admitted on leads to woodland walk, but not to walled garden

➜ **(6:** E5) Just N of Temple Sowerby, 6ml E of Penrith on A66 [91: NY612281] *Bus:* Stagecoach Cumberland 100 Penrith–Appleby (passes close ⊞ Penrith & ⊞ Appleby) (tel. 01946 63222) *Station:* Langwathby (U) 5ml; Penrith 6ml

---

BEATRIX POTTER GALLERY 🖼 *Cumbria*

Main Street, Hawkshead LA22 0NS Tel: 015394 36355

An annually changing exhibition of original sketches and watercolours from the celebrated children's stories. One of many historic buildings in this picturesque village, this was once the office of the author's husband, William Heelis. The interior remains substantially unaltered since his day

O 1 April to 1 Nov: Sun to Thur (closed Fri and Sat except Good Fri) 10.30–4.30. Last admission 4. Admission is by timed ticket (incl. NT members)

£ £2.80, children £1.40. No reduction for parties. Car- and coach-parking in village car park, 200m

🛍 Shop (30m) open 1 April to 24 Dec: daily 9.30–5.30. Out of season: daily except Thur & Fri 9.30–5 (tel. 015394 36471 to check)

♿ We regret Gallery unsuitable for wheelchairs

◉ Braille guide

◉ Available in Hawkshead

🚼 Children's quiz sheet and guidebook on Beatrix Potter. We regret the Gallery is not suitable for baby back carriers or pushchairs

➡ (6: C7) In The Square [96: SD352982] *Bus:* Stagecoach Cumberland 505/6 Ambleside–Coniston (connections from ⛟ Windermere) (tel. 01946 63222) *Station:* Windermere 6½ml via ferry

---

BORROWDALE 🌳 🏊 🚶   *Cumbria*

Tel: (Regional Office) 015394 35599 Fax: (Regional Office) 015394 35353

The location of the Trust's first acquisition in the Lake District: Brandelhow Woods, on the shore of Derwentwater. Total NT ownership in the area today amounts to 11,806ha (29,173 acres), including eleven farms, half of Derwentwater (including the main islands), the hamlets of Watendlath and Stonethwaite, and well-known sites such as the Bowder Stone, Friar's Crag and Ashness Bridge

What's new in 1998: Boat trips to Derwent Island in Derwentwater to see 18th-century house and restored garden: on Sun 17 May, Sun 7 June, Wed 22 July, Sun 16 Aug and Sun 20 Sept. Free admission to house and island (charge for non-members), charge for boat trip (incl. members). For booking form send s.a.e. to Regional Office

🅾 All year. Information Centre at Keswick Lakeside, open April to end Oct: daily 10–5; also some winter weekends, tel. 017687 73780 for details

£ Six pay-and-display car parks in valley (NT members free)

📕 Guided walks available; please tel. Regional Office for details

🏠 Shop in Information Centre at Keswick Lakeside

♿ Access to Friar's Crag, the Bowder Stone, Crow Park, Cat Bells Terrace, Calf Close Bay and to the shore of Derwentwater at Brandelhow; strong helper recommended at all sites

☕ Café at Caffle House, Watendlath; teas at the Flock Inn, Rosthwaite, at Knotts View, Stonethwaite and at Seathwaite - all these properties owned, but not managed, by the Trust

🚌 Please tel. Regional Office for details of minibus tours and resource information

➡ (6: B6) S of Keswick [90:NY266228 - Keswick Lakeside Information Centre] *Bus:* Cumbria Enquiry Line tel. 01228 606000

BUTTERMERE AND ENNERDALE 🖼️ 🏛️ 🚶 *Cumbria*

Tel: (Regional Office) 015394 35599 Fax: (Regional Office) 015394 35353

3588ha (8866 acres) of fell and commonland, including the lakes of Buttermere, Crummock and Loweswater, seven farms and woodland, as well as lakeshore access to Ennerdale Water. The high fells to the south include the famous Pilla Rock, and there are extensive prehistoric settlements on the fells south of Ennerdale

🅾 All year

💷 Three pay-and-display car parks (NT members free), including one on Honister Pass

📕 Guided walks available; please tel. Regional Office for details. Short firm gravel path to Crummock Water from car park at Lanthwaite Woods

♿ 2ml route along SW side of Buttermere lake; strong pusher recommended

🚌 Please tel. Regional Office for details of minibus tours and resource information

➡ (6: B6) 8ml S of Cockermouth [89:NY1815 - Buttermere] *Bus:* Cumbria Enquiry Line tel. 01228 606000

CARTMEL PRIORY GATEHOUSE 🏠 ✝ *Cumbria*

Cavendish Street, Cartmel, Grange-over-Sands LA11 6QA
Tel: (Regional Office) 015394 35599 Fax: 015394 35353

All that is left, apart from the church, of a 12th-century Augustinian priory, which was later strengthened following devastating raids by Robert the Bruce. After dissolution in the mid 16th century, it served as a grammar school from 1624 to 1790

🅾 Opening times under review; please tel. 015394 35599 for latest information

💷 Free. Parking in the village

➡ (6: C8) [96: SD378788] *Bus:* Stagecoach Cumberland 530/1 Kendal–Cartmel (passing 🚉 Grange-over-Sands) (tel. 01946 63222) *Station:* Cark (U) 2ml

CONISTON AND LITTLE LANGDALE 🐾 🏛 🕴   *Cumbria*

Tel: (Regional Office) 015394 35599 Fax: 015394 35353

A mixture of fell and woodland covering some 2608ha (6444 acres) and including eleven farms and the well-known Tarn Hows beauty spot, once owned by Beatrix Potter as part of the Monk Coniston Estate. There is also access to the lakeshore of Coniston Water. Little Langdale shows several signs of medieval settlement, including the Thingmound (a Norse meeting place) by Fell Foot Farm

O All year

£ Pay-and-display car park (NT members free) at Tarn Hows

🕴 Guided walks available; please tel. Regional Office for details

♿ Accessible path from car park (NT) to Blea Tarn, with views to Great Langdale. Circuit of Tarn Hows possible, but two strong pushers required

◉ Trail around Tarn Hows using audio cassette, from NT Land Rover in car park

🎦 Please tel. Regional Office for details of minibus tours and resource information

➔ (6: C7) Little Langdale valley starts 7ml N of Coniston village [89:NY2904 - Blea Tarn Farm] *Bus:* Cumbria Enquiry Line tel. 01228 606000; also NT minibus service 'Tarn Hows Tourer' linking Hawkshead and Tarn Hows, Sun only during main season; leaflet from Regional Office

DALTON CASTLE 🏠   *Cumbria*

Market Place, Dalton-in-Furness LA15 8AX
Tel: (Regional Office) 015394 35599 Fax: 015394 35353

A 14th-century tower in the main street of the town, with a local exhibition by the Friends of Dalton Castle

O Easter to end Sept: Sat 2–5

£ Free but donations welcome

➔ (6: B9) In main street of Dalton [96: SD226739] *Bus:* From surrounding areas (tel. 01946 63222) *Station:* Dalton ¼ml

DUNHAM MASSEY 🏠 🏠 🎭 ♣ ♠ 🕴 🛡   *Cheshire*

Altrincham WA14 4SJ
Tel: 0161 941 1025; Infoline 0161 928 4351 Fax: 0161 929 7508

An early Georgian house, Dunham Massey was extensively re-worked in the early years of this century. The result is one of Britain's most sumptuous Edwardian interiors, housing exceptional collections of walnut furniture, paintings and magnificent Huguenot silver. The richly planted garden contains extensive borders and late-flowering azaleas, as well as an orangery, Victorian bark house and well house. The surrounding deer park was laid out in the early 18th century and contains a series of beautiful avenues and walls

Note: Weekend crèche for children 2–5 yrs (tel. for details); NT minibus link to public transport; reduced admission for bus ticket holders; extended Christmas opening for restaurant

◯ House: 4 April to 1 Nov: daily except Thur & Fri 12–5; BH Sun & BH Mon 11–5). Closed Good Fri. Last admission 4.30. **Garden**: 4 April to 1 Nov: daily 11–5.30. Last admission 5. The Mill machinery will normally operate on Wed & Sun 2–4. **Park**: daily throughout the year. **Events**: concerts, theatre and walks. 10 May, Plantsman's Day. Please send s.a.e. for details

£ House & garden: £5, children £2.50; family ticket £12.50. House only: £3, children £1.50. Garden only £3, children £1.50. Reduced rate for booked parties Sat & Mon to Wed (but not BH Mon). Reduced admission for bus ticket holders at certain times. Park only: £2.80 per car, £1 per motorbike, £5 per coach/minibus. NT members and coaches bringing booked parties park free. Car park and adjacent picnic area 250m from house. Visitors to house must leave large bags, video cameras, pushchairs etc. at reception

🛠 Outside normal hours, guided tours for booked parties min. charge £200

🖾 Daily throughout the year 11–5.15 (11–4 from Nov to March 1999), closed 25 to 31 Dec; tel. 0161 928 6820

♿ Regret house difficult, steps to ground floor and throughout house. The less accessible rooms are illustrated in an album of photographs. Access to garden and park, on smooth, level paths; shop, refreshments and WCs in main lavatory block and next to restaurant accessible over cobbled yard (restaurant accessible by lift). Car-parking by prior arrangement. Wheelchairs and self-drive powered vehicles available, advance notice requested. Sympathetic Hearing Scheme

👁 Braille guide; large-print guide. Audio tour indicates those items which may be touched; Bechstein piano may be played by musicians

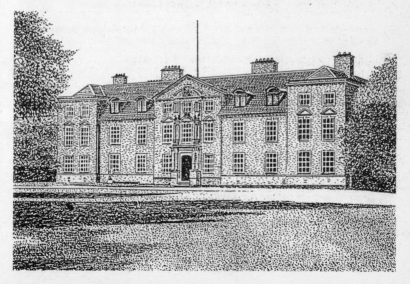

▣ Licensed self-service Stables Restaurant on first floor (accessible by lift) with variety of lunches and teas, vegetarian choice; open daily April to Oct, 11–5.15, Nov to March 1999 11–4 (closed 25 Dec). Seating for 150. Functions and parties welcome by arrangement. The Piers Davenport Room available for booked parties, except Sun (tel. 0161 941 2815). Picnics welcome in North Park adjacent to car park, but not in deer park or garden

🛉 Baby slings available; baby-changing unit in WC; children's menu, highchairs and activity table in restaurant; children's guidebook, seek & find quiz, garden trail, park trail. Please send s.a.e for details of children's activities

▣ Victorian living history in house and environmental studies in deer park based on National Curriculum Key Stages 1 & 2; by arrangement with Education Coordinator (tel. 0161 941 4986). Teachers' resource pack. Schoolrooms for booked parties

▣ Good walks in park for dogs on leads. No dogs in house or garden

➔ (6: K7) 3ml SW of Altrincham off A56; exit 19 off M6; exit 7 off M56 [109: SJ735874] *Bus:* Warrington Goldlines/Warrington Transport 38 ▣ Altrincham Interchange–Warrington (tel. 01244 602666); also NT minibus link to Altrincham Interchange (tel. 0161 941 1025). Reduced admission for bus ticket holders *Station:* Altrincham (▣ & Metro) 3ml; Hale 3ml

DUNHAM MASSEY: WHITE COTTAGE ▣ 𝑲   *Cheshire*

Little Bollington, Altrincham WA14 4TJ

An important timber-framed cottage, built c.1500 as a cruck trussed open hall and altered in the 17th century. Recently restored by the Trust using traditional materials and techniques and now a private residence, open to visitors by kind permission of our tenants

◙ April to end Oct: last Sun of month 2–5. All visits to be pre-booked through the Stamford Estate Office (tel. 0161 928 0075) open Mon to Fri 9–1 and 2–5

£ Voluntary contributions to be made at the White Cottage

➔ As Dunham Massey above

FELL FOOT PARK AND GARDEN ▣ ▣ ▣   *Cumbria*

Newby Bridge, Ulverston LA12 8NN Tel: 015395 31273 Fax: 015395 30049

A Victorian park and garden, currently being restored and landscaped to its former glory. Spring and early summer bring impressive displays of daffodils, followed by rhododendrons, and there are magnificent views of the Lakeland fells. The park has access to the lakeshore where there are boats for hire and fine picnic sites

Note: No launching or landing of speedboats or jet-skis

◙ All year 9–7 or dusk if sooner. Facilities (such as rowing boat hire) 28 March to 1 Nov: daily incl. Good Fri 11–4 (buoyancy aids available).
Events: held throughout the year, tel. for details

£ Car park £4 (over 2hrs), £1.50 (up to 2hrs). Coaches £10 by arrangement. Please note car park has pay and display meters so NT membership or season ticket must be displayed in car. Season tickets available from most NT outlets in Cumbria

⬜ 28 March to 1 Nov: daily 11–5

♿ Accessible but please be careful; slopes and unfenced water. Communications system, sponsored by BAe, now installed in both car parks. Access to tea-room and shop; WC beside tea-room. Two 2-seater self-drive buggies are available

👁 Braille guide planned

🍴 Hot and cold drinks, light lunches, teas and ice-creams in tea-room, 28 March to 1 Nov: 11–5. Tea-room available for evening functions all year and during the day out of season; please contact the Catering Manager

👶 Highchairs in tea-room, children's menu, scribble sheets

🐕 On leads only

➡ (6: C8) At the extreme S end of Lake Windermere on E shore, entrance from A592 [96/97: SD381869] *Bus*: Stagecoach Cumberland 518 Ulverston–Ambleside (passing ⊟ Windermere) (tel. 01946 63222)
Station: Grange-over-Sands 6ml; Windermere 8ml

FORMBY 🏊 📷 👶 🛡   *Sefton*

Victoria Road, Freshfield, Formby L37 1LJ Tel: 01704 878591 Fax: 01704 874949

A wonderful stretch of unspoilt coastline, made up of rolling sand dunes and attractive pine woods set between the sea and Formby town. There are interesting plants and birds to be found, and this is one of the last places in Britain where visitors may catch a glimpse of the rare red squirrel

🅾 All year during daylight hours. Country walks around the property and the Sefton coast. **Events**: details from Property Manager (s.a.e. please)

£ Entrance per car £2.70 (NT members free). Coaches £15 all year. Coaches should pre-book; details from Property Office

♿ Hard surface paths to red squirrel viewing area and Cornerstone Walk. Large car park in sand dunes gives access to beach via boardwalk. Picnic sites. WC (RADAR key)

👶 Red squirrel booklet for children £1. Baby-changing facilities in WC

📖 School groups must book in advance. Environmental education programme; for information tel./fax 01704 874949

🐕 On leads around the squirrel walk

➡ (6: G6) 15ml N of Liverpool, 2ml W of Formby, 2ml off A565 [108: SD275080] *Bus*: ABC 161/4/5, ⊟ Formby–⊟ Freshfield, to within ½ml (tel. 0151 236 7676)
Station: Freshfield 1ml

20 FORTHLIN ROAD 🏠 *Liverpool*

Allerton, Liverpool L18 9TN Tel: 0870 9000 256

This 1950s terraced house is the former home of the McCartney family, where the Beatles met, rehearsed and wrote many of their earliest songs. Displays include contemporary photographs by Mike McCartney and early Beatles memorabilia

O The property will open to the public in mid to late 1998; tel. 0870 9000 256 for details. **All visitors must book in advance and access will be by minibus from Speke Hall - there is no direct car access**

£ Prices to be confirmed; please tel. for details

🛍 Shop at nearby Speke Hall

☕ Refreshments at nearby Speke Hall

→ **(6: H7)** See entry for Speke Hall

GAWTHORPE HALL 🏠 ✿ 🛡 *Lancashire*

Padiham, nr Burnley BB12 8UA Tel: 01282 771004 Fax: 01282 770178

An Elizabethan gem in the heart of industrial Lancashire, Gawthorpe closely resembles the great Hardwick Hall and is very probably by the same architect, Robert Smythson. In the middle of the 19th century Sir Charles Barry was commissioned to restore the house, thereby creating the opulent interiors we see today. There are many notable paintings, including some on loan from the National Portait Gallery, and an unparalleled collection of needlework, assembled by the last family member to live here, Rachel Kay-Shuttleworth

Note: Gawthorpe Hall is financed and administered by Lancashire County Council

O **Hall**: 1 April to 31 Oct: daily except Mon & Fri, but open Good Fri & BH Mon, 1–5. Last admission 4.15. **Garden**: all year: daily 10–6. **Events**: exhibitions during high season

£ Hall: £2.90, children £1.30, concessions £1.45; family ticket £8. Garden: free. Parties by prior arrangement. Free parking 150m. We regret that the Hall is not suitable for baby back carriers or pushchairs

Access limited to grounds only; please tel. for details

Rose garden

Tea-room open same days as Hall, 12.30–4.30

Role-play for Key Stage 2. Through role-play and interactive sessions with our Victorian Butler and Housekeeper, children can gain valuable insight into how a grand Victorian house was organised and run. Available during term-time from 10am on days when house open; please tel. 01282 771004 for details

→ (6: L4) On E outskirts of Padiham; ¾ml drive to house on N of A671 [103: SD806340] *Bus:* Frequent services from Burnley. All pass close ⊞ Burnley Barracks & Burnley Manchester Road (tel. 01282 423125) *Station:* Rose Grove (U) 2ml

---

GRASMERE AND GREAT LANGDALE 🏵 ♿ 🚶   *Cumbria*

Tel: (Regional Office) 015394 35599 Fax: (Regional Office) 015394 35353

4925ha (12,170 acres) and eleven farms, including the protection of the famous Langdale Pikes. The area includes the popular White Moss Common, the glaciated valley of Mickleden, a Victorian garden at High Close (currently being restored) and dramatic Dungeon Ghyll, as well as the bed of Grasmere lake and part of Rydal Water

Note: There is a NT campsite at Great Langdale, open all year; charge (incl. NT members). Please tel. 015394 37668 for details

O All year. Grasmere Information Centre (near church) open as follows: April to end Oct: daily 10–5; Nov to mid Dec: 10–4 (tel. 015394 35621)

£ Three pay-and-display car parks (NT members free)

🚶 Guided walks available; please tel. Regional Office for details

Shop in Grasmere Information Centre

Accessible path at White Moss Common; designated car-parking, plus adapted WC

Please contact Regional Office for details of minibus tours and resource information

→ (6: C6) Great Langdale valley starts 4ml W of Ambleside [89:NY2906] *Bus:* Cumbria Enquiry Line tel. 01228 606000

HARE HILL 🏵 ♠   *Cheshire*

Over Alderley, Macclesfield SK10 4QB

A woodland garden with azaleas, rhododendrons and a delightful walled garden at its heart, containing a pergola and wire sculptures. The surrounding parkland has attractive walks, including a link path to Alderley Edge (2ml)

🅾 3 April to 30 Oct: Wed, Thur, Sat, Sun & BH Mon 10–5.30. Special opening to see rhododendrons and azaleas: 11 May to 1 June: daily 10–5.30. Closed Nov to March

💷 £2.50. Entrance per car £1.50 refundable on entry to garden. Parties either by written appointment c/o Garden Lodge, Oak Road, Over Alderley, Macclesfield SK10 4QB, or by tel. Gardener-in-charge on 01625 828981. Not suitable for school parties

♿ Ample car-parking, but on slope; gravel paths, strong companion advisable. Wheelchair available

👁 Braille guide. Scents & sounds of wooded parkland; scented plants in walled garden

🐕 No dogs in garden, elsewhere on leads

➔ (6: L7) Between Alderley Edge and Prestbury, turn off north at B5087 at Greyhound Road [118: SJ875765] *Bus:* Stevensons 287 ✒ Manchester Airport–Macclesfield (passing ✒ Prestbury), to within ¼ml (tel. 01244 602666) *Station:* Alderley Edge 2½ml; Prestbury 2½ml

HAWKSHEAD 🏠 🖼 🚶 *Cumbria*

Tel: (Regional Office) 015394 35599 Fax: (Regional Office) 015394 35353

Hawkshead is a classic Lakeland village, surrounded by beautiful scenery, much of which is owned by the Trust. Claife Woodlands and the low-lying small farms between the village and the lake are typical of the area. In Hawkshead itself there is the Courthouse, which dates from the 15th century and is all that remains of the village manorial buildings (once held by Furness Abbey). Claife Station, on the west bank of Windermere, is a former Victorian viewing station with spectacular views of the lake. Wray Castle is currently let as a college, with limited access to the grounds only

Note: There is a NT campsite at Low Wray, open Easter to end Oct; charge (incl. NT members); tel. 015394 32810

🅾 All year, except for Hawkshead Courthouse, which is open 1 April to 1 Nov: daily 10–5, access by key from NT shop, The Square, Hawkshead; free admission; but no parking facilities

💷 Pay-and-display car park (NT members free) at Ash Landing, close to Lake Windermere (Ferry Nab)

🚶 Guided walks available; please tel. Regional Office for details

🛍 NT shop in The Square, Hawkshead (see Beatrix Potter Gallery for opening times)

♿ Walks at Claife and Red Nab, on W shore of Windermere; tel. Regional Office for details. Adapted room at Low Wray campsite, with adapted shower, wash basin and WCs

🚌 Please contact Regional Office for details of minibus tours and resource information

➔ (6: C7) Hawkshead is 6ml SW of Ambleside [96/97:SD352982] *Bus:* Cumbria Enquiry Line tel. 01228 606000

HILL TOP 🏠 ❀   *Cumbria*

Near Sawrey, Ambleside LA22 0LF Tel: 015394 36269

Beatrix Potter wrote many of her famous children's stories in this little 17th-century stone house and it has been kept exactly as she left it, complete with her furniture and china. There is a traditional cottage garden attached. A selection of her original illustrations can be seen at the Beatrix Potter Gallery (p.233)

Note: Hill Top is a very small house and a timed entry system is operated, with a daily limit of 800 visitors. During the busiest periods this may give rise to long delays and some visitors may not gain admission at all. Tickets cannot be purchased in advance. Please help to preserve Hill Top by avoiding peak times if you can, particularly mornings in school holidays (closed Thur & Fri except Good Fri)

🅾 1 April to 1 Nov: Sat to Wed & Good Fri 11–5. Last admission 4.30

£ £3.80, children £1.70. No reduction for parties. Parking 200m; no parking for coaches

🛍 Shop daily 10–5 during season

♿ Ground floor access for wheelchairs by prior arrangement

👁 Accompanied visually impaired people welcome, but are advised to visit outside peak times as house is so small and often crowded. Some items in house may be touched; Braille guide

🍽 Bar lunches and evening meals at the Tower Bank Arms (NT owned, and let to tenant) next door, during licensing hours (tel. 015394 36334)

🚼 Unsuitable for back carriers or pushchairs. Children's guidebook on Beatrix Potter

➡ (6: C7) 2ml S of Hawkshead, in hamlet of Near Sawrey, behind the Tower Bank Arms [96/97: SD370955] *Bus:* Stagecoach Cumberland 505/6 Ambleside–Coniston service (connections from 🚆 Windermere); also frequent service from 🚆 Windermere to Bowness Pier, thence ferry and 2ml walk (tel. 01946 63222) *Station:* Windermere 4½ml via vehicle ferry

LITTLE MORETON HALL 🏠 ✚ ❀ 🛡   *Cheshire*

Congleton CW12 4SD Tel: 01260 272018

Britain's most famous and arguably finest timber-framed moated manor house. The drunkenly reeling south front, topped by a spectacular long gallery, opens onto a cobbled courtyard and the main body of the Hall. Magnificent wall-paintings and a notable knot garden are of special interest. The Hall was the location for Granada TV's recent (1996) adaptation of Daniel Defoe's Moll Flanders

What's new in 1998: Costumes used in the filming of Moll Flanders will be on display 21 March to 1 Nov

☉ 21 March to 1 Nov: daily except Mon & Tues 12–5.30 or dusk if earlier (open BH Mon 11–5.30 and opens at 11 Wed to Sun 25 July to 6 Sept). Last admission 5. 7 Nov to 20 Dec: Sat & Sun 12–4, access to Great Hall, Parlour, garden, shop and restaurant only. Special openings at other times, for pre-booked parties, including evening tours with buffet supper. **Events:** 22 March to 1 Nov: Chapel Service every Sun 3.45. Open-air theatre in July

£ £4; family ticket £10. Pre-booked parties £3. Joint ticket with Biddulph Grange Garden available £6; family ticket £15. 7 Nov to 20 Dec: free admission. Extra charge for special openings. Parking 150m £2, refundable on entry to Hall (NT members free); car park open from 11

⯅ Optional free guided tours most afternoons, 21 March to 1 Nov

🛍 Shop as house

♿ Access to ground floor; includes Great Hall, Parlour, chapel (ramp available), tea-room, shop, exhibition room. Cars may be driven to entrance, but then must park in car park. Garden accessible. Self-drive vehicle and wheelchairs available by arrangement. WC

◉ Braille and large-print guides; opportunities to touch

◖ Light lunches and home-made teas (waited service); licensed; limited seating – no reservations. Last admission 5. Picnic area adjacent to car park

⍓ Baby-changing unit; highchair and children's portions available; children's guidebook

▮ School parties April to end Oct: Wed, Thur & Fri mornings only, by prior arrangement with Property Manager. Schoolroom available; teachers' resource pack

🐕 In car park only

➜ **(6: L8)** 4ml SW of Congleton, on E side of A34 [118: SJ832589] *Bus:* PMT 77 Congleton–Hanley (passing close ⊠ Kidsgrove & Congleton), alight Brownlow Heath, 1½ml (tel. 01244 602666) *Station:* Kidsgrove 3ml; Congleton 4½ml

---

LYME PARK 🏠 ✿ ♠ ⯅ 🛡   *Cheshire*

Disley, Stockport SK12 2NX Tel: 01663 762023/766492 Fax: 01663 765035

The home of the Legh family for 600 years and originally a Tudor house, Lyme was transformed by the Venetian architect Leoni into an Italianate palace and one of the biggest houses in Cheshire. Some of the Elizabethan interiors survive and contrast dramatically with later rooms. The state rooms are adorned by Mortlake tapestries, Grinling Gibbons wood-carvings and an important collection of English clocks. Outside, the Victorian garden contains Lewis Wyatt's great conservatory and is surrounded by a medieval deer park, complete with hunting tower. Lyme appeared as 'Pemberley' in the BBC's recent adaptation of the Jane Austen novel Pride and Prejudice

Note: Lyme Park is owned and managed by the NT and partly financed by Stockport Metropolitan Borough Council

☉ **House:** 3 April to 31 Oct: daily except Wed & Thur 1–5 (BH Mon 11–5). Last

admission 4.30. **Garden:** 3 April to 31 Oct: Fri to Tues 11–5; also Wed & Thur 1–5; Nov to 20 Dec: Sat & Sun 12–3. **Park:** April to Oct: daily 8am–8.30pm; Nov to March: 8–6 daily. **Events:** details from Estate Office (please send s.a.e.)

£ House & garden £4; family £10. House only £3; garden only £2. Park only £3.30 per car (NT members free)

House: outside normal opening hours, by arrangement. Park or garden, by arrangement

Park shop open as park coffee shop (see below); hall shop open as hall tea-room (see below)

Limited parking at house. Refreshment facilities in park and hall courtyard accessible. First floor of house accessible, wheelchair users please telephone in advance. Direct wheelchair access through Rose Garden. Wheelchairs available. Steep terrain throughout park

Park shop and coffee shop open 3 April to 31 Oct: daily 11–5. Nov to March: Sat & Sun 12–4. Hall tea-room and shop open 3 April to 31 Oct: daily except Wed & Thur 11–5

Playground for 11-years and under. Highchairs available in hall tea-room and park coffee shop

Extensive education programme in house and park

No dogs in garden; under close control in park

(6: M7) Entrance on A6, 6½ml SE of Stockport, 9ml NW of Buxton (house and car park 1ml from entrance) *Bus:* Glossopdale 361 from Stockport to car park (Sun, May to Sept only); for other services from surrounding areas to park entrance (tel. 0161 228 7811) *Station:* Disley, ½ml from park entrance

NETHER ALDERLEY MILL ☒ ⬚ᴛ *Cheshire*

Congleton Road, Nether Alderley, Macclesfield SK10 4TW Tel: 01625 523012

A fascinating and unusual water-mill, dating from the 15th century. It has overshot tandem wheels and is powered by a reservoir, against which the mill is wedged. After lying derelict for thirty years, the Victorian machinery was restored in the 1960s and is now in full working order, with regular flour-grinding demonstrations

☉ 1 April to end May, Oct & 1 Nov: Wed, Sun & BH Mon 1–4.30. June to Sept: daily except Mon (but open BH Mon) 1–5

£ £2, child £1. Parties (max. 20) by prior arrangement. No WC

⬚ As required

⬚ Ladder stairs. No access for wheelchairs

⬚ Working machinery provides fascinating range of sounds

⬚ Visits by arrangement. Parking space for one coach at a time; must book in advance. Teachers' resource book available. Bookings: 7 Oak Cottages, Styal, Wilmslow SK9 4JQ (tel. 01625 523012)

⬚ No dogs

➜ (6: L7) 1½ml S of Alderley Edge, on E side of A34 [118: SJ844763]
Bus: Stevensons/Timeline 127, 130 Manchester–Macclesfield (passing ⬚ Alderley Edge) (tel. 01244 602666) *Station:* Alderley Edge 2ml

---

QUARRY BANK MILL ⬚ ☒ ⬚ ⬚ᴛ ⬚ *Cheshire*

Wilmslow SK9 4LA Tel: 01625 527468 Fax: 01625 539267

This working Georgian cotton mill, built in 1784 by entrepreneur Samuel Greg, provides a fascinating insight into the early Industrial Revolution. The complex of buildings which grew up around the magnificent 50-ton water-wheel charts the growth of cotton textile manufacture from cottage industry to noisy weaving factory. Through hands-on opportunities visitors can learn about the processes involved, and the restored Apprentice House, where pauper apprentice children lived, gives an insight into the arduous social conditions of the time

Note: See also entry for Styal Country Park (p.252)

What's new in 1998: From April 1998 an 1840s beam engine will be steamed daily and will be the highlight of the new Power Galleries and Audiovisual Theatre. These galleries are in the original engine house area, not previously open to the public

☉ **Open all year**. April to Sept: **Mill:** daily 11–6. Last admission 4.30. Also pre-booked specified evenings in May, June & Sept. **Apprentice House & garden:** (closed Mon except BH Mon) Tues to Fri 2–4.30. Weekends & during Aug: as Mill. Timed entry tickets: to avoid disappointment please reserve timed ticket at reception on arrival. Oct to March: **Mill:** daily 11–5 except Mon. Last admission 3.30. Pre-booked groups from 9.30 except weekends & BH Mon. **Apprentice House and garden:** Tues to Fri 2–4.30; weekends: as Mill. **Events:** details of programme available from property

£ Mill & Apprentice House £5.50, children/concessions £3.50; family ticket £15. Mill only £4.20, children/concessions £3. Apprentice House & garden only £3.50, children/concessions £2.50. Advance booking essential for groups of 10 or more (please apply for booking form at least 3 weeks in advance; guides may be booked at same time). Groups of 20 or more admitted at concessionary rate

Available for pre-booked parties

Mill shop sells goods made from cloth woven in the mill and wide range of gifts & souvenirs. Mail order catalogue for Styal Calico, send A5 s.a.e. (36p) plus £1, refunded against subsequent purchase

Exterior and partial access to interior including Power Galleries, Water-wheel and Audiovisual Theatre. Access to three rooms on ground floor of Apprentice House, photographic record of upper floors. Wheelchair available on request; cars may set down passengers in the Mill Yard. Please tel. for special access leaflet. WC. Sympathetic Hearing scheme; audiotapes and induction loop

Braille and large-print guides. Audiotape tour of mill. Talking map, varied smells and noises from machinery, etc; cotton samples and other items to handle

The Mill Kitchen: licensed. Mill Pantry for snacks, drinks and ice-cream. Conference and banqueting facilities

Parent & baby room; back carriers admitted; baby sling and back carriers available

Education programme (for pre-booked parties) linked to National Curriculum; living history, hands-on science and technology activities and textile workshops. Information available from Education Dept on tel. 01625 532034

➜ (6: L7) 1½ml N of Wilmslow off B5166, 2½ml from M56, exit 5, 10ml S of Manchester [109: SJ835835] *Bus:* Stevensons 187, 287 Manchester Airport–Macclesfield, passing ✇ Wilmslow (tel. 01244 602666) *Station:* Styal, ½ml (not Sun); Manchester Airport 2ml; Wilmslow 2½ml

RUFFORD OLD HALL 🏛 ✤ 🛡   *Lancashire*

Rufford, nr Ormskirk L40 1SG Tel/fax: 01704 821254

One of Lancashire's finest 16th-century buildings, famed for its spectacular Great Hall with its intricately carved movable wooden screen and dramatic hammerbeam roof. It is rumoured that Shakespeare performed in this hall for the owner, Sir Thomas Hesketh, in whose family Rufford remained for 250 years. The Carolean wing, altered in 1821, contains fine collections of 16th- and 17th-century oak furniture, arms, armour and tapestries

O **House**: 1 April to 1 Nov: Sat to Wed 1–5. Also open on selected Thur: 16 April, 28 May, from 23 July to 27 Aug & 29 Oct. Last admission 4.30. **Garden**: same days 12–5.30. **Events**: please send s.a.e. for details

£ House and garden £3.50, children £1.70; family ticket £9.50. Garden only £1.80. (Children free during school holidays.) Reduction for pre-booked parties £2.60 (but no parties Sun & BH Mon)

Shop open as garden. Also 3 Nov to 19 Dec: daily except Mon & Fri 12–4, Sun 2–5

Access to ground floor, Great Hall, tea-room, shop & garden only, otherwise many steps & narrow passages; two wheelchairs available. Photograph albums of rooms available to those unable to reach them. Parking on firm gravel; level paths to hall and garden

Braille guide and large-print house guide; great screen and carved oak doors may be touched

Old Kitchen Restaurant serves light lunches 12–2 (licensed for cider & wine) and teas 12–5 (last serving 4.30); 3 Nov to 19 Dec, as shop, see above. Picnic site adjacent to car park

House not suitable for baby back carriers or pushchairs, but following available: highchairs in tea-room, baby slings, children's menu, children's quiz sheet, scribble sheets, baby-changing facility in women's WC, bottle-warming service. Early learning toys

Accompanied visits and teachers' pack

In grounds only, on leads. Fresh water and bowl available. Tether rings in yard

➜ (6: H5) 7ml N of Ormskirk, in village of Rufford on E side of A59 [108: SD463160] *Bus*: Little White Bus 101 Preston–Ormskirk; Blackpool Transport X54, 754/8 Liverpool–Blackpool (tel. 01695 579062) *Station*: Rufford (U), not Sun, ½ml; Burscough Bridge 2½ml

SIZERGH CASTLE 🏛 ✿ 🛉 🎭 *Cumbria*

Sizergh, nr Kendal LA8 8AE Tel: 015395 60070

*The Strickland family has lived for over 750 years at Sizergh and the castle reflects the
turbulent history of this part of the country. Essentially defensive, its core is the 14th-
century pele tower, later extended and containing some exceptional Elizabethan carved
wooden chimney-pieces. There is a good collection of contemporary oak furniture and
portraits, and the castle is surrounded by handsome gardens which include a particularly
imposing and beautiful rock garden*

🅾 **Castle**: 1 April to 29 Oct: Sun to Thur 1.30–5.30. **Garden**: as Castle, but from
12.30. Last admission 5. **Events**: please tel. for details

💷 £4, children £2; family ticket £11. Garden only £2. Parties of 15+ £3.20 by
arrangement (not BH). Car park 100m

🏠 Shop open as garden. Also from 1 Nov to 21 Dec: Tues, Thur & Sun 12.30–4.30;
tel. 015395 60070

♿ Access to most of garden mainly via gravel paths; battery-powered and manual
wheelchairs available. Lower Hall & tea-room accessible. Photograph album of
inaccessible rooms available. Picnic tables with wheelchair access. WC

👁 Garden & first floor suitable for accompanied visually impaired visitors. Some
wooden articles may be touched; Braille guide

☕ Tea-room in basement of pele tower opens 1.30. Picnic tables in car park

🛉 Young Explorers, quiz sheet, garden treasure hunt. Unsuitable for baby back
carriers and pushchairs

🐕 Not allowed in garden

➡ **(6: D8)** 3½ml S of Kendal NW of interchange A590/A591 [97: SD498878]
Bus: Stagecoach Cumberland 555 Keswick–Lancaster (passing close ➣ Lancaster
and Kendal) (tel. 01946 63222) *Station*: Oxenholme 3ml; Kendal (U) 3½ml

SPEKE HALL 🏠 ✿ 👥 🎭 *Liverpool*

The Walk, Liverpool L24 1XD
Tel: 0151 427 7231; Infoline (local rate) 0345 585702 Fax: 0151 427 9860

*One of the most famous half-timbered houses in the country, dating from 1490. The unique
and atmospheric interior spans many periods: the Great Hall and priest holes evoke Tudor
times, while the Oak Parlour and smaller rooms, some with William Morris wallpapers,
show the Victorian desire for privacy and comfort. There is also fine Jacobean plasterwork and
intricately carved furniture. A fully equipped Victorian kitchen and servants' hall enable
visitors to see 'behind the scenes'. The restored garden has spring bulbs, a rose garden,
summer border and stream garden, and there are woodland walks and magnificent views of
the Mersey basin*

Note: Speke Hall is administered and financed by the National Trust with the help of a
grant from the National Museums & Galleries on Merseyside

O **House:** 4 April to 31 Oct: daily except Mon (but open BH Mon) 1–5.30 (closes 4.30 from 25 Oct). 1 Nov to 13 Dec: Sat & Sun 1–4.30. **Garden:** 4 April to 31 Oct: open as house from 12; Nov to March 1999: daily except Mon 12–4 (closed 24, 25, 26, 31 Dec & 1 Jan); last admission 30min before closing. *Note:* on BH Mon and summer weekends the house can become very crowded. **Events:** open-air theatre and Christmas events; for details please send s.a.e. to Events Manager

£ House, garden & grounds £4; family ticket £10. Garden & grounds only £1.40. Reduction for pre-booked groups. Car park 200m

⚟ Programme of roof tours and 20-minute 'tasters', also of gardens, estate & house (by arrangement)

⌷ Shop open same days as house, 12–5

♿ Close parking by arrangement; self-drive powered vehicle available for use in grounds. Wheelchairs available by arrangement on arrival or at house; access to ground floor (includes most principal rooms) and tea-room. WC; ramp and 5cm step to tea-room; cobbled dairy courtyard with paved path. Easy access to much of garden and woodlands; wheelchair path around Stocktons Wood. Sympathetic Hearing Scheme

👁 Braille and large-print guides; some objects may be touched; guided tours bookable

🍽 Refreshments and teas; tea-room open same days as house from 12; light lunches 12–2; parties should book. Also open Sun in March 1–4.30 for drinks; seating capacity 40. Picnics in orchard

👶 Children's guide. Children's table, highchairs and Trusty picnic boxes in tea-room; baby-changing facilities

🏛 School visits welcome, but must be pre-booked; details from Education Assistant

🐕 On leads in Stocktons Wood only. No dogs in garden

➜ (6: H7) On N bank of the Mersey, 1ml off A561 on W side of Liverpool airport. Follow airport signs from M62 exit 6, A5300; M56 exit 12 [108: SJ419825] *Bus:* North Western H25 ⊞ Garston–Runcorn, Sun, May to Oct only; otherwise Merseybus 80, 180 ⊞ Liverpool Lime Street–Liverpool Airport (passing ⊞ Garston) or 81/2 Bootle–Speke (passing ⊞ Hunt's Cross or Cressington), both to within ½ml (tel. 0151 236 7676) *Station:* Garston 2ml; Hunt's Cross 2ml

---

STAGSHAW GARDEN ❖   *Cumbria*

Ambleside LA22 0HE Tel: (Regional Office) 015394 35599 Fax: 015394 35353

A woodland garden, created by the late Cubby Acland, Regional Agent for the Trust. It contains a fine collection of shrubs, including many notable rhododendrons, azaleas and camellias

O 1 April to end June: daily 10–6.30. July to end Oct: by appointment with Regional Office. Please send s.a.e.

£ £1.30. No reduction for parties. Parking very limited; access dangerous; visitors may park at Waterhead car park and walk to Stagshaw. No access for coaches: park in Waterhead car park, Ambleside. No WC

[⛄] Difficult for pushchairs

[→] (6: C7) ½ml S of Ambleside on A591 [90: NY380030] *Bus:* Stagecoach
Cumberland 518, 555/9 from [≊] Windermere (tel. 01946 63222)
Station: Windermere 4ml

STEAM YACHT *GONDOLA* *Cumbria*

NT Gondola Bookings Office, The Hollens, Grasmere LA22 9QZ
Tel: 015394 63849

The steam yacht Gondola *was first launched in 1859 and now, completely renovated by the Trust, provides a steam-powered passenger service in its opulently upholstered saloons. The perfect way to view Coniston's spectacular scenery*

[O] **Sailings:** Steam yacht *Gondola* sails to a scheduled daily timetable 1 April to
1 Nov, weather permitting, starting at 11, except Sat, when sailings start at
12.05. The Trust reserves the right to cancel sailings in the event of high winds
or lack of demand. Piers at Coniston, Park-a-Moor at SE end of the lake and
Brantwood (not NT). Parties from Coniston Pier only. Free parking & WC at
Coniston Pier

[£] Ticket prices and timetable on application and published locally. Family ticket
available. No reduction for NT members as *Gondola* is an enterprise and not held
solely for preservation. Parties & private charters by prior arrangement. Contact
may be made direct between 9 and 10.30; answerphone in operation at other times

[📷] Guidebook and *Gondola* souvenirs available on board

[♿] Not suitable for wheelchairs

[👁] Access for visually impaired visitors; guide dogs admitted

[⛄] Children's quiz sheet

[→] (6: C8) Coniston (½ml to Coniston Pier) *Bus:* Stagecoach Cumberland 505/6 from
Ambleside (connections from [≊] Windermere) (tel. 01946 63222)
Station: Foxfield (U), not Sun, 10ml; Windermere 10ml via vehicle ferry

STYAL COUNTRY PARK 🏠 ✕ ✝ 🏕 🎿 *Cheshire*

Estate Office, 7 Oak Cottages, Styal, Wilmslow SK9 4JQ Tel: 01625 523012

Part of the valley of the River Bollin, with many pleasant riverside walks in attractive woodland. The Park includes Quarry Bank Mill (see p.246), the factory colony village of Styal and associated farmland

🅾 All year during daylight hours; gates close 9pm during summer

💷 £2 admission charge per car to country park

🏃 Guided tours of woodlands and village from main car park on second Sun in each month at 2.30

📷 Shop at mill

♿ A circular woodland route is available from the Twinnies Bridge car park (not NT) at the southern end of the country park. (No access from main car park)

👁 Braille and large-print guides available from Estate Office

📺 Available from Mill

🚼 Baby-changing facilities at Mill

🏛 Environmental education; booking as for Quarry Bank Mill, see p.246

🐕 Dogs allowed, but must be under close control

➡ (6: L7) As for Quarry Bank Mill *Bus:* As for Quarry Bank Mill *Station:* Styal ½ml (not Sun)

TATTON PARK 🏠 🏠 🍀 🍀 📷 👤 🛡 *Cheshire*

Knutsford WA16 6QN
Tel: 01565 654822 Infoline: 01565 750250 Fax: 01565 650179

One of the most complete historic estates open to visitors. The early 19th-century Wyatt house sits amid a landscaped deer park and is opulently decorated, providing a fine setting for the Egerton family collections of pictures, books, china, glass, silver and specially commissioned Gillow furniture. The theme of Victorian grandeur extends into the garden, with fernery, orangery, rose garden, pinetum and Italian and Japanese gardens. There is also a medieval old hall, a 1930s working farm and many varieties of wildfowl on the lake. An outdoor and sailing centre can be booked by groups in advance and walks include the 'Wartime Tatton' trail

Note: Tatton Park is financed, administered and maintained by Cheshire County Council. Without this commitment the Trust would not have been able to acquire this property, and members are only entitled to free admission to the Mansion and Gardens. Members must pay car park charges, and full admission to all other attractions – including the Old Hall, Farm and many special events (including the carriage-driving trials)

What's new in 1998: New exhibition rooms open in the Mansion, with Egerton family memorabilia and a cabinet room of paintings

3 April to 1 Nov: **Park:** 10–6 daily. **Gardens:** daily except Mon 10.30–5. **Mansion:** daily except Mon 12–4 (open Sat & Sun only 1 to 26 Oct); midweek Mansion opening times vary, so please tel. to check. 2 Nov to 31 March 1999: **Park:** Tues to Sun 11–4. **Gardens:** Tues to Sun 11–4. Opening times for Farm and Old Hall on request. **Events:** All NT members will be expected to pay the special charges which apply to events, including those at Christmas. Please send s.a.e. for full events programme

Park: (incl NT members) cars, motorcycles, mopeds £3 (disability badges £1); horse/horse-drawn vehicles £2; cyclists, pedestrians, coaches free. **Mansion:** adult £2.80, child £1.80; family ticket £8 (NT members free). **Gardens:** as Mansion. **Old Hall:** adult £2.50, child £1.50; family ticket £8. **Farm:** as Old Hall; charges apply to NT members. Explorer ticket (Park plus all 4 attractions): adult £8.50, child £5.50; family ticket £25. Mini Explorer (2 attractions): adult £4.50, child £2.50; family ticket £12.50. Discounts on all prices for groups of 12 adults or more; contact the property for details

Mansion: 3 April to 28 June & 1 to 27 Sept; hourly, on weekdays only except school holidays and busy periods. Old Hall: 2 April to 1 Nov: Tues to Fri at 3 & 4. *Note*: on weekdays access to Mansion is by guided tour only, on the hour 12–4, except during July & Aug

3 April to 27 Sept: Tues to Sun 11.30–5; 29 Sept to 1 Nov: Tues to Sun 11.30–4; 3 Nov to 22 Dec: Sat & Sun 11.30–4. Special opening 21 to 24 Oct & 29 Nov to 20 Dec for Christmas events. Jan to 28 March 1999: Sun only 11.30–4. Shop, housekeeper's store sells estate and local produce; kitchen sales area

Comprehensive leaflet available. Parking in stable yard, at Old Hall and Farm. Ramped access to ground floor of Mansion; contact cashier for access. Garden, park, farm, restaurant & shop easily accessible. Walking and fishing facilities. WC. Sungift electric vehicles available at garden and farm. Arrangements can be made for sign language interpreters and lip-speakers

Braille guide available at garden entrance. Some objects in Mansion may be touched; also farm animals

3 April to 1 Nov: daily 10.30–5; 2 Nov to 31 March 1999: Tues to Sun 11.30–3

Adventure playground. Nursing mothers invited to use rest-room (ask for directions)

■ Living history and education programme available for schools. Please tel. 01565 750790 for details. Tatton Outdoor Sailing Centre for group instruction. Please tel. 01565 653141 for details

🐕 On leads at farm and in park under close control. No dogs in garden

➡ (6: K7) 3½ml N of Knutsford, 4ml S of Altrincham, 5ml from M6, exit 19; 3ml from M56, exit 7, well signposted on A556; entrance on Ashley Road, 1½ml NE of jn. A5034 with A50 [109/118: SJ745815] *Bus:* Executive Mini Travel X2 ⊞ Altrincham Interchange–Chester, Sun only, otherwise from surrounding areas to Knutsford, thence 2ml (tel. 01244 602666) *Station:* Knutsford 2ml

TOWNEND 🏠 *Cumbria*

Troutbeck, Windermere LA23 1LB Tel: (015394) 32628

A very fine example of Lake District vernacular architecture and an exceptional survival. Largely 17th-century, the solid stone and slate house belonged to a wealthy yeoman farming family and contains carved woodwork, books, papers, furniture and fascinating domestic implements from the past, largely accumulated by the Browne family who have lived here since 1943

🕐 1 April to 1 Nov: Tues to Fri, Sun & BH Mon, 1–5 or dusk if earlier. Last admission 4.30

£ £2.80, children £1.40; family ticket £7.50. No reduction for parties which must be pre-booked. Townend and the village are unsuitable for coaches; 12–15-seater minibuses are acceptable; permission to take coaches to Townend must be obtained from the Transportation and Highways Dept, Cumbria CC, Carlisle, Cumbria (tel. 01228 23456). Car park (no coaches)

♿ Unsuitable for wheelchairs

👁 Access for accompanied visually impaired visitors; Braille guide

🍴 Refreshments available in the village

👶 Unsuitable for baby back carriers or pushchairs. Children's quiz sheet

➡ (6: C7) 3ml SE of Ambleside at S end of Troutbeck village [90: NY407020] *Bus:* From surrounding areas (many passing ⊞ Windermere) to within 1ml (tel. 01946 63222) *Station:* Windermere 3ml

ULLSWATER 🍴 🚻 🚹 *Cumbria*

Tel: (Regional Office) 015394 35599 Fax: (Regional Office) 015394 35353

Aira Force waterfalls provide one of the highlights of the Trust's ownership in this valley, which totals 5173ha (12,782 acres) of fell and woodland, as well as six farms (including Glencoyne, the largest). There is access to parts of Ullswater and Brotherswater lakes

🕐 All year

£ Two pay-and-display car parks (NT members free)

[K] Guided walks available; please tel. Regional Office for details

[access] Access to lower bridge on Aira Beck, to Aira Green and the shore of Ullswater, and to the tea-room at Aira Force

[audio] Trail around Victorian arboretum at Aira Force using audio cassette, available from NT Land Rover in car park for small deposit

[tea] Tea-room at Aira Force (not NT)

[minibus] Please tel. Regional Office for details of minibus tours and resource information

[→] (6: C6) 7ml S of Penrith [90:NY4020 - Aira Force] *Bus:* Cumbria Enquiry Line tel. 01228 606000

WASDALE, ESKDALE AND DUDDON [icons] *Cumbria*

Tel: (Regional Office) 015394 35599 Fax: (Regional Office) 015394 35353

Here the Trust owns England's highest mountain, Scafell Pike, and her deepest lake, Wastwater. Almost the whole of the head of Wasdale valley is NT-owned, including the Great Gable and the famous historic wall patterns at the valley head. Lower down, there is the wooded and tranquil estate at Nether Wasdale. Over 7000ha (17,000 acres) and eleven farms are covered in total. In neighbouring Eskdale, Trust ownership covers extensive areas of fell and commonland, including Hardknott Roman Fort and Hardknott Pass. The beautiful and tranquil Duddon valley covers almost 3000ha (7400 acres) and nine farms

Note: There is a NT campsite at Wasdale Head, open Easter to end Oct; charge (incl. NT members); tel. 019467 26220

[O] All year

[£] Pay-and-display car park (NT members free) at Wasdale Head

[K] Guided walks available; please tel. Regional Office for details

[access] Adapted WC at Wasdale Head campsite. 300m of accessible footpath at Gill Force waterfall in Eskdale

[minibus] Please tel. Regional Office for details of minibus tours and resource information

[→] (6: B7) 8ml E of A595 Cumbrian coast road from Barrow to Whitehaven, turning by Santon Bridge [89:NY178003 - Boot] *Bus:* Cumbria Enquiry Line tel. 01228 606000

WINDERMERE AND TROUTBECK [icons] *Cumbria*

Tel: (Regional Office) 015394 35599 Fax: (Regional Office) 015394 35353

This property includes the beautiful and secluded Troutbeck valley, as well as several sites next to Lake Windermere and six farms. One of these, Troutbeck Park, was once farmed by Beatrix Potter and was her largest farm. Ambleside Roman Fort, tiny Bridge House in Ambleside, and Cockshott Point on the lake at Bowness-on-Windermere, are all popular places to visit. See also Townend, p.254

O	All year, except Bridge House, which is now an Information Centre and shop, open: April to end Oct, daily 10–5 (tel. Regional Office for further details)
𝕏	Guided walks available; tel. Regional Office for details
🛍	Shop at Bridge House
▌	Please tel. Regional Office for details of minibus tours and resource information
→	(6: C7) Troutbeck is signposted E of the A591 Windermere to Ambleside road [90: NY407020 - Townend House] *Bus:* Cumbria Enquiry Line tel. 01228 606000

WORDSWORTH HOUSE 🏠 ✿ 🛡 *Cumbria*

Main Street, Cockermouth CA13 9RX Tel: 01900 824805

The Georgian town house where William Wordsworth was born in 1770. Several rooms are furnished in contemporary style and contain some of the poet's personal effects. His childhood garden, with terraced walk, leads down to the River Derwent

O	1 April to 30 Oct: weekdays 11–5. Also Sat 11 April, 2 & 23 May, all Sats 27 June to 5 Sept and Sat 24 Oct. Closed remaining Sats and all Suns. Last admission 4.30. **Events:** concerts and other events during the season; tel for details
£	£2.80, children £1.40; family ticket £7.50. Pre-booked parties £2 per person. Parking in the town. Reciprocal discount ticket, available from Wordsworth House, allows visitors to enjoy Dove Cottage, the Wordsworth Museum and Rydal Mount (nr Grasmere, not NT) at reduced prices; please ask for details
🛍	Shop same months as house: Mon to Sat 10–5. Also 2 Nov to 23 Dec: Mon to Wed, Fri and Sat 10–4 (also open Thur 17 Dec)
♿	Unsuitable for severely disabled people; steps at access points. Shop accessible from Main Street. Garden possible over gravel paths by prior arrangement
👁	Suitable for accompanied visually impaired visitors; Braille guide
🍴	Morning coffee, light lunches & refreshments (licensed for beer and wine); teas in the old kitchen
👶	We regret the house is not suitable for baby back carriers, pushchairs or wheelchairs. Baby sling available (up to 2 yrs), children's menu, children's quiz sheet, toys and books, highchair, mother and baby facilities.
🐕	Only guide dogs allowed
→	(6: B5) [89: NY118307] *Bus:* Stagecoach Cumberland X5, 34 ⬛ Penrith–Workington (passing close ⬛ Workington); 58 from Maryport (passing close ⬛ Maryport) (tel. 01946 63222) *Station:* Maryport 6½ml

Introduction to the North East

England's North East offers magnificent scenery, with wide open stretches of unspoilt moorland and upland pasture, and a long and dramatic coastline. This beautiful landscape provides a fitting context to some of England's greatest country houses.

The upland properties of **Malham Tarn Estate** and **Upper Wharfedale** protect some of the finest landscapes in the Yorkshire Dales, with limestone pavements, waterfalls, flower-rich hay meadows criss-crossed with stone walls and studded with traditional field barns, and an internationally important wetland nature reserve at Malham Tarn (free leaflet available). This is magnificent walking country through dramatic and varied scenery.

The spine of the Pennine chain runs through the south west of the area, and at **Hardcastle Crags**, near Hebden Bridge, there are waymarked trails through steep-sided valleys covered in woodland. There is a rich variety of birdlife here, and at the heart of Hebden Dale lies Gibson Mill, an old textile mill currently being restored. Information on site provides details on what there is to see and do in the area. Not far away is **East Riddlesden Hall**, a classic West Riding manor house.

To the south lies the **Marsden Moor Estate**, over 2400ha (5900 acres) of wild and open SSSI moorland. There are many interesting archeological remains and much wildlife interest, including significant numbers of breeding birds such as red grouse, curlew and golden plover. There are guided walks and events throughout the year and an information caravan tours the estate during the main season. For a leaflet on self-guided walks please send a s.a.e. to: The Estate Office, Marsden, Huddersfield HD7 6DH.

There are also good walking opportunities at the strange and fantastic geological formations of **Brimham Rocks** near Ripon, set in open moorland overlooking Nidderdale. Due to nesting birds, dogs must be kept on leads during April, May and June, and under strict control thereafter. Nearby is the magnificent **Fountains Abbey** and **Studley Royal**, one of Europe's most important designed landscapes.

In the heart of the historic city of York, **Treasurer's House** provides a splendid backdrop to the Minster and within easy travelling distance are **Beningbrough Hall** and **Nunnington Hall**. Near Wakefield is **Nostell Priory**, one of Robert Adam's great masterpieces.

The Trust also owns **Bridestones Moor**, within the North York Moors National Park. Part of this property is a nature reserve (access via the Forestry Enterprise Dalby Forest Drive, for which a charge is made) sheltering a variety of plants and animals typical of heather moorland. The Trust is carrying out scrub clearance at the site and a nature trail leaflet is available. To the north is the bent pinnacle of **Roseberry Topping**, reaching 317m above sea level and used as a beacon station at the time of the Armada and again when Napoleon threatened invasion.

The Trust cares for 10½ miles of Yorkshire's wild and rugged coastline, including **Cayton Bay** and **Hayburn Wyke** near Scarborough. These areas of wooded valley and cliffs are notable for their abundance of wild flowers. Further north, Trust land at **Runswick** and **Port Mulgrave** is best viewed from the Cleveland Way long distance footpath. At **Ravenscar** the Trust's Coastal Centre provides a fascinating insight into the local wildlife and geology and the **Peak Alum Works** explain the alum industry and history of this early industrial site.

The spectacular coastline runs north to the dramatic **Souter Lighthouse**, the famous bird colony on **Marsden Rock** and thence to **Druridge Bay**, where the Trust owns a mile of coast backed by golden sand dunes and grassland. From **Craster** Trust ownership runs for 5 miles and includes the brooding ruins of **Dunstanburgh Castle**, as well as **Embleton Links** and **Low Newton-by-Sea**, where **Newton Pool** provides a superb habitat for many water birds. There are interesting 18th-century lime kilns at **Beadnell Harbour** and a Trust information centre and shop at **Seahouses**, from where there is access to the **Farne Islands**. Just to the north is the dramatic **Lindisfarne Castle**, perched atop Holy Island.

Northumberland's hinterland is as stunning as its coastline. There are magnificent walks around **Allen Banks** and **Staward Gorge**, along the River Allen, and the **Hadrian's Wall Estate** offers breathtaking views, as well as some of England's best preserved Roman remains at **Housesteads Fort.** Circular walks are possible in the beautiful countryside around **Wallington** near Rothbury and at **Cragside** there are 40 miles of paths and the fascinating Power Circuit, designed to show visitors the industrial archaeology of the property.

Highlights for Disabled Visitors
Newton Pool has a boarded walkway and specially adapted bird hide; special arrangements for disabled visitors at **Malham Tarn** and **Brimham Rocks** (tel. for details).

... and for Families
Ravenscar Coastal Centre has a rock pool aquarium; **Townhead Barn** at Malham has hands-on displays for children.

Further Information
NT Regional Offices:

- **Northumbria** (tel. 01670 774691) – for properties in Northumberland, Durham and Tyneside.

- **Yorkshire** (tel. 01904 702021)

Malham Tarn Estate and **Upper Wharfedale** both have free interpretation centres with exhibitions. Townhead Barn at Malham is open Easter to Sept: daily except Mon, 10–4; Sun only for rest of year. Town Head Barn at Buckden is open Easter to Sept: daily except Fri, 10–4; Sun only for rest of year. For further information and a free leaflet detailing walks in Upper Wharfedale, please tel/fax 01729 830416.

Hardcastle Crags; an information vehicle is present Sun all year, weekends in April, May, June & Oct, daily from last week of June to first week of Sept. Parking £2 (£1.50 midweek), coaches £15 and by arrangement only, minibuses £5, motorcycles 60p. A programme of events and walks runs thoughout the year.

Brimham Rocks; information centre, shop and refreshment kiosk are open 11–5 daily from June to Sept, weekends only in April, May & Oct, plus Bank Hols and local school holidays and some winter weekends. Parking £1.80, coaches £7, minibuses £3, motorcycles 70p. Tel. 01423 780688; fax 01423 781020.

Ravenscar Coastal Centre; open 4 April to 4 Oct, daily 10.30–5.30.

BENINGBROUGH HALL AND GARDENS
🏠 🏠 ✂️ 🧍 😀   *North Yorkshire*

Shipton-by-Beningbrough, York YO6 1DD Tel: 01904 470666 Fax: 01904 470002

An imposing Georgian mansion, built in 1716 and containing one of the most impressive baroque interiors in England. Exceptional wood carving, an unusual central corridor running the full length of the house, and over 100 pictures on loan from the National Portrait Gallery can be found inside. There is also a fully equipped Victorian laundry and exciting new walled garden

Note: Most rooms have no electric lights. Visitors wishing to make a close study of the interior and portraits should avoid dull days early and late in the season. The house may be closed for up to 1hr on Fri for wedding ceremonies to take place. Contact the property for more information

O 4 April to 1 Nov: Sat to Wed, Good Fri & Fri in July and Aug. **House:** 11–5. Last admission 4.30. **Grounds:** 11–5.30. Last admission 5. **Events:** 17 May, Spring Plant Fair; 13 Sept, Autumn Plant Fair. Licensed for wedding ceremonies and receptions; please contact Assistant Property Manager for details

£ House, garden & exhibition: £5, children £2.50; family ticket (2 adults & 3 children) £12.50. Discount for cyclists. Party rates available; for full details tel. 01765 601005 and ask for group visits information or contact the Assistant Property Manager (tel. 01904 470666). Garden & exhibition only: £3, children £1.50; family ticket £7.50

Guided garden walks most weekends

Open as grounds

Access to ground floor only, by ramp; inform reception on arrival. Level garden paths (embedded gravel); walled garden designed for wheelchair access, with wide level paths; parking spaces by stable block. Restaurant, shop, garden exhibition and laundry accessible; WC in stable block. Wheelchairs available

Braille guides for house and garden; guided tours by arrangement

Home-made hot & cold lunches, coffee & teas in licensed restaurant, open as grounds. Kiosk open busy days. Special functions and pre-booked parties by arrangement

Baby-changing and feeding room. For conservation reasons pushchairs are not allowed in the house, baby slings available. Children's menu & highchairs in restaurant. Children's guidebook. Wilderness playground. Full programme of events for families

School groups by prior arrangement. Victorian 'Below-stairs'; artwork with portraits; archive of materials

Strictly no dogs allowed in house or garden

➔ (7: E7) 8ml NW of York, 2ml W of Shipton, 2ml SE of Linton-on-Ouse (A19) [105: SE516586] *Bus:* Rider York 30, 31/B, 32A from ➡ York–Newton-on-Ouse, thence 1ml (tel. 01904 435637) *Station:* York 8ml; also, on Route 65 of National Cycle Network

BRAITHWAITE HALL    *North Yorkshire*

East Witton, Leyburn DL8 4SY Tel: 01969 640287

A remote 17th-century stone farmhouse, with fine original features including fireplaces, panelling and oak staircase

O By arrangement with the tenant, Mrs David Duffus

£ £1, incl. leaflet. No reduction for children. No access for coaches. No WC

→ (7: C6) 1½ml SW of Middleham, 2ml W of East Witton (A6108) [99: SE117857]

CHERRYBURN   *Northumberland*

Station Bank, Mickley, Nr Stocksfield NE43 7DB Tel: 01661 843276

The birthplace of Thomas Bewick (b.1753), Northumberland's greatest artist, wood-engraver and naturalist. The 19th-century farmhouse, latter home of the Bewick family, houses an exhibition on Bewick's life and work. There is a printing press in the adjoining barn, plus Bewick's birthplace cottage, a farmyard and garden for picnics. There are beautiful views over the Tyne valley and a short walk from the south bank of the River Tyne, where Bewick spent much of his childhood

What's new in 1998: Improved access to main events lawn for disabled visitors

O 2 April to 1 Nov: daily except Tues and Wed 1–5.30. Last admission 5.
Events: First May BHol, May Day celebration with maypole dancing and children's entertainment; 28 June, Scottish country dancing; plant sales throughout summer season; engraving, bookbinding and printing demonstrations on most days; please send s.a.e to Administrator for details

£ £2.80. Pre-booked coach parties welcome; exclusive use of property Mon, Thur & Fri mornings only (s.a.e. to Administrator for booking form)

🛍 Shop selling prints from Bewick's original engravings, books & gifts, located in the farmhouse at Cherryburn

♿ Some gravel paths; cobbled farmyard; 100m sloping ramped pathway from car park, companion necessary for wheelchair users; level entry to front of property (usual visitor entrance), then three steps inside property and two steps to rear of property. WC. Car park 100m from house entrance

👁 Braille booklet 'Discover Thomas Bewick at Cherryburn'; smooth and engraved woodblocks may be touched

☕ Morning coffee available for pre-booked parties

The Jay, BY THOMAS BEWICK

Farmyard animals usually include donkeys, pigs, poultry, lambs. Picnicking in grounds. Play lawn. Annual art competition. Join in maypole dancing on first BHol in May (prize for best-dressed May King or Queen)

Pre-booked school parties welcome Mon, Thur & Fri mornings only (exclusive use of property). Wood-engraving, printing and bookbinding demonstrations. Art, artists, countryside, local history and country life in 18th and 19th centuries. Farmyard animals. Maypole and country dancing with instruction. School Visits leaflet available (s.a.e. to Administrator)

No dogs

(7: K4) 11ml W of Newcastle, 11ml E of Hexham; ¼ml N of Mickley Square (leave A695 at Mickley Square and follow signposts). Cherryburn situated close to S bank of River Tyne [88: NZ075627]. Free car park at property *Bus:* Northumbria 602 Newcastle–Hexham (passes ✸ Newcastle) (tel: 0191 212 3000) *Station:* Stocksfield (U) 1½ml; Prudhoe (U) 1¼ml

CRAGSIDE HOUSE, GARDEN AND GROUNDS

🏛 🦇 ✿ ♣ ⬆ ♿ ♥   *Northumberland*

Rothbury, Morpeth NE65 7PX Tel: 01669 620150/620333

A Victorian mansion, designed by R. Norman Shaw for the 1st Lord Armstrong and the first house in the world to be lit by hydroelectricity, a system developed by Armstrong using man-made lakes and underground piping. He also created extensive pleasure grounds surrounding the house, planting millions of trees and building forty miles of drives and footpaths. The 'Power Circuit', a 1½ml walk alongside Debdon Burn, includes the Ram and Power houses in which hydraulic and hydroelectric machinery is displayed. The Victorian Terraced Garden contains a remarkable Orchard House, ferneries, loggia, Italian garden and restored 19th-century clock tower

House: 1 April to 1 Nov: daily except Mon but open BH Mon, 1–5.30. Last admission 4.45. **Grounds:** same days as house 10.30–7. Last admission 5. Also selected days in Nov & Dec. **Events:** for details please send s.a.e. to Property Manager

House, garden, grounds & visitor centre £6; family ticket (2 adults, 2 children) £15; pre-booked parties £5.70. Garden, grounds & visitor centre only £3.80; pre-booked parties £3.50. Accompanied children 12 and under free during school holidays. Car park 100m from house (9 car parks in grounds). New car park to rear of gardens: access from main entrance. Coach park 350m (advance booking essential). Please note coaches cannot tour grounds as drive is too narrow in places. Mini-bus for tour of grounds available to groups visiting by coach, must be booked in advance

🏠 Visitor centre (including shop), Vickers Rooms restaurant, information centre, Armstrong Energy Centre and natural history exhibition: same days as house: 10.30–5.30; weekends and selected days in Nov & Dec (tel. 01669 620448)

♿ Parking for disabled drivers in designated areas of car parks; disabled passengers may be set down at house. Access to house (lift to first floor) & shop and restaurant in Visitor Centre. WC at visitor centre & by house and Crozier Drive car park; wheelchair path, adapted picnic tables & parking at Nelly's Moss Upper Lake

👁 Braille guides

🍴 Morning coffee, lunches and teas in Vickers Rooms restaurant in visitor centre (tel. 01669 620134). Picnicking in all car parks and around Nelly's Moss Lakes

👶 Front sling baby carriers available; facilities for parents and babies, including use of private room for nursing mothers. Adventure playground at Dunkirk car park. Children's guide

🏫 Education room/school party base. School parties may visit all attractions with a guide. Resource book for teachers available. Pre-book with Education Officer (tel. 01669 621445)

🐕 In grounds only (not in formal garden)

➔ (7: K3) 13ml SW of Alnwick (B6341) and 15ml NW of Morpeth on Wooler road (A697), turn left on to B6341 at Moorhouse Crossroads, entrance ¾ml N of Rothbury; public transport passengers enter by Reivers Well Gate from Morpeth Road (B6344) [81: NU073022] *Bus:* Northumbria 516 Morpeth–Thropton, Postbus 817 (both passing 🚉 Morpeth) with connections from Newcastle (passing Tyne & Wear Metro Haymarket), alight Reivers Well Gate, ¾ml (tel. 01670 533128)

DUNSTANBURGH CASTLE 🏰 🏛 🐕 *Northumberland*

Craster, Alnwick   Tel: 01665 576231

A magnificent ruin, dominating a lonely stretch of Northumberland's beautiful coastline. Originally built in 1316, the castle was later enlarged by John of Gaunt and then severely damaged during the Wars of the Roses, since when it has been derelict

Note: Dunstanburgh Castle is in the guardianship of English Heritage

🕐 1 April to 1 Nov: daily 10–6 (or dusk if earlier); 2 Nov to 31 March 1999: Wed to Sun 10–4 (closed 24 to 26 Dec & 1 Jan)

£ £1.70 adult, £1.30 concession, 90p child. Car parks at Craster & Embleton, 1½ml (no coaches at Embleton)

🏠 Shop

♿ Castle unsuitable for wheelchairs. WC at Craster car park

🍴 In Craster (not NT)

🏫 Free school visits. Book through EH (tel. 0191 261 1585)

🐕 Must be kept on leads

→ (7: L2) 9ml NE of Alnwick, approached from Craster on S and Embleton on N (pedestrians only) [75: NU258220] *Bus:* Northumbria 501 Alnwick–Berwick-upon-Tweed (passing close ≋ Berwick-upon-Tweed) with connections from Newcastle (passing Tyne & Wear Metro Haymarket), alight Craster, 1½ml (tel. 0191 212 3000) *Station:* Chathill (U), not Sun, 5ml from Embleton, 7ml from Castle; Alnmouth, 7ml from Craster, 8¼ml from Castle

---

EAST RIDDLESDEN HALL 🏠 🏠 ✽ 🛡 *Bradford*

Bradford Road, Keighley BD20 5EL Tel: 01535 607075 Fax: 01535 691462

A charming 17th-century West Riding manor house, with panelled rooms, fine plasterwork and mullioned windows. There are embroideries, pewter and Yorkshire oak furniture inside, and an attractive garden with herbaceous borders. The impressive Great Barn houses a collection of traditional agricultural implements

What's new in 1998: The Hall is now licensed for wedding ceremonies

🅾 1 April to 1 Nov: daily except Thur & Fri (but open Good Fri, & Thur in July & Aug) 12–5, but 1–5 on Sat. Last admission 4.30. **Events:** 18/19 July, Viking Saga; July & Aug, costumed interpretation; for details of this and of full events programme send s.a.e. marked 'Events'

💷 £3.30, child £1.60; family ticket (2 adults & 3 children) £8. Party rates available; please tel. for details. Parking 100m; coaches must book as space limited. Open for pre-booked parties outside normal opening hours, private functions and wedding ceremonies and receptions

🛍 Shop and information area in Bothy, open at 12 on house open days. Also some Christmas opening

♿ Access to ground floor and garden; some uneven surfaces; loose gravel paths. Spaces reserved for disabled drivers in car park, visitors may be set down near house. Shop accessible via some steps. Tea-room on first floor of Bothy. Access to Great Barn (uneven floor) and Airedale Barn for events only. Sympathetic Hearing Scheme. WC

👁 Braille guide, large-print guide and tactile book; panelling, carving and some kitchen items may be touched

🍽 Tea-room serving lunches and afternoon teas, open at 12 on house open days; also some Christmas openings. Open for pre-booked parties during and outside normal opening hours. Tea-room and Airedale Barn available for private functions. Picnic area in field

👶 Changing facilities. Highchairs and children's menu in tea-room. Children's guidebook. Children's activity days & workshops

🏫 School groups by prior arrangement. Living History for schools

🐕 In grounds only, on leads. Not permitted in garden

→ (7: C8) 1ml NE of Keighley on S side of the Bradford Road in Riddlesden, close to Leeds & Liverpool Canal [104: SE079421] *Bus:* Frequent services from ≋ Bradford Interchange, Bingley & Keighley (tel. 0113 245 7676) *Station:* Keighley 1ml

FARNE ISLANDS ✝ 🏛 🐦 🚶 *Northumberland*

Tel: Information Centre 01665 721099 Warden 01665 720651

One of Britain's most important seabird sanctuaries, home to many different species including puffins, eider ducks and four species of tern. Many of the birds are extremely confiding and visitors can enjoy close views. There is also a large colony of seals. St Cuthbert died on Inner Farne in 687 and the chapel built in his memory can be visited

◎ Inner Farne and Staple Islands only are open to visitors. 1–30 April & 1 Aug to 30 Sept: daily 10.30–6. During breeding season (1 May to 31 July) access is limited to Staple 10.30–1.30, Inner Farne 1.30–5. Visitors to Inner Farne are advised to wear hats!

£ May to end July £3.90; pre-booked school parties £1.90 (per island). At other times £3; pre-booked school parties £1.60 (per island). Public car park in Seahouses opposite harbour. Admission fees do not include boatmen's charges. Tickets may be bought from Warden on landing and boat tickets from boatmen in Seahouses Harbour. No landing in bad weather. Enquiries about landing answered by Property Manager: The Sheiling, 8 St Aidan's, Seahouses, Northumberland NE68 7SR (tel. 01665 720651). WC on Inner Farne

🏠 NT Information Centre and shop at 16 Main Street, Seahouses (tel. 01665 721099); open 24 March to 30 Sept: 10–5 (till 6 during July & Aug); Oct: daily 11–4.30 (except half-term, when 10–5); Nov to 24 Dec: Wed to Sun 11–4

♿ Nature walks on Inner Farne & Staple Island. Islands are difficult for disabled or visually impaired visitors and largely unsuitable for wheelchairs; some wheelchair access to Inner Farne. Please tel. Property Manager before attempting this. WC on Inner Farne

🍽 Refreshments (not NT) in Seahouses (none on islands)

🏴 Teachers' resource book. Guided walks available

➡ (7: L1) 2–5ml off the Northumberland coast, opposite Bamburgh: trips every day from Seahouses Harbour, weather permitting [75: NU2337] *Bus:* As for Dunstanburgh Castle, but alight Seahouses *Station:* Chathill (U), not Sun, 4ml

FOUNTAINS ABBEY & STUDLEY ROYAL WATER GARDEN
🏰 🏠 ✝ ♣ 🍽 🚶 🎭 *North Yorkshire*

Fountains, Ripon HG4 3DY Estate Office tel: 01765 608888; fax: 01765 608889
Visitor Centre tel: 01765 601005; fax: 01765 601002

One of the most remarkable places in Europe and a World Heritage Site, comprising the spectacular ruin of a 12th-century Cistercian abbey, an Elizabethan mansion and one of the best surviving examples of a Georgian water garden. Elegant ornamental lakes, avenues, temples and cascades provide a succession of dramatic eye-catching vistas. St Mary's Church provides a dramatic focus to the medieval deer park, home to over 600 deer

Note: Audiovisual programme and exhibition at visitor centre; small museum near to Abbey; exhibitions in Fountains Hall and Swanley Grange. Abbey maintained by English Heritage; St Mary's Church owned by English Heritage, managed by the NT

What's new in 1998: A new access route through the water garden is open for walks and picnics

Abbey & water garden: open all year daily except Fri in Nov, Dec, Jan and 24/25 Dec. April to Sept: 10–7 (closes at 4 on 10/11 July & 8 Aug); Oct to March 1998: 10–5 (dusk if earlier). Last admission 1hr before closing. **Deer park**: open all year daily during daylight hours. **Floodlighting**: Abbey is floodlit on Fri & Sat evenings until 10pm, 28 Aug to 17 Oct. **Fountains Hall & St Mary's Church**: restoration in progress, apply to Estate Office for opening times. Charge may be reduced on and around event days (10/11 July) due to restricted access to parts of estate. **Events**: extensive programme of concerts, plays, walks & talks available all year, incl. 18 to 20 June, Shakespeare theatre; 10/11 July, Music by Moonlight; 26 to 18 July, theatre; 8 Aug, outdoor promenade entertainment. Details from Box Office (tel. 01765 609999). All outside events wheelchair-accessible. Join free events mailing list. We also offer wedding receptions, corporate hospitality/entertaining and conference facilities; tel. Elaine Clarke on 01765 601003 for details

Fountains Abbey and Studley Royal water garden: £4.20, children £2; family ticket (2 adults & 3 children) £10. Parties over 15 £3.70, children £1.90; parties over 40 (pre-booked only) £3.20, children £1.70. Visitor centre, deer park, St Mary's Church: free. Parking: visitor centre free; deer park £2

Free guided tours of the Abbey and water garden plus extended tours of the complete estate. Floodlit tours of the Abbey 28 Aug to 17 Oct, Fri 7.45pm & 8.15pm. Specialist guides for pre-booked parties (50p per person) (tel. 01765 601005)

Visitor centre shop: open all year except 24/25 Dec & Fri in Jan, April to Aug 10–6, Sept to March 10–5 (or dusk if earlier) (tel. 01765 601004). Lakeside shop open as estate

♿ Minibus available from visitor centre; wheelchairs and self-drive powered vehicle available by prior booking only (tel. 01765 601005); Sympathetic Hearing Scheme. WCs at visitor centre, lakeside tea-room and near Fountains Hall. Wheelchair access: most of the estate accessible, enquire for best route. Wheelchairs available; please book. Paths from visitor centre unsuitable for any self-drive vehicle, including wheelchairs, due to gradient; it is also strongly advised that three-wheeled powered vehicles are not used elsewhere on the estate because of the terrain. Four-wheel battery cars restricted to certain areas. For level access to Abbey use West Gate entrance via Bishop Thornton–Aldfield road (see information boards in designated car park)

👁 Large-print and Braille guides available from visitor centre. Tactile wall frieze and model of Abbey at visitor centre

☕ Visitor centre restaurant: licensed, serving coffee, teas and a wide variety of home-made lunches; party bookings and functions welcome (tel. 01765 601003). Open daily, same times as visitor centre shop. Lakeside tea-room: light lunches, teas & refreshments; open daily April to end Sept 10–5.30 or dusk if earlier (tel. 01765 604246). *Note*: tea-room may close for major building work Oct to March 1999

👪 Parent & baby rooms available at visitor centre and near Fountains Hall. Highchairs & children's menu in restaurant. Children's guide, programme of family and children's activities

🏫 Special facilities linked to National Curriculum for pre-booked parties; for details contact Education Officer (tel. 01765 608888); also new study centre at Swanley Grange

🐕 On short leads

➔ (**7**: D6) 4ml W of Ripon off B6265 to Pateley Bridge, signposted from the A1, 10ml N of Harrogate (A61) [99: SE271683] *Bus:* Keighley & District 802 Bradford–Ripon (with connections from ≢ Harrogate), Sun, June to Aug only (tel. 01535 603284); otherwise Harrogate & District 145 from Ripon (with connections from ≢ Harrogate), Thur & Sat only (tel. 01423 566061)

GEORGE STEPHENSON'S BIRTHPLACE ⚑ ♿ 🛁 *Northumberland*

Wylam NE41 8BP Tel: 01661 853457

A small stone tenement, built c.1760 to accommodate mining families. The furnishings reflect the year of Stephenson's birth here (1781), his whole family living in the one room

🕑 1 April to 1 Nov: Thur, Sat & Sun, BH Mon & Good Fri 1–5.30. Last admission 5. The property may be closed for building works for part of the season. Please contact the Regional Office before visiting (tel. 01670 774691)

£ 80p. Accompanied children aged 12 and under free during school summer holidays. No parties. No WC. Parking by War Memorial in Wylam village, ½ml

➔ (**7**: K4) 8ml W of Newcastle, 1½ml S of A69 at Wylam. Access on foot and bicycle through Country Park, ½ml E of Wylam [88: NZ126650] *Bus:* OK Travel 684 Newcastle–Ovington, alight Wylam, 1ml (tel. 01388 450000) *Station:* Wylam (U) ½ml

GIBSIDE ✚ 🐦 ♿ 🏛 🚹 🎭   *Gateshead*

nr Rowlands Gill, Burnopfield, Newcastle upon Tyne NE16 6BG
Tel: 01207 542255

One of the North's finest landscapes, a 'forest garden' currently under restoration and embracing many miles of walks with fine views. There are several outstanding buildings, including a Palladian chapel, the Column of Liberty, a banqueting house (a Landmark Trust property) and others, still awaiting repair

🅾 1 April to 1 Nov: **Grounds & chapel**, daily except Mon (open BH Mon) 11–5. Last admission 4.30. Note: the property will be closed 3 to 8 November incl. Winter opening (grounds only) 8 Nov to end March 1999: Sun only, 10–4.
Events: service in chapel first Sun each month at 3; 17/18 July, open-air concerts; for details of these and other events, including guided walks, please send s.a.e. to Administrator

💷 £3. Pre-booked parties £2.60. Winter opening (grounds only) £2. Accompanied childred aged 12 and under free during school summer holidays

🖥 Shop (tel. 01207 545801)

♿ Please contact Administrator for access arrangements. One wheelchair available. WC

◉ Braille guide

🍽 Tea-room (tel. 01207 545801). Picnic area in car park

🐕 In the grounds, on leads only

➡ (7: L4) 6ml SW of Gateshead, 20ml W of Durham; entrance on B6314 between Burnopfield and Rowlands Gill [88: NZ172583] *Bus:* Go-Ahead Gateshead 611, M21; Northern 745 from Newcastle (passing close ≋ Newcastle). On all, alight Rowlands Gill, ½ml (tel. 0191 232 5325) *Station:* Blaydon (U) 5ml

---

HADRIAN'S WALL & HOUSESTEADS FORT
♿ 🏦   *Northumberland*

Bardon Mill, Hexham NE47 6NN Tel: (EH Custodian) 01434 344363

One of Rome's most northerly outposts, the Wall was built when the Roman Empire was at its height. Snaking across dramatic countryside, it remains one of Britain's most impressive ruins. Housesteads Fort, one of thirteen permanent bases along the Wall, is one of the best-preserved and conjures an evocative picture of Roman military life

Note: The Trust owns approx. 5ml of the Wall running west from Housesteads Fort (including the Fort itself) to Cawfields Quarry and over 1000ha of farmland. Access to the Wall and the public rights of way is from car parks at Housesteads and Cawfields. Housesteads Fort is owned by the National Trust, and maintained and managed by English Heritage

🅾 **Housesteads Fort & Museum:** 1 April to 1 Nov: daily, 10–6. 2 Nov to 31 March 1999: daily 10–4 (closed 24 to 26 Dec & 1 Jan)

£ Hadrian's Wall, NT information centre and shop free. Housesteads Museum & Fort: Adults £2.70. OAP/UB40/students £2, children £1.40. Free admission to NT and English Heritage members. Car & coach parks at Housesteads (car park charge, incl. NT members), ½ml walk to the Fort, and at the western end at Cawfields Quarry, managed by Northumberland National Park

🏃 For details of guided walks send s.a.e. to information centre and shop. Please note that stout footwear is advisable

📷 Shop & information centre at Housesteads car park (times subject to revision): March: Sat & Sun 11–5; April & Oct: daily 11–5; May to end Sept: daily 10–5; Nov: Sat & Sun 11–dusk (tel. 01434 344525)

♿ Access to information centre and shop only; parking available near Housesteads Fort; ask at information centre for details. WC at information centre and shop. Fort not suitable for wheelchair users

📢 Braille guides

☕ Hot and cold drinks, sandwiches and ice-cream at kiosk. Picnic tables outside information centre

🧒 Children's guide

🐕 Must be kept on leads

➔ (7: J4) 6ml NE of Haltwhistle, 3ml N of Bardon Mill rly station; ½ml N of B6318; best access from car parks at Housesteads and Cawfields [87: NY790688] *Bus:* Waugh's 890 Hadrian's Wall service, Apr–Oct only, ☒ Hexham– ☒ Haltwhistle (tel. 01670 533128) *Station:* Bardon Mill (U) 4ml

---

LINDISFARNE CASTLE 🏰 ✿ 🖼 🍴 *Northumberland*

Holy Island, Berwick-upon-Tweed TD15 2SH Tel: 01289 389244

Perched atop a rocky crag and accessible over a causeway at low tide only, the castle presents an exciting and alluring aspect. Originally a Tudor fort, it was converted into a private house in 1903 by a young Edwin Lutyens. The small rooms are full of intimate decoration and design, the windows looking down upon the charming walled garden, planned by Gertrude Jekyll

Note: It is impossible to cross the island between the 2hrs before high tide and the 3½hrs following. Tide tables are printed in local newspapers, and displayed at the causeway. *Special note:* To avoid disappointment please check safe crossing times coincide with castle opening times before making a long/special journey

What's new in 1998: Essential conservation work may be in progress, and could affect visitor access to the castle

O 1 April to 29 Oct: daily except Fri (but open Good Fri) 1–5.30. Last admission 5. Castle *may* open at the earlier time of 11–5, tide and staff permitting; please tel. to check. Admission to garden only when gardener is in attendance (usually Fri but please check with Administrator before making a special journey).

£ £4; family ticket (2 adults, 2 children under 17) £10. No party rate. Parties of 15 or more must pre-book. No WC. Main public car park approx. 1ml away; parking off approach road to castle for disabled orange badge holders only, car-parking charges (incl. NT members). No large camera cases, boxes or rucksacks

🛍 NT shop in Main Street, Holy Island Village (tel. 01289 389253)

♿ Difficult for ambulant disabled people and not recommended to wheelchair users; steep, cobbled access ramp, many steps and stairs within castle

◉ Braille guide

🅿 In Holy Island Village (not NT)

👶 No back carriers in castle (including framed baby carriers); front sling baby carriers available

🐕 On leads as far as Lower Battery only

→ (7: K1) On Holy Island, 6ml E of A1 across causeway [75: NU136417]
Bus: Northumbria 477 from Berwick-upon-Tweed (passing close ⊟ Berwick-upon-Tweed). Times vary with tides (tel. 01670 533128 – bus times only)
Station: Berwick-upon-Tweed 10ml from causeway

MAISTER HOUSE 🏠   *Kingston-upon-Hull*

160 High Street, Hull HU1 1NL Tel: 01482 324114

Rebuilt in 1743 during Hull's heyday as an affluent trading centre, this house is a typical but rare survivor of a contemporary merchant's residence. The restrained exterior belies the spectacular plasterwork staircase inside. The house is now let as offices

🅾 Staircase and entrance hall only: all year: Mon to Fri 10–4; closed BH Mon, Good Fri & 1 Jan

£ 80p, incl. guidebook. Unsuitable for parties. No parking at property. No WC

→ (7: G8) Hull city centre *Bus:* Local services to within 100m (tel. 01482 222222); services from surrounding areas (tel. 01482 327146) *Station:* Hull ¾ml

---

MOULTON HALL 🏠 🔑   *North Yorkshire*

Moulton, Richmond DL10 6QH Tel: 01325 377227

A compact stone manor house, dating from 1650 and with a very fine carved wood staircase

🅾 By arrangement with tenant, the Hon. J. D. Eccles

£ 50p. Unsuitable for coaches

♿ Please enquire about access when arranging a visit

→ (7: D5) 5ml E of Richmond; turn off A1, ½ml S of Scotch Corner [99: NZ235035]
Bus: United 35/A Darlington–Richmond (passing close ⊟ Darlington), alight Moulton village, ½ml (tel. 0345 124125) *Station:* Darlington 9½ml

MOUNT GRACE PRIORY ✚ 🏃 🎽 *North Yorkshire*

Osmotherley, Northallerton DL6 3JG Tel: 01609 883494

England's most important Carthusian ruin, the remains of a 14th-century priory. The individual cells reflect the hermit-like isolation of the Carthusian monks; a reconstruction enables visitors to see the austere and simple furnishings. There is a small herb garden and nature trail

Note: The priory is financed, administered and maintained by English Heritage

🅾 1 April to 31 October: daily 10–6 (closes 4 in Oct). 1 Nov to 31 March: Wed to Sun 10–4; closed 1–2. **Events:** diary of events available in shop free of charge, or tel. 0191 261 1585

£ £2.70; OAPs, students and UB40 holders £2.20; children (under 16) £1.40. Parties of 11 or more 15% discount. NT members free, except on certain special event days, when full admission price will be charged. School visits Mon to Fri, free, but must be booked with EH (tel. 0191-261 1585). Bulky bags and pushchairs may be left in reception

🛍 Shop; herbs for sale May to Aug

♿ Disabled visitors may bring car up to entrance. Access to grounds, shop and ground floor of reconstructed cell and the herb garden

🐦 Wild flowers and herbs; bird song and animal sounds

🍴 Light refreshments, ie canned drinks, biscuits, available in shop. Picnics welcome

🏫 School visits free Mon to Fri. Must be booked in advance through EH (tel. 0191 261 1585)

🐕 No dogs, except guide dogs

➡ (7; E5) 6ml NE of Northallerton, ½ml E of A19 and ½ml S of its junction with A172 [99: SE449985] *Bus:* Tees 90 /190 Northallerton–Middlesbrough, alight Priory Road End, ½ml (tel. 0345 124125) *Station:* Northallerton 6ml

NOSTELL PRIORY 🏰 ❀ 🏃 🎽 *Wakefield*

Doncaster Road, Nostell, nr Wakefield WF4 1QE
Tel: 01924 863892 Fax: 01924 865282

One of Yorkshire's finest Palladian houses, built in the mid 18th century and set in parkland with delightful lakeside walks. The spectacular interiors are an unusual mixture of the rococo and classical styles, designed by Paine and Adam respectively. The state rooms house an exceptionally fine collection of Chippendale furniture, as well as many important paintings and exquisite Chinese wallpapers

🅾 4 April to 1 Nov: April to June & 5 Sept to 1 Nov: Sat & Sun 12–5 (closed Good Fri); 1 July to 3 Sept: daily except Fri 12–5, BH Mon 12–5. Last admission 4.30. **Events:** Easter Sat, Sun & Mon, Living Heritage Craft Fair; 24/25 May, Craft, Garden & Flower Show; 19 July, Country Fair (charge for admission to grounds, incl. NT members); 12/13 Sept, Living Heritage Craft Fair

£ House & grounds: £4, children £2; family ticket (2 adults & 3 children) £9.50. Party rates available; for full details tel. 01924 863892 and ask for group visits information or contact the Visitor Services Manager. Grounds only: £2.50, children £1.50; family ticket £6.50. Pre-booked parties welcome outside published opening times (no reduction and charge made for NT members). Min. charge for parties of fewer than 30. Parking 350m. NT members may be expected to pay additional charge for access to grounds during special events

⚐ Guided tours only on weekdays (last tour 4); free-flow visiting at weekends

⚑ Gift shops

♿ Disabled visitors may usually be driven to front door. Level access to ground floor. Lift to first floor; grounds accessible; wheelchairs, walking aid and powered self-drive vehicle available. Restaurant accessible. WC. Tape guide; loop system; rollators

◉ Braille guide and audio tour; tactile books

◗ Light lunches and teas in stable block. Meals available to parties, by arrangement (tel. 01924 862205 or 863892). Picnic site

⚐ Baby-changing facilities and feeding area. For conservation reasons pushchairs must be left in reception; baby carriers

⚐ In grounds only, on leads

➔ (7: E8) On the A638 out of Wakefield towards Doncaster [111: SE407172] *Bus:* W Riding/Yorkshire Traction/Yorkshire Rider 485, 497/8 Wakefield–Doncaster; W Riding 123 from Wakefield; Yorkshire Traction 245 from Pontefract (tel. 0113 245 7676) *Station:* Fitzwilliam 1½ml

---

NUNNINGTON HALL ⚐ ⚑ ⚐   *North Yorkshire*

Nunnington, York YO6 5UY Tel: 01439 748283 Fax: 01439 748284

The sheltered walled garden on the bank of the River Rye with its peacocks, ducks, old varieties of fruit trees and clematis collection, complements this mellow 17th-century manor house. From the magnificent oak-panelled hall, follow three staircases to discover family rooms, the nursery, the haunted room and the attics, with their fascinating Carlisle collection of miniature rooms fully furnished to reflect different periods.

◯ 1 April to 1 Nov: daily except Mon & Tues (but open BH Mon & every Tues during June, July & Aug) 1.30–6 (1.30–5.30 April & Oct); last admission 1hr before house closes. **Events:** 20 June, outdoor concert; other exhibitions and events through the year; contact Visitor Manager for details

£ House & garden £4, children £2; family ticket £10. Party rates available, please tel. the Visitor Manager for details. Garden only £1; children free. Car parking 50m; unsuitable for trailer caravans

⚑ Open as house

♿ Access to ground floor and tea-room only. Garden tables by river. Ramp to main garden; loose gravel paths. For close parking please apply at reception; adapted WC. Wheelchairs available

Braille guide; river, peacock and duck sounds; garden scents

Tea-room and tea-garden serving home-made teas, sandwiches, scones, cakes and pastries. Open 12.30 for light lunches, closes 30min after last admission

For conservation reasons pushchairs, prams and back carriers are not allowed in the house. Baby-changing facilities. Children's menu and highchairs in tea-room. Winner of 1997 Egon Ronay award for child-friendly tea-room. Collection of miniature rooms. Children's guide. Quiz

Contact the Visitor Manager for details

In car park only (shaded woodland)

(7: F6) In Ryedale, 4½ml SE of Helmsley (A170) Helmsley–Pickering road; 1½ml N of B1257 Malton–Helmsley road [100: SE670795]; 21ml N of York, B1363. Nunnington Hall is 7½ml SE of the NT Rievaulx Terrace and Temples
Bus: Yorkshire Coastliner 94 ⮌ Malton–Helmsley (tel. 01653 692556); otherwise Scarborough & District/Stephensons 128 Scarborough–Helmsley (passing close ⮌ Scarborough & Seamer), alight Wombleton, 3ml (tel. (01609 780780)

ORMESBY HALL 🏠 🏛 ✿ 🌳 🛡 *Middlesbrough*

Ormesby, Middlesbrough TS7 9AS Tel: 01642 324188 Fax: 01642 300937

A mid 18th-century Palladian mansion, notable for its fine plasterwork and carved wood decoration. The Victorian laundry and kitchen with scullery and game larder are especially interesting, and there is a particularly beautiful stable block (let to the Cleveland Mounted Police). A large model railway exhibition is on show. There is also an attractive garden and holly walk

What's new in 1998: The Hall is now licensed for wedding ceremonies

1 April to 1 Nov: Tues, Wed, Thur & Sun 2–5.30; also open Good Fri & BH Mon. Last admission 5. Guided tours on Tues only, last tour 3.30.
Events: full events programme, including Victorian Sundays, family days, concerts and plays; please write or tel. for details

£ House, garden, railway & exhibitions: £3.30, children £1.60; family ticket (2 adults & 3 children) £8. Party rates available; please contact the House Manager for details. Garden, railway & exhibitions: £2, children £1. Parking 100m

🎫 On Tues only (see above), plus special evening tours for pre-booked parties

🛍 Shop as house. Also certain dates in Nov & Dec. Tel. for details

♿ Access via one shallow step to ground floor of house, shop, tea-room & garden; cars may bring disabled visitors to front door; disabled drivers may park near house. WC

👁 Braille guide. Specialist tours for groups by arrangement

🍴 Tea-room serving home-made teas open as house and certain dates in Nov & Dec

👶 Baby-changing facilities; children's menu, highchairs in tea-room; children's play area

🏫 School groups on Mon & Tues mornings during season. Laundry and kitchen visits

🐕 In park only, on leads

➔ (7: E4) 3ml SE of Middlesbrough, W of A171 [93: NZ530167]. From the A19 take the A174 to the A172. Follow signs for Ormesby Hall. Car entrance on Ladgate Lane (B1380) *Bus:* From Middlesbrough (passing close ⇌ Middlesbrough) (tel. 01642 444777) *Station:* Marton (U), not Sun, except May to Sept, 1½ml; Middlesbrough 3ml

---

RIEVAULX TERRACE & TEMPLES 🏫📷🎫🛡 *North Yorkshire*

Rievaulx, Helmsley, York YO6 5LJ Tel: 01439 798340 Fax: 01439 748284

A ½ml long grass terrace and adjoining woodland, with vistas over Rievaulx Abbey (English Heritage) to Ryedale and the Hambleton Hills. There is an abundance of spring flowers and two mid 18th-century temples. The Ionic temple, intended as a banqueting house, has elaborate ceiling paintings and fine 18th-century furniture

Note: No access to Rievaulx Abbey from Terrace. No access to property Nov to end March

🕙 1 April to 1 Nov: daily 10.30–6 (closes at 5 in April & Oct). Last admission 1hr before closing. Ionic Temple closed 1–2. **Events:** contact the Visitor Manager at Nunnington Hall for information (tel. 01439 748283)

£ £2.80, children £1.40; family ticket £7. Party rates available; for full details please contact the Visitor Manager at Nunnington Hall. Parking at reception, but coach park 200m; unsuitable for trailer caravans

🛍 Shop and information centre open as property

♿ Terrace recommended; access to Ionic Temple not possible because of steps. Unadapted WCs. Powered self-drive vehicle available; level gravel path through woods. Ramped access to shop and reception. Manual wheelchair available

Braille guide

Ice-cream only. Teas at Nunnington Hall, 7ml (see p.271)

Baby-changing facilities. Nature quizzes

Contact the Visitor Manager at Nunnington Hall for information

On leads only

(7: E6) 2½ml NW of Helmsley on B1257 [100: SE579848] *Bus:* Moorsbus from Helmsley (connections from ▣ Scarborough), Sun, June to Sept, plus Tues & Wed in Aug; otherwise Scarborough & District 128 from Scarborough or Stephensons 57 from ▣ York, alight Helmsley, thence 2½ml (tel. 01609 780780)

SOUTER LIGHTHOUSE 🏠 🖼 🔦 🍴 🎭 *South Tyneside*

Coast Road, Whitburn, Sunderland SR6 7NR Tel: 0191 529 3161

Boldly painted in red and white stripes, this rocket-like lighthouse opened in 1871, the first to be powered by alternating electric current. The engine room, light tower and keeper's cottage are all on view, and there is a video, model and information display

What's new in 1998: Closed circuit TV now allows view from the top for those unable to ascend light tower

O 1 April to 1 Nov: daily except Fri (but open Good Fri) 11–5. Last admission 4.30. **Events:** Story-telling sessions for schools, Christmas lunches and talks; for full details please send s.a.e. to Property Manager

£ £2.50. Pre-booked parties £2. Two accompanied children aged 12 and under free during school summer holidays. Car and coach park 100m

For pre-booked parties

Access to shop is free. Open as lighthouse

Good access to ground floor of lighthouse, including engine room, shop and interpretation area with video. WC (limited wheelchair access). Restaurant, limited access. Light tower not accessible for wheelchairs, but closed circuit TV camera enables visitors unable to ascend the tower to enjoy the view from the top

Braille guide. Engines and Morse code signaller are among items to touch

Tea-room serving morning coffee, lunch and teas, open as lighthouse. Access is free. Children's pirate parties, meetings and other functions by arrangement; details from Property Manager. Picnicking in grounds

Education room; school base for single class groups only. School visits may take place on property open days before opening to public, and must be booked in advance; full details from Education Officer or Property Manager

Dogs in grounds only

(7: E2) 2½ml S of South Shields on A183, 5ml N of Sunderland on A183 [88: NZ641408] *Bus:* Stagecoach Economic E1 ▣ Sunderland–South Shields (passes ▣ Sunderland & Tyne & Wear Metro South Shields) (tel. 0191 232 5325) *Station:* East Boldon (U) 3ml

TREASURER'S HOUSE 🏠 ❀ 🎭 🎭 *York*

Chapter House Street, York YO1 2JD Tel: 01904 624247

York's 'hidden treasure', this elegant house stands within the tranquil surroundings of the Minster Close. Medieval in origin (and with even earlier - Roman - links), the house was rescued from neglect by the wealthy local industrialist Frank Green, who carefully restored it and made it his home. It is as he left it, with many fine pieces of furniture and notable collections of china, pottery and glass

What's new in 1998: The property is now licensed for weddings

🅾 28 March to 1 Nov: daily except Fri 10.30–5. Last admission 4.30.
Events: contact Property Manager for details of function hire and full calendar of special events

💷 House & garden: £3.50, children £1.75; family ticket (2 adults & 3 children) £8. Party rates available; please tel. Property Manager for details. No parking facilities, but car park nearby in Lord Mayor's Walk

🎟 Guided tours by arrangement. Evening opening for pre-booked parties £4.50 per person (min. charge £90) incl. guided tour; contact Property Manager

🛍 NT shop at 32 Goodramgate open all year, Mon to Sat 9–5.30

♿ Cars may set down passengers with disabilities at the door. Ground floor accessible with helper. Introductory video (with induction loop) for those who find stairs difficult. Access to tea-room difficult, but possible to have refreshments brought up. Garden level

👁 Braille guide. Tactile pictures in exhibition and short 'scented' pathway in garden

🍴 Licensed tea-room for coffee, lunches & teas. Open for pre-booked parties during and outside normal opening hours and for private functions (tel. 01904 646757)

Facilities for babies & nursing mothers; children's guidebook, activity sheets, children's menu and highchair. Recipient of York City Council's Child Friendly Award 1997. For conservation reasons pushchairs are not allowed in the house

Pre-booked school parties welcome, with 'Butler's Tours' available; please tel. for details

In garden only, on leads

(7: E7) In Minster Yard, on N side of Minster [105: SE604523]
Bus: From surrounding areas (tel. 01904 435637). Park-and-ride scheme from outskirts of city *Station:* York ½ml

---

WALLINGTON 🏛 🖼 ❖ 🌳 ⛱ 👤 🛡   *Northumberland*

Cambo, Morpeth NE61 4AR Tel: 01670 774283

The family home of the Trevelyans, Wallington is largely a mid 18th century creation. The restrained Palladian exterior gives way to magnificent rococo plasterwork inside and there are later, Victorian, additions including the magnificent paintings of Northumbrian history carried out by William Bell Scott. The delightful grounds include a splendid walled garden and conservatory, with fine walks along the River Wansbeck

What's new in 1998: Adventure playground

House: 1 April to 30 Sept: daily except Tues 1–5.30. Last admission 5. 1 Oct to 1 Nov: daily except Tues 1–4.30. Last admission 4. **Walled garden:** 1 April to end Sept: daily 10–7; Oct: daily 10–6; Nov to March 1999: daily 10–4 (or dusk if earlier). **Grounds:** all year during daylight hours. **Events:** Easter egg hunt, open air-concerts, Family Fun Day, Shakespeare on the lawn; for details send s.a.e. to House Manager. Wallington is available for weddings, corporate bookings and special events

House, walled garden & grounds £4.80; family ticket (2 adults & their children) £12. Parties £4.30. Walled garden & grounds £2.80; parties £2.30. Parties must book in advance

Guided tours available outside normal opening hours; contact House Manager for details (tel. 01670 774283)

Shop open 1 April to 30 Sept: daily except Tues 10.30–5.30; 1 Oct to 2 Nov: daily except Tues 10.30–5; 4 Nov to 20 Dec: Wed to Sun 12–4 (tel. 01670 774249). Plant centre (access through shop) 1 April to 30 Sept (except Tues) 10.30–5.30

Access via ramp to ground floor of house only; wheelchairs available. Apply to parking attendant for reserved bays in main car park and walled garden; most of grounds, conservatory and walled garden accessible, self-drive powered vehicle. WC in courtyard and restaurant. Tea-room upstairs, but refreshments available in Harness Room on ground floor on request

Braille guides to house, garden, park and estate; scented roses in garden

Coffee, lunches & teas in Clock Tower tea-room (tel. 01670 774274) same times as shop, see above. Picnics in grounds. Access to shop and tea-room is free from 4 Nov to 20 Dec, daily except Mon & Tues

⊞ Front sling baby carriers to be used in house, provided at front desk; please enquire about other facilities for parents & babies. Doll's houses and toy soldier collections. Children's guide. 'Spot the odd thing out' competition during summer holidays

▦ School visits welcome, please book in advance with House Manager (tel. 01670 774283)

⊞ In grounds and in walled garden on leads

➡ (7: K3) 12ml W of Morpeth (B6343), 6ml NW of Belsay (A696), take B6342 to Cambo [81: NZ030843] *Bus:* Northumbria 419, from Morpeth (Wed, Fri, Sat only) (passing close ⊞ Morpeth); Northumbria 508 from ⊞ Newcastle, Sun, May to Aug only; otherwise National Express from Newcastle (passing close ⊞ Newcastle), alight Capheaton Road End, 2ml (tel. 01670 533128)

WASHINGTON OLD HALL ⊞ ✻ ⊡ *Sunderland*

The Avenue, Washington Village NE38 7LE Tel: 0191 416 6879

A modest and unpretentious 17th-century manor house, incorporating the 12th-century remains of the home of George Washington's ancestors, and from where the family drew its name

What's new in 1998: Video on the Washington family; re-created Jacobean garden

◉ 1 April to 1 Nov: daily, but closed to visitors Thur, Fri & Sat when the property is available for private function hire (open Good Fri) 11–5. Last admission 4.30. **Events:** Independence Day celebrations; 17 Sept, wedding exhibition. In addition, the Old Hall and garden are available for various functions; please tel. for full details

£ £2.50. Accompanied children aged 12 and under free during school summer holidays. Parties £2 on application. Coaches must park on the Avenue

⌐ Introductory talks for group visits

⌂ Souvenir desk in entrance hall, open as house

♿ Access to ground floor only and to part of garden. Please contact property for access arrangements. Adapted WC

◈ Please ask about tactile opportunities. Braille guide. Garden has scented plants

☕ Tea, coffee and cake available during opening hours

▦ Teachers' notes available; please contact the Property Manager

⊞ Dogs allowed on leads in garden only

➡ (7: D3) 5ml W of Sunderland, 2ml E of A1, S of Tyne tunnel, follow signs to Washington, District 4, then Washington village; situated on E side of Avenue [88: NZ312566] *Bus:* Wear Buses 191/4, 291/3/4/7, 394, 638, OK 297 from Tyne & Wear Metro Heworth; also other services from surrounding areas (tel. 0191 232 5325) *Station:* Heworth (Tyne & Wear Metro) 4ml; E Boldon (U) 6ml; Newcastle 7ml

Introduction to Wales

Mae'r wybodaeth sydd yn y llawlyfr hwn am feddiannau'r Ymddiriedolaeth Genedlaethol yng Nghymru ar gael yn Gymraeg o Swyddfa'r Ymddiriedolaeth Genedlaethol, Sgwar y Drindod, Llandudno LL30 2DE, ffôn 01492 860123.

Wales is famous for its spectacular coastline, rugged mountain scenery and lush green valleys. With three national parks and thousands of hectares designated as Areas of Outstanding Natural Beauty, visitors do not have to travel far to reach beautiful open countryside offering a wide variety of recreational opportunities. The Trust plays an active role in protecting and managing this countryside and owns 132 miles of the Welsh coastline. In fact, the first property ever given to the Trust was in Wales, at **Dinas Oleu** above Barmouth on the Cardigan Bay coast, given in 1895.

The **Gower Peninsula**, near Swansea, was the first place in Britain to be given AONB status and offers a diversity of habitats, including stunning beaches and walks with breathtaking views. In Pembrokeshire, the 186 mile Coastal Path starts at Amroth and runs through several areas owned by the Trust, including the **Colby Estate and Woodland Garden**, from where there are dramatic views of Somerset and Carmarthen Bay. To the west lies the fascinating **Stackpole Estate**, which includes **Barafundle Bay** and the delightful freshwater lily ponds at **Bosherston**. At Stackpole Quay itself there is a tea-room and several holiday cottages, as well as an exhibition on the local mansion Stackpole Court, which was demolished in 1963. There are NT car parks at the Quay and at **Broadhaven**, an excellent bathing beach.

Further west, the Trust owns 15½ miles of the coastline of **St Bride's Bay**, including the **Deer Park** at Marloes and the tiny harbour of **St Martin's Haven**, where there is a NT car park and information panel. Nearby **Marloes Sands** offer wonderful walks. This part of the coast is excellent for wildlife, with ravens, choughs and grey seals to be seen, as well as a wide variety of interesting plants and insects.

The city of **St David's**, dedicated to the patron saint of Wales, is located in an area of spectacular geology, with rocky outcrops and coastal plateau, much of which is Trust-owned. There are seasonal NT shops in St David's and at **Solva**. The spectacular coastline and wonderful views continue northwards to Ceredigion, where the beaches at **Mwnt** and **Penbryn** are especially popular and offer a range of facilities for visitors.

Behind the coast lies a fascinating hinterland of green meadows, rivers and rolling hills. Much of this countryside is unspoilt and ideal for a relaxing holiday. At the heart of it lies **Dinefwr Park** near Llandeilo, the historic seat of the former Welsh princes of South Wales and an ancient deer park of much wildlife interest. The recently refurbished **Newton House** is now open to visitors and nearby is **Paxton's Tower**, an early 19th century folly dedicated to Lord Nelson, and from which there are fine views of the Towy Valley. To the north is the **Dolaucothi Estate**, over 1000ha (2500 acres) of delightful countryside with woodland walks and a visitor centre in the village of Pumsaint. The unique Roman gold mines here are also open to visitors.

The industrial heritage of Wales has left its scars on some of the southern valleys, but **Aberdulais Falls** near Neath provides a fascinating insight into how natural energy was harnessed to power the Industrial Revolution. Just north of the valleys, there is some of the country's most spectacular scenery in the **Brecon Beacons**, where the Trust owns over 3500ha (9000 acres) of the main range, including **Pen-y-Fan**, the highest point in southern Britain and **Henrhyd Falls**, the highest single drop waterfall in South Wales. Other notable vantage points are the **Sugarloaf** and **Skirrid Fawr**. Near the border town of Monmouth is **The Kymin**, a hill upon which is an enigmatic tower known as the Round House, built by a dining club in 1794.

The turbulent history of the Welsh Marches is reflected in the local style of architecture, from the Norman castle at **Skenfrith** in the south to the rather more comfortable **Chirk Castle** near Wrexham. But Wales also has its fair share of classic country houses, including **Powis Castle** with its stunning gardens, the brooding **Penrhyn Castle**, **Erddig**, with its fascinating social history, and Anglesey's **Plas Newydd**, which commands some of the finest views in Europe. The spectacular gardens at **Bodnant** are equally celebrated.

Snowdonia is justly famous for its epic upland landscapes, and the Trust owns ten of the main mountain peaks, including **Tryfan**, where the first successful Everest climbers trained. The **Carneddau Estate** and **Ysbyty Estate**, together covering over 15,000ha (37,000 acres), contain some of the most exciting scenery of all and include **Cwm Idwal**, a nature reserve famous for its flora since the 17th century. South west of Betws y Coed is **Tŷ Mawr** in the charming little valley of Wybrnant, which offers many delightful walks.

In the south of the National Park at **Cregennan**, there are splendid walks amidst hill farms and upland lakes, with fine views towards Cadair Idris and over Cardigan Bay. The **Dolmelynllyn Estate** near Dolgellau contains one of Wales's most impressive waterfalls, **Rhaeadr Ddu**, which can be reached by footpath from Ganllwyd, as well as sheepwalks on **Y Llethr**, the highest peak in the Rhinog Mountains. This whole area is full of wildlife interest and is particularly noted for its late summer and autumn colours.

The north arm of Wales – the beautiful **Llŷn Peninsula** – is noted for its spectacular coastal scenery and since the delightful manor house of **Plas yn Rhiw** was given in 1951 by the three Misses Keating, the Trust has worked to consolidate its ownership in this unspoilt and tranquil corner. Through the success of Enterprise Neptune, it has been possible to acquire and protect such wonderful places as **Porthdinllaen**, a charming fishing village, and the famous 'whistling sands' of **Porthor**.

Highlights for Disabled Visitors
There is a wheelchair accessible footpath through delightful riverside scenery at **Aberglaslyn**, and many excellent paths on the **Stackpole Estate**, where there is also an accessible bird hide. On the Gower at **Rhossili** there is an accessible path leading to the old coastguard lookout. Disabled picnic areas are located on the **Dolmelynllyn Estate** at Ganllwyd, at **Glan Faenol** on the Menai Strait and at **Cwrt** on Llŷn. Further west, the car park at **Uwchmynydd** provides stunning views across to Bardsey Island.

... and for Families
Particularly recommended are the beaches at **Porthdinllaen** and **Porthor**, as well as **Rhossili**, where shipwrecks become visible at low tide, and **Mwnt**, from where dolphins can often be seen.

Further Information
NT Regional Office in Llandudno, tel. 01492 860123

Please contact the above office for a free copy of the NT Countryside Guide to Wales, sponsored by Barclays, which gives full details of a range of Trust coast and countryside properties.

ABERCONWY HOUSE 🏠

Conwy

Castle Street, Conwy LL32 8AY Tel: 01492 592246 Fax: 01492 585153

Dating from the 14th century, this is the only medieval merchant's house in Conwy to have survived the turbulent history of this walled town for nearly six centuries. Furnished rooms and an audiovisual presentation show daily life from different periods in its history

Note: The house has limited electric lighting and therefore is dark on dull days

◯ 1 April to 1 Nov: daily except Tues 10–5. Last admission 4.30

£ £2, children £1; family ticket (max. 2 adults & 2 children) £5. Pre-booked groups £1.80 per person. NT members free

🛍 Shop open all year: daily 9.30–5.30, except 25/26 Dec

♿ No WC. Steps up to entrance

▦ Educational visits welcome. Pre-booked groups only

➜ (8: F1) At junction of Castle Street and High Street [115: SH781777]
Bus: From surrounding areas (tel. 01492 575415) *Station:* Conwy 300m

ABERDULAIS FALLS 🛶 🍴 🛡

Neath & Port Talbot

Aberdulais, nr Neath SA10 8EU Tel: 01639 636674 Fax: 01639 645069

For over 300 years this famous waterfall on the River Dulais has provided the energy to drive the wheels of industry, from the first manufacture of copper in 1584 to present-day remains of the tinplate works. The site today houses a unique hydroelectric scheme and the new water-wheel, the largest currently used in Britain to generate electricity, makes Aberdulais Falls self-sufficient in environmentally friendly energy. The Turbine House provides access to an interactive computer, fish pass, and display panels. A special lift has been installed to allow disabled visitors access to the roof level, which affords excellent views of the Falls

Note: The operation of the fish pass, water-wheel and turbine is subject to river levels

What's new in 1998: Scissor lifts giving access to views over the falls and the upper reaches of the River Dulais

◯ March: Sat & Sun only 11–4; 1 April to 1 Nov: Mon to Fri 10–5, Sat, Sun, BHols 11–6. Last admission 30min before closing. **Events:** Spring BHol, Model Steam & Railway exhibition; August BHol, Craft Fair; other events throughout the year

£ £2.80, children £1.40; family ticket (max 2 adults & 2 children) £7. Special offer July/Aug, one child (16 or under) free with each paying adult. Parties (min. 15) by prior arrangement with Property Warden: adults £2.20, children £1.10. Children should be accompanied by an adult. NT members free. Car park signposted to Dulais Rock Inn, 2min walk. Also, on-road parking on A4109 outside the property entrance; coaches please check beforehand as parking is limited

🎧 Audio tours available. Guided tours every day during July and Aug, at other times by arrangement for pre-booked parties

⬛ Located near the entrance and open during normal property opening times, April to Nov. Christmas shop open Nov & Dec: daily except Mon 11–4

♿ Much of the property is accessible to disabled visitors. In the Turbine House a special lift, capable of carrying two wheelchair visitors and their helpers, provides access to the roof level with excellent views of the falls, gorge and water-wheel. New scissor lifts give access to further views of the Falls and River Dulais. WC and wheelchair available. *Note*: Won British Gas ADAPT Commendation 1993 for access

👁 Taped guide with information for sighted companions

🍴 Light refreshments are served in the Old Works Library and Victorian schoolroom by Friends of Aberdulais Falls during summer weekends and public holidays. At other times by arrangement. Lunches and bar meals available at Dulais Rock Inn (not NT)

🏫 Educational facilities provided for pre-booked groups by arrangement with the Property Warden. In Victorian schoolroom: tours and talks on hydroelectric scheme, industrial archaeology, history for educational and other groups. Teachers' resource pack available

🐕 Must be kept on leads

➡ (8: G9) On A4109, 3ml NE of Neath [170: SS772995]. 4ml from M4 exit 43 at Llandarcy, take A465 signposted Vale of Neath *Bus*: SWT 158: Swansea–Banwen 161, N10 from Neath, X75 Swansea–Merthyr Tydfil (tel. 01792 580580). All pass close ⊞ Neath *Station*: Neath 3ml

---

BODNANT GARDEN 🏠 �souvenir 🎭   *Conwy*

Tal-y-Cafn, Colwyn Bay LL28 5RE Tel: 01492 650460 Fax: 01492 650448

One of the world's most spectacular gardens, situated high above the River Conwy with stunning views across Snowdonia. Begun in 1875, Bodnant features huge Italianate terraces and formal lawns on its upper level, with a wooded valley, stream and wild garden below. There are dramatic colours throughout the season, with notable collections of rhododendrons, magnolias and camellias and the spectacular laburnum arch, a 36-metre tunnel of golden blooms in May

Note: The garden and refreshment pavilion are managed by Lord Aberconway, VMH

🕐 14 March to 31 Oct: daily 10–5. Last admission 4.30

£ £4.60, children £2.30. Parties of 20 or more £4.20 per person. NT members free. Car park 50m from garden entrance

⬛ Plant centre and gift shop (not NT), open as garden

♿ The garden is steep in places, has many steps, and is not recommended for wheelchair users. Five wheelchairs available, but cannot be reserved. Refreshment pavilion and plant centre accessible. WC

👁 Braille guide. Scented roses and other plants

🍴 Refreshment pavilion serving light lunches and teas, open as garden: daily 11–5. Picnicking in car park area only

👶 Baby-changing facilities. Baby slings available. Highchairs in refreshment pavilion

🐕 No dogs allowed

➡️ (8: G2) 8ml S of Llandudno and Colwyn Bay off A470, entrance ½ml along the Eglwysbach road [115/116: SH801723]. Signposted from A55 *Bus:* Crosville Cymru 25 from Llandudno (passing ⊠ Llandudno Junction) (tel. 01492 575412) *Station:* Tal-y-Cafn (U) 1½ml

---

CHIRK CASTLE ▦ ✝ ❊ ♣ 🧍 😈 *Wrexham*

Chirk, Wrexham LL14 5AF Tel: 01691 777701 Fax: 01691 774706

A magnificent Marcher fortress, completed in 1310 and commanding fine views over the surrounding countryside. The rather austere exterior belies the comfortable and elegant state rooms inside, with elaborate plasterwork, superb Adam-style furniture, tapestries and portraits. In the formal gardens there are clipped yews, roses and a variety of flowering shrubs. The beautiful 18th-century parkland contains many mature trees and elaborate entrance gates, made in 1719 by the Davies brothers

🅾️ 1 April to 30 Sept: daily except Mon & Tues but open BH Mon; 3 Oct to 1 Nov: Sat & Sun only. **Castle:** 12–5. **Garden:** 11–6. Last admission 4.30. **Events:** please contact Property Manager for details of programme, which includes open-air plays, family fun days and snowdrop walks

💷 £4.60, children £2.30; family ticket (max. 2 adults & 2 children) £11.50. Pre-booked parties of 15 or more £3.70 per person. Garden only, adults £2.40, children £1.20. NT members free. Parking 200m

🧍 Connoisseurs' tour by prior arrangement (minimum group of 20), Wed am only

🛍️ Shop open as castle

♿ Access to state rooms by stairclimber. Garden mostly accessible; gravel paths. Tea-room accessible. Courtesy coach from car park. Room for CAPD. WC

👁️ Braille guide. Many touchable items

📺 Licensed tea-room: morning coffee, light lunches and teas; open 11–5. Picnicking in car park only

🚼 Parent & baby room. Baby carriers for loan. Highchairs in tea-room

📖 Educational visits particularly welcome. 'Hands-on' facilities. Education Officer and room available. School parties must be pre-booked

🐕 Allowed on walks and in car park

➡ (8: H3) Gates are ½ml W of Chirk village off A5; 8ml S of Wrexham, signposted off A483. 1½ml driveway from main gates *Bus:* Midland Red 2/A Wrexham–Oswestry (tel. 01978 363760) *Station:* Chirk (U) ½ml to gates

---

CILGERRAN CASTLE 🏰 🎭 *Pembrokeshire*

nr Cardigan, Pembrokeshire SA43 2SF Tel: 01239 615007

This 13th-century ruin is perched overlooking the spectacular Teifi gorge and has inspired many artists, including Turner

Note: Cilgerran Castle is in the guardianship of Cadw (Welsh Historic Monuments)

🅾 All year: daily. Summer (late March to late Oct): 9.30–6.30. Winter (late Oct to late March 1999): 9.30–4. **Events:** Shakespeare plays held each year; contact Custodian for details

💷 NT members free. Otherwise please check current admission prices on 01239 615007.

🛍 Shop open daily except Sat, same hours as castle

♿ Access to grounds and inner bailey only

🐕 No dogs allowed

➡ (8: D7) On rock above left bank of the Teifi, 3ml SE of Cardigan, 1½ml E of A478 [145: SN195431] *Bus:* Midway 430 from Cardigan; otherwise Davies Bros 460/1 ➤ Carmarthen–Cardigan, alight Llechryd. 1¼ml by footpath (tel. 01437 764551)

COLBY WOODLAND GARDEN 🌼 🌳 🎣 🏛 🚻 🎭 *Pembrokeshire*

Amroth, Narberth SA67 8PP Tel: 01834 811885

Attractive woodland garden with a fine collection of rhododendrons and azaleas. There are beautiful walks through secluded valleys along open and wooded pathways. The early 19th-century house is not open (Mr & Mrs A. Scourfield Lewis kindly allow access to the walled garden during visiting hours)

🅾 1 April to 31 Oct: daily 10–5. **Walled garden:** 1 April to 30 Oct: 11–5. **Events:** Guided walks with Gardener-in-charge held regularly throughout the season; Celtic Music evening; Shakespeare in the Meadow; Family Fun Days

💷 £2.80, children £1.40; family ticket £7. Group: adult £2.30, child £1.15. Coaches welcome (narrow approaches). Open evenings by arrangement

⬜ Shop, gallery and plant sales, open as property

♿ Limited facilities, shop and parts of garden accessible; disabled visitors may park closer to the garden on request. Wheelchair and walking stick available

🦮 Braille guide; advisable to bring companion as parts of garden are steep

🍽 Tea-room (not NT) serving morning coffee, home-made light lunches and afternoon tea; open as property. Large car park with picnic facilities

🚼 Baby-changing facilities. Children's quiz and safari fun packs

🐾 Not in walled garden

→ (8: D9) 1½ml inland from Amroth beside Carmarthen Bay [158: SN155080]. Follow brown signs from A477 Tenby–Carmarthen road or off coast road at Amroth Castle *Bus:* Silcox 350/1 from Tenby (passing ⮀ Kilgetty) (tel. 01437 764551) *Station:* Kilgetty (U) 2½ml

---

CONWY SUSPENSION BRIDGE 🔟   *Conwy*

Conwy LL32 8LD Tel: 01492 573282

Designed and built by Thomas Telford, this elegant suspension bridge was completed in 1826. It replaced the ferry, which was previously the only means of crossing the river. The toll-keeper's house has recently been restored and furnished as it would have been a century ago

🔵 1 April to 30 June and 1 Sept to 1 Nov: daily except Tues 10–5. July & August: daily 10–5. Last admission 4.30

💷 Adults £1, children 50p. NT members free

🎒 Educational visits welcome; pre-booked groups only

→ (8: F1) 100m from Conwy town centre, adjacent to Conwy Castle [115: SH785775] *Bus:* From surrounding areas (tel. 01492 575412) *Station:* Conwy ¼ml; Llandudno Junction ½ml

---

DINEFWR PARK 🏠 ♣ 🛡   *Carmarthenshire*

Llandeilo SA19 6RT Tel: 01558 823902 Fax: 01558 822036

A beautiful 18th-century landscape park surrounding Newton House, originally 17th-century but now with a Victorian Gothic façade. The ground floor and basement are now open after restoration and an exhibition explains the importance of Dinefwr in Welsh history. The Victorian garden at the rear of the house is currently under restoration and overlooks the ancient deer park, in which live fallow deer and the famous Dinefwr White Park cattle. There are fine views over the Towy Valley and a boardwalk, suitable for families and wheelchair users, which meanders through Bog Wood. There is limited access to the privately owned walled garden, as well as access to Dinefwr Castle

🔵 **House, garden, deer park, parkland & boardwalk:** 2 April to 1 Nov: daily except Tues & Wed 11–5. Last admission 4.30. The library and old drawing room are available for conferences on Tues & Wed. Parkland also open during winter in daylight hours. **Events**: for details of programme please send s.a.e. marked 'Events' to Property Manager

£ £2.80, children £1.40; family ticket (max. 2 adults & 2 children) £7; 1 child (16 and under) free per paying adult from 23 July to 30 Aug. Parties £2.60, children/school groups £1.30. Coaches by prior appointment only due to narrow access. WCs in car park

Guided tours through the deer park by prior arrangement with Warden

Christmas shop and tea-room open Nov & Dec: Fri to Sun 10.30–4.30

Ramped access to ground floor of house, exhibition and tea-room. WC. Parts of grounds accessible: boardwalk through Bog Wood to lake

Braille guide; many touchable items (please contact in advance)

Tea-room (not NT) open as house

Baby-changing facilities, highchairs & children's menu. Active events programme and quizzes

In outer park only, on leads. No dogs in deer park

→ (**8**: F8) On W outskirts of Llandeilo A40(T); from Swansea take M4 to Pont Abraham, thence A48(T) to Cross Hands and A476 to Llandeilo; entrance by police station [159: SN625225] *Bus:* From surrounding areas to Llandeilo, thence 1ml (tel. 01267 231817) *Station:* Llandeilo 1ml

DOLAUCOTHI GOLD MINES

Carmarthenshire

Pumsaint, Llanwrda SA19 8RR Tel: 01558 650359

These *unique Roman gold mines are set amid wooded hillsides overlooking the beautiful Cothi Valley. Exploited by the Celts and Romans some 2,000 years ago and last worked in 1938, the ancient and modern mine workings remain in good condition and are vividly illustrated in the Exhibition Centre. A guided tour takes visitors on a trail to a Roman* adit *or mine entrance and there are displays of gold-panning and 1930s mining machinery in the mine yard, with video and bilingual interpretation*

◯ 1 April to 30 Sept: daily except Thur & Fri 10–5 (open daily during July & Aug 10–5). Underground tours, 16 May to 13 Sept during normal open hours. Underground tours last about 1hr, involving hillside walking; helmets with lights are provided and stout footwear is recommended. The underground tour is unsuitable for disabled or infirm visitors; the Trust regrets children under 5 not allowed underground. Limited places are available on underground tours; tours are very busy during July and Aug; please come early or book in advance to avoid disappointment

£ Site admission £3, children £1.50; family ticket (max. 2 adults, 2 children) £7.50; NT members free. Price includes guided site tour, gold-panning and access to audio-visual displays. In addition, guided underground tour: £3.50, children £1.75; family ticket (max. 2 adults, 2 children) £8.50. NT members £2, members' children £1; members' family ticket £5. All-inclusive family ticket £15

🏃 Stout footwear recommended. Unsuitable for disabled or infirm visitors and under-5s

🏠 Shop and tea-room open as property

♿ Wheelchair access to reception and exhibition centre; mines not accessible

🍴 Light lunches and refreshments available

🏫 Room available for school groups

🐕 On leads, but no dogs on tours

➔ (8: F7) Between Lampeter and Llanwrda on A482 [146: SN6640]
  Bus: Thomas Bros 284 from Llandeilo, Tues only (tel. 01267 231817)
  Station: Llanwrda (U), not Sun, except June to Sept, 8ml

ERDDIG 🏠🏡✝🎡♣🏊🏃🎭 *Wrexham*

nr Wrexham LL13 0YT Tel: 01978 355314 Fax/Infoline: 01978 313333

One of the most fascinating houses in Britain, not least because of the unusually close relationship that existed between the family of the house and their servants. The beautiful and evocative range of outbuildings includes kitchen, laundry, bakehouse, stables, sawmill, smithy and joiner's shop, while the stunning state rooms display most of their original 18th- and 19th-century furniture and furnishings, including some exquisite Chinese wallpaper. The large walled garden has been restored to its 18th-century formal design and has a Victorian parterre and yew walk. It also contains the National Collection of Ivies. There is an extensive park with woodland walks

Note: Due to the extreme fragility of their contents, the Tapestry and Small Chinese Rooms are open on Wed & Sat only. Most rooms have no electric light; visitors wishing to make close study of pictures and textiles should avoid dull days

◯ 21 March to 1 Nov: daily, except Thur & Fri (open Good Fri); **House:** 12–5; **Garden:** 11–6 (July & Aug: 10–6); from 3 Oct house & garden close 1hr earlier. Last admission to house 1hr before closing. **Events:** 19–21 June, Craft Show in gardens (charge, incl. NT members). Also outdoor opera, jazz and Last Night of the Proms. Please send s.a.e. to Property Manager for full events programme

💷 All-inclusive ticket £5.60, children £2.80; family ticket (max. 2 adults & 2 children) £14. Parties (15 or more) £4.60 per person. Below stairs (incl. outbuildings & garden) £3.60, children £1.80; family ticket (max. 2 adults & 2 children) £9. Parties (15 or more) £2.90 per person. NT members free. Parking 200m

🛠 Garden tours available by prior arrangement (15 or more)

🏠 Shop and plant sales open as property. Christmas shop: 6 Nov to 20 Dec: Fri, Sat & Sun 11–4 (tel. 01978 311919)

♿ Access over rough gravel and cobbled yard to ground floor, garden (ramps) and outbuildings only; not an easy property for wheelchair users; please discuss visits in advance with the Property Manager. Tea-room difficult but table by shop accessible. WC in main yard; wheelchairs provided. Good access provided in Country Park; 2200m 'improved access' area at Felin Puleston; RADAR key WCs

👁 Braille guide; furniture, panelling, pewter and other items may be touched (prior notice appreciated)

☕ Licensed restaurant: morning coffee, lunches and teas, open as property 21 March to 1 Nov. Also open for pre-booked functions, incl. pre-booked Christmas lunches. Catering Manager (tel. 01978 311919). Picnicking in car park area only

👶 Feeding and baby-changing facilities. Highchairs in restaurant. Baby carriers on loan. Children's guide

📖 School and youth groups Mon, Tues & Wed am only by prior arrangement. Please send s.a.e. to Education Officer for details of education programme at the house and on the estate

🦮 In car park and country park only, on leads

➔ (8: H3) 2ml S of Wrexham, signposted A525 Whitchurch road, or A483/A5152 Oswestry road [117: SJ326482] *Station:* Wrexham Central (U) 1ml, Wrexham General 1½ml via Erddig Rd & footpath

---

LLANERCHAERON 🧒 🎭   *Ceredigion*

nr Aberaeron SA48 8DG Tel: 01545 570200 Fax: 01545 571759

A rare survivor of a classic Welsh gentry estate of the late 18th century. The elegant house was designed and built by John Nash in 1794–6, with an equally well-proportioned service wing and courtyard. The model home farm, kennels and stables complete the picture. The estate park was landscaped in the spirit of the Picturesque and commands fine views over the surrounding countryside

Note: The property has been accepted unendowed. An ambitious programme of repair and regeneration has commenced with minimal finance and will only continue for as long as funds permit. Access may be restricted in some areas for safety reasons. The house is under restoration

🅾 **Home farm, gardens and grounds**: 2 April to 4 Oct: Thur to Sun & BH Mon 11–5. Last admission 4.30. **Parkland**: all year, dawn to dusk. **Events**: details from Property Manager (s.a.e. please)

💷 £2, children £1. Parties £1.60/80p. Guided tours: 90p in addition to admission (incl. NT members)

🧒 At 2 every Thur June to Sept; also at 2 on Sun 5 July to 16 Aug. Groups of 15+ please book in advance

♿ Access to whole site including walled garden. WCs. Wheelchair available

👁 Braille guide

🦮 On leads in parkland only

➔ (8: F6) 2ml east of Aberaeron off A482 [146:SN480 602] *Bus:* Davies Bros 202 🚆 Carmarthen–Aberaeron (with connections from 🚆 Aberystwyth (tel. 01267 231817)

LLYWELYN COTTAGE/BWTHYN LLYWELYN 🏠 🛍 🧒 *Gwynedd*

Beddgelert LL55 4YA Tel: 01766 890293 Fax: 01766 890545

A shop and exhibtion are housed in this 17th-century cottage, situated in the picturesque village of Beddgelert, near the Aberglaslyn Pass and within the Snowdonia National Park. There are superb walks in the area, including a stroll to the legendary Gelert's grave, and a level path along the track of the former Welsh Highland Railway. An interactive display helps visitors learn about the area's history, wildlife and other attractions

🅾 1 April to 1 Nov: daily 11–5

💷 Free admission

⌂ Open 1 April to 1 Nov: daily 11–5

♿ Accessible to wheelchairs; interactive display accessible

➔ (8:F3) At junction of A498 and A4085. Beddgelert is well-signposted from A5 and A487 [115:SH590481] *Bus:* KMP/Crosville Cymru 95 from Caernarfon (with connections from ⊟ Bangor), Express 97 from Porthmadog (passes close ⊟ Porthmadog) (tel. 01286 679535) *Station:* Penrhyndeudraeth (U) or Porthmadog (U) both 6ml

---

PENRHYN CASTLE 🏰 ✝ ♣ 🍴 👁 *Gwynedd*

Bangor LL57 4HN Tel: 01248 353084 Infoline: 01248 371337 Fax: 01248 371281

This dramatic neo-Norman castle sits between Snowdonia and the Menai Strait and was built by Thomas Hopper between 1820 and 1845 for the wealthy Pennant family, who made their fortune from the local slate quarries. The extraordinarily grand staircase and extravagant stone carving of the interior create an almost cathedral-like atmosphere. The castle contains fascinating 'Norman' furniture, panelling and plasterwork all designed by Hopper, and houses an outstanding collection of paintings. There is also an industrial railway museum, a countryside exhibition, a Victorian terraced walled garden and an extensive tree and shrub collection, as well as attractive walks in the grounds

◐ 25 March to 1 Nov: daily except Tues. **Castle:** 12–5 (July & Aug 11–5). **Grounds and stable block exhibitions:** 11–5.30 (July & Aug 10–5.30). Last admission 30min before closing (last audio tour 4). **Events:** a programme including open-air plays, concerts and family fun days runs throughout the season; send s.a.e. for details. Events information line (tel. 01248 371337)

£ £4.80, children £2.40; family ticket £12 (max. 2 adults & 2 children). Booked parties of 15 or more £3.80 per person. Garden and stable block exhibitions only £3, children £1.50. NT members free. Audio tour (charge), for adults and children in Welsh and English. School and youth groups by arrangement. Parking 200m

🕊 Garden tours arranged throughout the season. Specialist guided tours by prior arrangement

🛍 Shop opens 1hr before Castle

♿ Access to all ground-floor rooms; access ramps and handrail (but no access to shop in basement). Wheelchair available. Castle is least congested on Sat. Park paths are firm. Volunteer-driven golf buggy seating 3, for garden and park by arrangement. WC. Induction loop audio tour for hard of hearing, Sympathetic Hearing Scheme

👁 Braille guides to Castle and garden. Audio tour

🍴 Licensed tea-room; morning coffee, light lunches and teas. Tea-room opens 1hr before Castle. Picnicking in grounds only

🧒 Industrial railway museum. Adventure playground. Young Adventurers' audio tour. Baby-changing facilities; baby carriers on loan but no baby back carriers allowed in Castle. Highchairs in tea-room. Permanent orienteering course in grounds; maps and instructions available from shop. Activity sheets for children

🖥 Pre-booked educational visits particularly welcome. Hands-on educational facilities, Education Officer on site. Permanent orienteering course. Send s.a.e. for education programme

🐕 In grounds only, on leads

➔ (8: F2) 1ml E of Bangor, at Llandegai on A5122 [115: SH602720]. Signposted from junction of A55 and A5 *Bus:* Crosville Cymru 5/B Caernarfon–Llandudno; Purple 6/7 Bangor–Bethesda; D & G 66 Bangor–Gerlan. All pass close ➔ Bangor and end of drive to Castle (tel. 01286 679535) *Station:* Bangor 2ml

---

PLAS NEWYDD 🏠 ✿ ♣ 🏛 🛡   *Anglesey*

Llanfairpwll, Anglesey LL61 6DQ Tel: 01248 714795 Fax: 01248 713673

Set amidst breathtakingly beautiful scenery and with spectacular views of Snowdonia, this elegant 18th-century house was built by James Wyatt and is an interesting mixture of classical and Gothick. The comfortable interior, re-styled in the 1930s, is famous for its association with Rex Whistler, whose largest wallpainting is here. There is also an exhibition about his work. A military museum contains campaign relics of the 1st Marquess of Anglesey and the Battle of Waterloo. There is a fine spring garden, summer terrace and, later, massed hydrangeas and autumn colour, and a woodland walk gives access to a marine walk on the Menai Strait

Note: The Rhododendron Garden is open from 1 April to early June only; woodland walk and newly reinstated Marine Walk remain open throughout the season

🅾 **House:** 1 April to 1 Nov: daily except Fri & Sat 12–5. **Garden:** same days as house 11–5.30. Last admission 30min before closing. **Events:** extensive programme of tours, plays, music and family events (incl. 18 July, open-air concert; 22 Aug, open-air jazz concert); please send s.a.e for full events list

💷 £4.20, children £2.10; family ticket (max. 2 adults, 2 children) £10.50. Pre-booked parties of 15+ £3.40 per person. Garden only £2, children £1. NT members free. Parking 400m

[icon] Connoisseurs' and garden tours by prior arrangement

[icon] Shop open daily (incl. Fri & Sat) 11–5. Also Christmas shop: 6 Nov to 20 Dec: Fri, Sat & Sun 11–4

[icon] Ground floor and Whistler Room accessible via ramps. Stairclimber to first floor. Close parking, enquire at reception desk; wheelchairs available. Easy access to garden (all main paths accessible), tea-room and shop. WC near tea-room

[icon] Braille guide. Aromatic shrubs; fragrant azaleas in spring

[icon] Licensed tea-room: morning coffee, light lunches & teas; open daily (incl. Fri & Sat) 11–5. Picnicking in car park and playground area

[icon] Parent & baby facilities. Baby carriers available. No back carriers or pushchairs in house. Highchairs in tea-room. Children's quiz and adventure playground

[icon] Pre-booked school groups welcome

[icon] No dogs allowed in house or gardens

[icon] (8: F2) 1ml SW of Llanfairpwll and A5 on A4080 to Brynsiencyn; turn off A5 at W end of Britannia Bridge [114/115: SH521696] *Bus:* Crosville Cymru 42 from Bangor (passing [rail] Bangor & Llanfairpwll) (tel. 01248 351879) *Station:* Llanfairpwll (U), no practical Sun service, 1¼ml

PLAS YN RHIW [icons] *Gwynedd*

Rhiw, Pwllheli LL53 8AB Tel/fax: 01758 780219

A small manor house, rescued from neglect and lovingly restored by the three Keating sisters, who bought it in 1938. The views across Cardigan Bay are among the most spectacular in Britain and there are delightful grounds tumbling down to the sea. The house is part-medieval, with Tudor and Georgian additions, and the ornamental gardens contain many interesting flowering trees and shrubs, with beds framed by box hedges and grass paths. Brilliant displays of snowdrops and bluebells can be found in the wood above at the appropriate season

Note: In the interests of preservation, numbers of visitors admitted to the house at any one time may be limited, particularly in July and Aug and on BHols

🅾️ 1 April to 18 May: daily (except Tues & Wed) 12–5. 20 May to 30 Sept: daily (except Tues) 12–5. Last admission 4.30. Timed tickets may be in operation on BHols and during July & Aug. **Events:** open-air play; tel. for details

💷 £3.20, children £1.60; family ticket (max. 2 adults & 2 children) £8. NT members free. Pre-booked parties evenings only (incl. full guided tour) £4 per person. Parking 80m. No coaches

🚶 Advance notice is required; no tours during July & Aug

🏠 Shop open as house

♿ Wheelchair access to ground-floor rooms only; most of garden very difficult for wheelchairs. WC

🔡 Braille guides

🏫 School visits are encouraged, but Custodian must be informed 2 weeks in advance

🐕 On the woodland walk, on leads only

➡️ (8: D4) 12ml from Pwllheli, signposted from B4413 to Aberdaron (drive gate at the bottom of Rhiw Hill) [123: SH237282] *Bus:* Crosville Cymru 17B Pwllheli–Aberdaron (passing ≽ Pwllheli) (tel. 01248 351879) *Station:* Pwllheli 12ml

---

POWIS CASTLE & GARDEN 🏫 ❄️ 😀 *Powys*

Welshpool SY21 8RF Tel: 01938 554338 Fax/Infoline: 01938 554336

The world-famous garden, overhung with enormous clipped yews, shelters rare and tender plants. Laid out under the influence of Italian and French styles, the garden retains its original lead statues, an orangery and an aviary on the terraces. In the 18th century an informal woodland wilderness was created on the opposing ridge. Perched on a rock above the garden terraces, the medieval castle contains one of the finest collections in Wales. It was originally built c.1200 by Welsh princes and was subsequently adapted and embellished by generations of Herberts and Clives, who furnished the castle with a wealth of fine paintings and furniture. A beautiful collection of treasures from India is displayed in the Clive Museum.

🅾️ **Castle & museum:** 1 April to 28 June & 2 Sept to 1 Nov: daily except Mon & Tues 1–5; July & Aug: daily except Mon 1–5 (open BH Mon during season). **Garden:** same days as castle & museum, 11–6. Last admission to the garden, castle and museum each 30min before closing. **Events:** programme of concerts, plays, walks, talks and demonstrations throughout the year: for details tel. 01938 554338

💷 Garden £5, children £2.50; family ticket (max. 2 adults & 2 children) £12.50. Parties £4 per person. All-in ticket (incl. castle, museum & garden) £7.50, children £3.75; family ticket (max. 2 adults & 2 children) £18.75. Parties for castle, museum & garden £6.50 (NT members free). All groups by written appointment only and coaches limited to four per day. No group rates Sun & BH Mon

Out of hours guided tours of the castle and/or garden by prior arrangement; please tel. for details

Open same days as castle & garden. Also Christmas shop open 6 Nov to 20 Dec: Fri, Sat, Sun 11–4

Please tel. in advance of a visit: due to the layout of the garden and design of the castle, access for disabled visitors is very limited and it is not possible to use wheelchairs inside the castle. The garden is very steep, and not recommended for disabled walkers or wheelchair-users, but access to the tea-room, shop and plant shop is good. Wheelchair available. Elderly and disabled visitors may be driven up to entrance but drivers should return car to car park; disabled drivers should park on the reserved area near the coach park. Adapted WC

Recommended for accompanied visually impaired visitors. Braille guide; scented flowers

Licensed tea-room; counter service for morning coffee, light lunches and teas. Open same days as castle & garden, 11–5. Also open for festive food, 6 Nov to 20 Dec: Fri, Sat & Sun 11–4

Baby-feeding and changing facilities. Front baby carriers available on loan. Castle unsuitable for back baby carriers and pushchairs. Highchairs in restaurant. Children's guides and questionnaires. Family quiz trails and activities in garden during school holidays

Children's guides and questionnaires. School groups by appointment

Guide dogs only, allowed in castle and garden. Dogs cannot be walked in the park as it does not belong to the Trust and there is no public access on this private land

(8: H4) 1ml S of Welshpool; pedestrian access from High Street (A490); cars turn right 1ml along main road to Newtown (A483); enter by first drive gate on right [126: SJ216064] *Bus:* Midland Red D71 Oswestry–Welshpool; D75 Shrewsbury–Llanidloes, alight High Street, 1ml (tel. 0345 056785)
Station: Welshpool 1¼ml via footpath from town

RHOSSILI VISITOR CENTRE 🏛 🚶

Swansea

Coastguard Cottages, Rhossili, Gower SA3 1PR Tel: 01792 390707

The Trust owns and protects much land on the beautiful Gower peninsula. The Visitor Centre is situated adjacent to the Raised Terrace, the Down, Worm's Head and beach and coastal cliffs, and provides information about the area. There is also an exhibition and shop

🅾 1 Feb to 20 March: Sat & Sun 11–4; 21 March to 24 Oct: daily 10.30–5.30; 25 Oct to 31 Oct: daily 11–4; 1 Nov to 20 Dec: daily except Mon & Tues 11–4

£ Free admission to Visitor Centre. Car park and WC nearby (not NT): charge for parking

♿ Visitor Centre ground floor and shop accessible. Rough surface in car park (not NT); disabled visitors may be set down at Visitor Centre. No separate parking facilities. Excellent view from outside building

☕ Available nearby (not NT)

🐕 Guide dogs only in the Visitor Centre

➜ (8: E9) SW tip of Gower Peninsula, approached from Swansea via A4118 and then B4247 *Bus:* South Wales 18/A/C from Swansea (passing close ≋ Swansea) (tel. 01792 580580)

SEGONTIUM 🏛

Gwynedd

Caernarfon LL55 2LN Tel: 01286 675625

The remains of a Roman fort, built to defend the Roman Empire against rebellious tribes and later plundered to provide stone for Edward I's castle at Caernarfon. There is a museum containing relics found on-site

Note: Segontium is in the guardianship of Cadw (Welsh Historic Monuments)

🅾 All year. March, April & Oct: Mon to Sat 9.30–5.30, Sun 2-5. May to Sept: Mon to Sat, 9.30–6, Sun 2–6. Nov to end Feb: Mon to Sat 9.30–4, Sun 2–4. Closed 24 to 26 Dec & New Year's Day

£ Please check current admission prices: 01286 675625. NT members free. Parking on main road nearby

♿ Wheelchair access to most parts of site. Reduced entry

🐕 No dogs

➜ (8: E2) On Llanbeblig road, A4085, on SE outskirts of Caernarfon [115: SH485624] *Bus:* From surrounding areas to Caernarfon, KMP 95 from Beddgelert & Arvonia 93, KMP89 pass museum, on others ½ml walk to fort (tel. 01286 679535) *Station:* Bangor 9ml

SKENFRITH CASTLE 🏰 _Monmouthshire_

Skenfrith, nr Abergavenny

A Norman castle, built to command one of the main routes between England and Wales. A keep stands on the remains of the motte, and the 13th-century curtain wall with towers has also survived

Note: Skenfrith Castle is in the guardianship of Cadw (Welsh Historic Monuments)

🅾 All year

💷 Free

♿ Wheelchair access

➡ (8: J8) 6ml NW of Monmouth, 12ml NE of Abergavenny, on N side of the Ross road (B4521) [161: SO456203]

TUDOR MERCHANT'S HOUSE 🏠 _Pembrokeshire_

Quay Hill, Tenby SA70 7BX Tel: 01834 842279

A late 15th-century town house, characteristic of the area and of the time when Tenby was a thriving trading port. The ground-floor chimney at the rear of the house is a fine vernacular example, and the original scarfed roof-trusses survive. The remains of early frescos can be seen on three interior walls and the furniture and fittings re-create the atmosphere from the time when a Tudor family was in residence. There is access to the small herb garden, weather permitting

🅾 2 April to 30 Sept: Mon to Sat (except Wed) 10–5, Sun 1–5; 1 to 31 Oct: Mon, Tues, Thur & Fri 10–3, Sun 12–3

💷 £1.80, children 90p. Groups £1.40 per person, children 70p. NT members free. No WC. Car-parking in town

♿ Not recommended for wheelchair users; difficult steps and stairs

➡ (8: D9) [158: SN135004] _Bus:_ From surrounding areas (tel. 01437 764551) _Station:_ Tenby 700m

TŶ MAWR WYBRNANT 🏠👥🚶 _Conwy_

Penmachno, Betws-y-Coed LL25 0HJ Tel: 01690 760213

Situated in the beautiful and secluded Wybrnant Valley, Tŷ Mawr was the birthplace of Bishop William Morgan, first translator of the entire Bible into Welsh. The house has been

restored to its probable 16th-17th-century appearance and houses a display of Welsh Bibles. A footpath leads from the house through woodland and the surrounding fields, which are traditionally managed

Note: No access for coaches

O 2 April to 29 Sept: Thur to Sun & BH Mon 12–5; Last admission 30min before closing. 1 Oct to 1 Nov: Thur, Fri & Sun 12–4

£ £2, children £1; family ticket (max. 2 adults & 2 children) £5. Pre-booked parties (20 or more) £1.60 per person. NT members free.

& Wheelchair access to ground floor only

■ Educational visits particularly welcome for house and nature trail tours. Pre-booked school parties only

►| In countryside only

→ (8: F2) At the head of the Wybrnant valley. From A5 3ml S of Betws-y-Coed, take B4406 to Penmachno. House is 2½ml NW of Penmachno by forest road [115: SH770524] *Bus:* Crosville Cymru 64 Llanrwst–Cwm (passing ⬛ Betws-y-Coed), alight Penmachno, thence 2½ml (tel. 01492 575412)
Station: Pont-y-pant (U) 1½ml

TY'N-Y-COED UCHAF 🎞 🏫 📷 🏃 *Conwy*

Penmachno, Betws-y-Coed LL24 0PS Tel: 01690 760229

A traditional smallholding with 19th-century farmhouse and outbuildings, providing a fascinating record of an almost-vanished way of life. The house is approached by an interesting walk along the River Machno through fields of nature and conservation interest

Note: As the property is extremely small, there may on occasions be a delay in gaining admission

O 2 April to 29 Sept: Thur, Fri & Sun: 12–5; 1 Oct to 1 Nov: Thur, Fri & Sun 12–4. Last admission 30min before closing. Ty'n-y-Coed Uchaf is occupied by a tenant family, so please observe the property opening times. Car park can be approached through the car park for Penmachno Woollen Mill

£ £2, children £1; family ticket (max. 2 adults & 2 children) £5. Parking at Penmachno Woollen Mill ¾ml

& Wheelchair-accessible path through first 3 fields only from Penmachno Woollen Mill car park; thereafter access not possible

■ Educational groups are especially welcome. Pre-booked only

►| No dogs allowed

→ (8: F2) 1½ml S of Betws-y-Coed on the A5. Turn right at the sign for Penmachno Woollen Mill, then follow B4406 for ½ml [116: SH803521] *Bus:* Crosville Cymru 64 Llanrwst–Cwm (passes ⬛ Betws-y-Coed) (tel. 01492 575412)
Station: Betws-y-Coed (U) 3ml

Introduction to Northern Ireland

Northern Ireland is famed worldwide for its beauty. The spectacular and varied coastline, rolling green scenery and evocative mountains, interspersed with areas of wetland and open water, combine to produce a singularly attractive landscape.

Many of the properties owned by the Trust in Ulster are important for their wildlife interest, offering a wide range of opportunities to enjoy unspoilt habitats and fascinating flora and fauna. **Murlough National Nature Reserve**, near Newcastle, was Ireland's first nature reserve. The oldest sand dunes here are at least 5,000 years old and the soil ranges from lime-rich to acid, supporting a wide variety of plants which in turn provide nesting sites for birds in spring. Nearby are the beautiful Mourne Mountains, where the Trust owns **Slieve Donard**, the highest peak and from the foot of which there is a footpath connecting with the **Mourne Coastal Path**. Further south, at the mouth of Carlingford Lough, are **Blockhouse** and **Green Islands**, important breeding locations for terns and leased to the RSPB.

Strangford Lough is one of Europe's most important wildlife sites. In order to protect this habitat and the interesting birds and animals it supports, the Trust operates a Wildlife Scheme embracing the entire foreshore of the Lough and some fifty islands. Depending on the season, visitors may see vast flocks of wintering wildfowl and nesting birds. Seals, otters and other marine animals can also be seen, as well as interesting flowers. The Strangford Lough Wildlife Centre is located in the grounds of the **Castle Ward Estate** and has exhibitions, leaflets and other information. Also on the shores of the Lough is **Mount Stewart**, with its magnificent garden and splendid views over the surrounding countryside.

The County Down coastline has much to offer the walker and naturalist, with rocky shore and heathland at **Ballymacormick Point** and wildfowl, wading birds and gulls to be seen at **Orlock Point**. Offshore is **Lighthouse Island**, which has a bird observatory and can be visited by arrangement with Mr Neville NcKee, 67 Temple Rise, Templepatrick, Co. Down (tel. 01849 433068). On the outer arm of the Ards peninsula is the picturesque former fishing village of **Kearney**, where the Trust owns thirteen houses and from where there are attractive walks to the beach at **Knockinelder**.

The north coast of Counties Londonderry and Antrim are even more dramatic than that of Co. Down, and much of this coastline is also under Trust ownership. In the far west is the landscaped estate of **Downhill**, where the **Mussenden Temple** perches on the cliff-edge. East of Downhill is **Portstewart Strand**, a 2 mile-long stretch of dunes and sandy beach. (Visitor facilities are open here from May to the end of Aug, daily 10–6, car-parking £2.50, dogs must be kept on leads during summer months). Nearby at the mouth of the River Bann are the **Bar Mouth** and **Grangemore Dunes**, a wildlife sanctuary with observation hide.

Further east still, the **Giant's Causeway** needs no introduction, but it is only one part of the beautiful **North Antrim Cliff Path**, of which the Trust owns 6 miles between the Causeway and the ruins of **Dunseverick Castle**. East of Dunseverick is the majestic sweep of **Whitepark Bay**, with its sandy beach and backdrop of white chalk cliffs. Beyond this bay is the tiny stack of basalt rock, **Carrick-a-Rede** (the 'rock on the road'), which is connected to the mainland in summer by a swinging rope bridge. There is a car park at **Larrybane**, from where there is access to the bridge and good views of seabird colonies, Rathlin Island and, in good weather, the west coast of Scotland. (Visitor facilities, including a tea-room, at Larrybane are open April, May & Sept, weekends only 11–6, June to Aug, daily 11–6, car-parking £2, coaches £6).

The distinctive headland of **Fair Head** rises 190m and gives dramatic views of the nearby **Murlough Bay** and the Western Isles of Scotland. This is fine walking country and full of wildlife, but much of the land is grazed by livestock and so dogs must be on leads at all times. To the south east is **Cushleake Mountain**, an exceptional example of raised blanket peat bog and home to rare plants and birds, and the delightful coastal village of **Cushendun**, where there are cottages designed by Clough Williams-Ellis, architect of Portmeirion in Wales. The Trust has recently acquired the townland of **Ballyconagan** on Rathlin Island, a traditional farm which has remained unchanged for centuries.

The interior of the province is full of interest and beauty. Here can be found the delightful country houses of **Springhill**, **The Argory** and **Ardress House**, as well as fascinating reminders of Northern Ireland's industrial heritage, such as **Wellbrook Beetling Mill** near Cookstown and **Patterson's Spade Mill** near Belfast, where the Trust also owns the magnificent **Crown Liquor Saloon**. In the west, the lush valleys and pastures of County Fermanagh provide a splendid setting for **Florence Court** and **Castle Coole**, as well as for the spectacular woodland and wetlands of the **Crom Estate** around Lough Erne.

Highlights for Disabled Visitors

Murlough Nature Reserve offers a boarded walkway to the dunes and beach (strong pusher needed), with wheelchair and adapted WC available in summer; at **Giant's Causeway** a bus service to the Causeway stones is available and is equipped with a hoist for wheelchairs; there is also easy access to the shop and tea-room; at **Carrick-a-Rede** there is a special viewing platform for disabled visitors.

... and for Families

The beach at **Portstewart Strand** is an ideal place for a family day out – there is a wardening service and areas where vehicles are not permitted; **Strangford Lough Wildlife Centre** at Castle Ward has a theatre with wildlife films and information, and around the Lough there are many hides and observation points from which wildlife can be seen. Several properties have children's play areas and activities .

Further Information

NT Regional Office tel. 01238 510721; please contact for copies of free leaflets on 'County Down' and 'The North Coast', as well as other information.

ARDRESS HOUSE 🏠 📷 🚶 🎷 😀 *Armagh*

64 Ardress Road, Portadown, BT62 1SQ Tel: 01762 851236

Originally a simple 17th-century farmhouse, Ardress was gentrified in the 18th century and boasts an elegant Adam-style drawing-room, as well as neo-classical plasterwork, good furniture and pictures. Farm implements and livestock can be seen in the farmyard, and there is an attractive garden with woodland and riverside walks

🅾 **House & farmyard**: April: weekends & Easter (10 to 14 April) 2–6; May & Sept: Sat, Sun & BH 2–6; June to end Aug: daily (except Tues) 2–6. **Events**: range of events and demonstrations during season; tel. 01762 851236 for details

💷 £2.30, children £1.15; family ticket £5.75. Parties £2. Parties outside normal opening hours £3 per person

🛍 Shop open as house

♿ Access to 3 rooms on ground floor via 3 steps or side door from farmyard, picnic area and part of farmyard; ground-floor farm exhibits in information room accessible. WC in car park by farm. Gravel paths in garden. Sympathetic Hearing Scheme

👁 Touch tours by prior arrangement

🍴 No on-site facilities but picnics welcome. Picnic area opens at 12

🧍 Children's play area

🎒 Pre-booked school groups welcome, especially those involved in the Cross-Community Contact Scheme. Farmyard tours and trails available

🐕 In garden only

➡ (9: H6) 7ml from Portadown on Moy road (B28), 5ml from Moy, 3ml from Loughgall intersection 13 on M1, 9ml from Armagh [H914559] *Bus:* Ulsterbus 67 Portadown–Kesquin Bridge (passing close NIR Portadown Stn) to within ¼ml (tel. 01762 342511) *Station:* Portadown 7ml

THE ARGORY 🏠 🏡 ❖ 🖼 🚶 🎷 😀 *Armagh*

Moy, Dungannon BT71 6NA Tel: 01868 784753 Fax: 01868 789598

This 1820 house remains largely unaltered and its cluttered interiors evoke the lifestyle of the Irish gentry of the time. Among the fascinating furniture and contents is an 1824 Bishop's barrel organ and interesting possessions left by the Bond family. There is a an imposing stableyard with coach house and carriages, harness room, laundry and acetylene gas plant. The handsome garden and pleasure grounds provide attractive walks

Note: The house has no electric light. Visitors wishing to make a close study of the interior and paintings should avoid dull days early and late in the season

🅾 Easter (10 to 14 April): daily 2–6. April, May & Sept: Sat, Sun & BH 2–6; June to end Aug: daily (except Tues) 2–6. Open 1–6 on all BH. Last tour 5.15. **Events**: range of events during season, tel. for details

£ £2.50, children £1.25; family ticket £6.25. Parties £2. Parties outside normal opening hours £3 per person. Car park £1.50. Parking 100m. Coaches must book with Administrator

𝕀 Please note that numbers on any one tour are restricted. All visitors, including NT members, please report to reception on arrival

🛍 Shop open as house, but weekends only in June 2–6; BHols 1–6; weekdays July & Aug 3–5

♿ Access to ground floor of house, all driveways, garden and pleasure grounds, walks, tea-room and reception area; some deep gravel round house; wheelchair available. Car-parking near east door of house (ramp) by arrangement at reception; WC by reception area. Sympathetic Hearing Scheme. Special tours for partially sighted visitors by prior arrangement

☕ Light refreshments in tea-room, open as shop. Picnics welcome

🧒 Adventure playground

📕 Pre-booked school groups welcome, especially those in the Cross-Community Contact Scheme. Study centre; teachers' pack and pupil worksheets; Key Stages 1 & 2 tours available

🐕 In grounds and garden only, on leads

➔ (9; G6) 4ml from Moy, 3ml from M1, exit 13 or 14 (signposted). NB coaches must use exit 13; weight restrictions at Bonds Bridge [H872580] *Bus:* Ulsterbus 67, 75 Portadown–Dungannon (both pass close NIR Portadown Stn), alight Charlemont on 67, Verner's Inn on 75, 2½ml from both (tel. 01762 342511)

CASTLE COOLE 🏛 ♣ 𝕀 🛡   *Fermanagh*

Enniskillen, BT74 6JY Tel: 01365 322690 Fax: 01365 325665

A James Wyatt masterpiece and certainly one of the finest neo-classical buildings in the British Isles. The clean and elegant exterior contains opulent Regency rooms, still with their original décor and furniture. Upstairs there is a magnificent state bedroom, refurbished in typical Regency style in 1821 for George IV. An interesting range of service buildings include servants' tunnel, laundry house, dairy and ice house, and there are delightful walks in the wooded landscape park

O Easter (10 to 14 April): daily 1–6; April & Sept: Sat, Sun & BH only, 1–6; May to end Aug: daily except Thur 1–6. Last tour begins 5.15. Grounds open to pedestrians during daylight hours. **Events:** concerts and displays in the house, cricket on the south lawn; tel. for details

£ £2.80, children £1.40; family ticket £7. Parties £2.50 per person. Parties outside normal opening hours £3.50 per person. Estate £2 per car

🛍 Shop in Tallow House, open same days as house 1–5 (weekends and BHs only in May & June)

♿ Ramped access to ground floor of house and reception area in car park; after reporting to reception, disabled visitors may be driven to the house. Wheelchair available. WC in reception centre. Sympathetic Hearing Scheme

🍴 Tea-room in Tallow House, open as shop (shop and tea-room opening times may vary according to demand)

👶 Baby-changing facilities in disabled WC

🏛 Pre-booked school groups welcome, especially those involved in the Cross-Community Contact Scheme

🐕 In grounds, on leads only

➡ (9: E6) 1½ml SE of Enniskillen on main Belfast–Enniskillen road (A4) [H260430]
Bus: Ulsterbus 95, Enniskillen–Clones (tel. 01365 322633)

CASTLE WARD 🏠 🏡 ✳ 🍴 🚣 ⛰ 🚻 🧒 🛡 *Down*

Strangford, Downpatrick, BT30 7LS Tel: 01396 881204 Fax: 01396 881729

A bizarre 18th-century mansion with opposing façades in different styles; the east front is classical, the west front Gothick, reflecting the divergence in taste of the owner and his wife. There is a Victorian laundry and Pastime Centre, as well as a sawmill and cornmill, driven by an outflow from the Temple Water. The setting for the house is magnificent, within a beautiful walled landscape park running down to the shores of Strangford Lough, where the Wildlife Centre features audiovisual shows

🅾 **House:** Easter (10 to 19 April): daily 1–6; April, Sept & Oct: Sat & Sun 1–6; May to end Aug: daily except Thur 1–6. Last tour 5.15. **Estate & grounds:** open all year dawn to dusk (charge for car park only). **Strangford Lough Wildlife Centre:** open as house 2–6, except May & June when open Sat, Sun & BH only 2–6. **Events:** craft fairs, guided walks, concerts, opera season and other events; tel. for details.

💷 £2.60, children £1.30; family ticket £6.50. Parties £2 per person. Parties outside normal opening hours £3 per person. Three car parks; parking £3.50 (£1.75 when house and other facilities are closed). Coaches: booked parties to house free; others £15. Horses (using bridlepath) £5 per single horsebox

🛍 Shop open same days as house (but weekends & BH only in May): weekdays 1–5; Sat, Sun & BH 1–6

[♿] Access to formal garden, restaurant and interpretation centre; wheelchairs available. Disabled visitors may be set down at house; car park for disabled drivers behind stables; limited spaces. House accessible via six steps. WC in stableyard and in farmyard and caravan park. Sympathetic Hearing Scheme. Wheelchair access to shore of Strangford Lough

[👁] Braille guide available. Scented plants

[🍴] Light refreshments, lunches and teas, open as shop. Party organisers should book visits and arrange teas in advance with receptionist. Picnics welcome

[🧒] Changing facilities in WC. Adventure playground. Victorian Pastime Centre; toys & dressing up

[🏫] Pre-booked school groups welcome especially those involved in the Cross-Community Contact Scheme. Teachers' pack available and pupil worksheet. Nature trails. Key Stage 2 tour available based on 'life in the big house'

[🐕] In grounds only, on leads

[→] (9: K6) 7ml NE of Downpatrick, 1½ml W of Strangford village on A25, on S shore of Strangford Lough, entrance by Ballyculter Lodge [J752494] *Bus:* Ulsterbus 16E Downpatrick–Strangford, with connections from Belfast (passing close NIR Belfast Great Victoria Street Stn); alight Ballyculter crossroads, 1ml (tel. 01396 612384)

CROM ESTATE [🏠][🌳][♿][🧒][🧍][🛡] *Fermanagh*

Newtownbutler BT92 8AP
Tel: 01365 738174; Visitor Centre 01365 738118

One of Ireland's most important nature conservation areas and of international significance, the estate covers woodland, parkland and wetland on the shores of Upper Lough Erne. There are nature trails along the shore and to the ruins of Crom Old Castle. Visitor facilities include holiday cottages, boat hire, overnight woodland hide and coarse angling

Note: The 19th-century castle is private and not open to the public

[O] 1 April to end Sept: daily 10–6 (Sun 12–6). **Events:** programme available: please contact the visitor centre

[£] Admission £3 per car or boat

[🚶] Guided walks programme available or by special arrangement

[🛍] Shop in visitor centre open April, May, June & Sept: Sat, Sun & BH 2.30–5.30; July & Aug: daily 2.30–5.30

[♿] Designated spaces in car park. Wheelchair and self-drive vehicle available from visitor centre. Full access to exhibition, shop and tea-room in visitor centre. Gravel paths on Estate; strong companions necessary. WCs in visitor centre in stableyard. Sympathetic Hearing Scheme

[🍴] Tea-room open as shop; also by arrangement

[🧒] Children's area in information centre; also baby-changing facilities

[🏫] Pre-booked school groups welcome, especially those involved in the Cross-Community Contact Scheme

🐕 On lead only

➡️ (9: F7) 3ml W of Newtownbutler, on Newtownbutler–Crom road [J363245], or follow signs from Lisnaskea *Bus:* Ulsterbus 95 Enniskillen–Clones (with connections from Belfast), alight Newtownbutler, 3ml (tel. 01365 322633)

CROWN LIQUOR SALOON 🏠 *Antrim*

46 Great Victoria Street, Belfast BT2 7BA Tel: 01232 249476

A magnificent High Victorian public house, with rich ornamentation and fine woodwork, glass and tiles, built at the end of the 19th century; now managed by Tennents Taverns

🕐 Daily, during licensed hours 11.30am–11pm; Sun 12.30–2.30 & 7–10

🍽️ Full bar facilities, snack lunches

➡️ (9: J5) [J738332] *Bus:* From surrounding areas (tel. 01232 246485 (Citybus) or 333000 (Ulsterbus)) *Station:* Belfast Great Victoria Street, few mins walk

---

DERRYMORE HOUSE 🏠 *Armagh*

Bessbrook, Newry, BT35 7EF Tel: 01693 830353

An elegant late 18th-century thatched cottage, built by Isaac Corry, who represented Newry in the Irish House of Commons for thirty years from 1776. Set amidst a picturesque estate it is typical of the informal thatched retreats boasted by many estates in the 18th century

🕐 10 to 14 April: daily 2–5.30; May to end Aug: Thurs, Fri & Sat 2–5.30

💷 £1.80, children 90p; family ticket £4.50. Parties £1.30 per person

♿ Access to grounds and one room on ground floor. No WC

🐕 In grounds on lead please

➡️ (9: H7) Off the Newry–Camlough road at Bessbrook, 1½ml from Newry [J056279] *Bus:* Ulsterbus 41/2/4 from Newry (passing close NIR Newry) (tel. 01693 63531) *Station:* Newry 2ml

---

DOWNHILL CASTLE, MUSSENDEN TEMPLE, BISHOP'S GATE & BLACK GLEN 🏰🏠❀🍽️🎢👤 *Londonderry*

Bishop's Gate, 42 Mussenden Road, Castlerock, Coleraine BT51 4RP Tel: 01265 848728

A dramatic landscaped estate on a stretch of wild coastline laid out in the late 18th century by the energetic Earl-Bishop, Frederick Hervey, Earl of Bristol and Bishop of Derry. The estate includes the ruins of his palatial house, family memorials, garden, fishpond, woodland and cliff walks, as well as the celebrated Mussenden Temple, perched on the cliff edge

Note: Mussenden Temple may be closed for several weeks during 1998 for repairs

⭘ **Temple:** Easter (10 to 14 April): daily 12–6; April, May, June & Sept: Sat, Sun & BH 12–6; July & Aug: daily 12–6. **Grounds:** open all year, dawn to dusk. Open for groups at other times by arrangement (tel. 01265 848728)

£ Free. Limited access for coaches. WC in Walled Garden (Lion's Gate)

♿ Paths through garden; cars may be taken to Bishop's Gate. Glen Walk partly accessible

◗ Picnics welcome

🐕 Must be kept on leads

➔ (9: G2) 1ml W of Castlerock and 5M W of Coleraine on the Coleraine–Downhill coast road (A2) [J757357] *Bus:* Ulsterbus 134 Coleraine–Limavady (tel. 01265 43334) *Station:* Castlerock ½ml

---

FLORENCE COURT 🏠 👜 ❀ ♠ 🚹 🍴 🛡 *Fermanagh*

Enniskillen, Co. Fermanagh BT92 1DB Tel: 01365 348249 Fax: 01365 348873

One of Ulster's most important houses, built in the mid 18th century by John Cole, father of the 1st Earl of Enniskillen, and famous for its rococo plasterwork and fine pieces of Irish furniture. There are interesting service quarters grouped around cobbled courtyards and a water-powered sawmill, as well as a walled garden, ice house and spectacular views. The magnificent park contains many notable mature trees

What's new in 1998: The return of many original paintings, furniture and other artifacts to the house; new 1400m path suitable for wheelchair users

⭘ Easter (10 to 14 April): daily 1–6; April & Sept: Sat, Sun & BH only 1–6; May to end Aug: daily except Tues 1–6. Last admission 5.15. Grounds open all year 10–7 (Oct to March 10–4). Closed Christmas Day. **Events:** country fairs, craft fairs and other events; tel. for details

£ House: £2.80, children £1.40; family ticket £7. Parties £2.50 per person. Parties outside normal opening hours £3.50 per person. Estate: £2. Parking 50m. Information room

🛍 Shop open as house 1–6 (weekends and BHols only in May & June). Open from 12 noon July and Aug (tel. 01365 348788)

♿ Access to garden & ground floor only. North Pavilion restaurant accessible. WCs and parking. Two wheelchairs and self-drive powered vehicle available. New countryside path suitable for wheelchair users. Sympathetic Hearing Scheme

🍽 Teas & lunches downstairs in North Pavilion; open as shop. Picnic area

👶 Parent and baby room, baby slings and highchair available. Play area

🏫 Pre-booked school groups welcome, especially those involved in the Cross-Community Contact Scheme. Teachers' pack and pupil worksheets available. Key Stages 1 & 2 tours available

🐕 In grounds and garden, on leads

➔ (9: E6) 8ml SW of Enniskillen via A4 Sligo road and A32 Swanlinbar road [H175344], 4ml from Marble Arch Caves *Bus:* Ulsterbus 192 Enniskillen–Swanlinbar to within 1ml (tel. 01365 322633)

GIANT'S CAUSEWAY 🖼 👤   *Antrim*

44a Causeway Road, Bushmills, Co. Antrim BT57 8SU
Tel: 012657 31159/31582 Fax: 012657 32963

The famous and unusual rock formations are of basalt, small polygonal stacks resulting from a volcanic eruption 60 million years ago and which now present a stunning panorama. This beautiful stretch of coastline has attracted visitors for centuries and harbours a wealth of local and natural history, which can be enjoyed from the cliff-paths. The Armada treasure ship Girona *was wrecked (in 1588) at nearby Port-na-Spaniagh*

Note: The visitor centre, with interpretative displays, audiovisual theatre and tourist information, is owned by Moyle District Council

🅾 **Giant's Causeway**: all year. **NT shop in visitor centre**: 6 March to end May: daily 10–5; June: daily 10–6; July & Aug: daily 10–7; Sept & Oct: daily 10–5. **Tea-room**: open same days as shop 11–5 (closing times may vary according to demand)

£ Free. Parking £2.50, incl. NT members (Moyle District Council car park)

🛍 Open as visitor centre

♿ Parking access close to buildings; minibus with hoist for transport to Causeway during season; ramps to shop, tea-room & visitor centre; accessible walks; WC. Sympathetic Hearing Scheme at visitor centre

👁 Braille guide

🍽 Lunch, tea, snacks in tea-room at visitor centre (closes 6.15 in July & Aug)

🏫 Pre-booked school visits welcome, especially those involved in the Cross-Community Contact Scheme. Activity trail available. Coastal Guardians Scheme

🐕 On leads only, outdoors

➔ (9: H2) On B146 Causeway–Dunseverick road [C945438] *Bus:* Ulsterbus 138 from Coleraine (passing NIR Coleraine Stn & connecting with trains from Belfast Central Stn); 172 Ballycastle–Portrush (tel. 01265 43334) *Station:* Portrush 8ml

GRAY'S PRINTING PRESS 🔲 🔲 🔲 *Tyrone*

49 Main Street, Strabane, BT82 8AU Tel: 01504 884094

An 18th-century printing press, where John Dunlap, the printer of the American Declaration of Independence, and James Wilson, grandfather of President Woodrow Wilson, learned their trade. There is a collection of 19th-century hand-printing machines, as well as an audio-visual display

🅾 April to end Sept: daily except Thur, Sun & BH 2–5.30. At other times by prior arrangement. **Events:** compositor demonstrations once a fortnight; tel. for details

£ £1.50, children 75p; family ticket £3.75. Parties £1. Public car park 100m

🔲 Guided tours by arrangement

🔲 Access to audiovisual display only

🔲 In town (not NT)

🔲 Pre-booked school visits welcome, especially those involved in the Cross-Community Contact Scheme

➡ (9: F4) [H345977] *Bus:* Ulsterbus Express 273 Belfast–Londonderry (passing close NIR Londonderry Stn), alight Strabane centre; few mins walk (tel. 01232 333000)

HEZLETT HOUSE 🔲 *Londonderry*

107 Sea Road, Castlerock, Coleraine, Co. Londonderry BT51 4TW
Tel: 01265 848567

One of few buildings in Ireland surviving from before the 18th century, this 17th-century thatched house has an interesting cruck-truss roof construction and is simply furnished in late Victorian style. There is a small museum of farm implements

🅾 Easter (10 to 14 April): daily 12–5; April, May & Sept: Sat, Sun & BH only 12–5; June to Aug: daily, except Tues 12–5. Guided tours. Parties must book in advance (max. number in house 15 at any one time)

£ £1.80, children 90p; family ticket £4.50. Parties £1.30 per person. Parties outside normal opening hours £2 per person. Cycles can be parked at side of house

🔲 Access to ground floor only

🔲 Pre-booked school groups welcome

🔲 In garden only, on leads

➡ (9: G2) 5ml W of Coleraine on Coleraine–Downhill coast road, A2 [C772349] *Bus:* Ulsterbus 134 Coleraine–Limavady, alight crossroads, few mins walk (tel. 01265 43334) *Station:* Castlerock ¼ml

MOUNT STEWART HOUSE, GARDEN & TEMPLE OF THE WINDS 🏠 🏠 ❖ 𝕂 ☻ *Down*

Newtownards, Co. Down BT22 2AD Tel: 012477 88387/88487 Fax: 012477 88569

A fascinating 18th-century house with 19th-century additions, the childhood home of Lord Castlereagh and famous for its magnificent garden, the creation of Edith, Lady Londonderry. The formal series of outdoor rooms contains an unrivalled collection of plants from all over the world, set in vibrant parterres and lush borders and with superb vistas. The Temple of the Winds, James 'Athenian' Stuart's banqueting hall of 1785, dramatically overlooks Strangford Lough

O **House:** Easter (10 to 19 April): daily 1–6; April & Oct: Sat & Sun 1–6; May to end Sept: daily except Tues 1–6. Last tour 5. **Garden:** March: Sun only 2–5; April to end Sept: daily 11-6; Oct: Sat & Sun only 11–6. **Temple of the Winds:** open same days as house 2–5. **Events:** seasonal guided walks & band concerts; tel. for details

£ House & garden £3.50, children £1.75; family ticket £8.75. Parties £3 per person. Parties outside normal opening hours £5 per person. Garden £3, children £1.50; family ticket £7.50. Parties £2.50. Parking 300m. Temple of the Winds only £1, children 50p; parties 80p per person

🛍 Open same days as house 12.30–5.30, Sun until 6. BH open 12.30–6. Also open Sun in March 2–5; Tues May to Sept, 12.30–5.30 (tel. 012477 88878)

♿ Ramped access to ground floor of house and large parts of garden; restaurant and shop accessible from house; wheelchairs available. Disabled visitors may be set down at house. WCs. Two powered buggies available; free route-map of garden; mostly level path round lake. Sympathetic Hearing Scheme

🔊 Scented plants

🍴 Light refreshments and teas (tel. 012477 88801) same times as shop

🚼 Baby-changing facilities

🎒 Pre-booked school groups welcome, especially those involved in the Cross-Community Contact Scheme; please tel. 012477 88830 for details

🐕 On leads only

➔ **(9**: K5) 15ml SE of Belfast on Newtownards–Portaferry road, A20, 5ml SE of Newtownards [J553695] *Bus:* Ulsterbus 9, 10 Belfast–Portaferry (passing close NIR Belfast Central Stn) to within ½ml (tel. 01232 333000) *Station:* Bangor 10ml

PATTERSON'S SPADE MILL 🏠 ✖ 🔧 𝕂 ☻ *Antrim*

Antrim Road, Templepatrick, Co. Antrim BT39 0AP Tel: 01849 433619

Ireland's last water-driven spade mill, founded in 1919 and still making spades until 1990. The original equipment has been fully restored and spade-making demonstrations are given regularly

O Easter (10 to 14 April): daily 2–6; April, May & Sept: Sat, Sun & BH only 2–6; June to end of August: daily except Tues 2–6. **Events:** vintage-vehicle displays; tel. for details

£ £2.50, children £1.25; family ticket £6.25. Parties £1.75. Parties outside normal opening hours £3

♿ Accessible throughout. Ramp gives access to viewing platform. WC in reception area. Wheelchair

👁 Machinery sounds; items and raw materials may be touched

■ Pre-booked school groups welcome, especially those involved in the Cross-Community Contact Scheme

→ (9: J5) 2ml SE of Templepatrick on Antrim–Belfast road, A6; exit 4 or 5 of M2 [J263/856] *Bus:* Ulsterbus 120 Belfast to Ballymena (passing close to NIR Belfast Central & Antrim stations): alight Templepatrick (tel. 01232 333000) *Station:* Antrim 8ml

---

ROWALLANE GARDEN ✿ 🛡 *Down*

Saintfield, Ballynahinch, Co. Down BT24 7LH
Tel: 01238 510131 Fax: 01238 511242

A unique tree and shrub garden, containing many exotic species from around the world. There are spectacular displays of azaleas and rhododendrons and a notable rock garden with primulas, alpines and heathers. The walled garden has mixed borders which include the National Collection of Penstemon; there are also several areas managed as wildflower meadows

O 1 April to end Oct: daily (weekdays 10.30–6; weekends 2–6); Nov to end March 1999: daily except Sat & Sun 10.30–5. Closed 25, 26 Dec & 1 Jan. **Events:** concerts, teddy bears' picnics, Yuletide market; tel. for details

£ Easter to Oct £2.50, children £1.25; family ticket £6.25. Parties £1.75. Parties outside opening hours £3 per person. Nov to end March 1999 £1.40, children 70p. Parties 80p

♿ Close parking by arrangement. Majority of garden accessible; wheelchair available. WC. Tea-room accessible. Sympathetic Hearing Scheme

👁 Scented plants. Tours arranged by Head Gardener

👣 Light refreshments. Open 10 to 14 April: daily 2–6; April & Sept: Sat & Sun only 2–6; May & June: daily 12.30–5; July & Aug: daily 1–5

🐶 Must be kept on leads

→ (9: K6) 11ml SE of Belfast, 1ml S of Saintfield, W of the Downpatrick road (A7) [J412581] *Bus:* Ulsterbus 15 Belfast–Downpatrick (passing NIR Belfast Great Victoria Street Stn) (tel. 01232 333000)

SPRINGHILL  *Londonderry*

20 Springhill Road, Moneymore, Magherafelt BT45 7NQ Tel: 01648 748210

A 17th-century 'Planter' house with later additions, Springhill was the home of ten generations of a family originally from Ayrshire. The house presents a curiously French aspect and contains family furniture, refurbished nursery, paintings, 18th-century hand-blocked wallpaper and an exceptional collection of books. The outbuildings house an extensive costume collection and there are walled gardens and attractive woodland walks

☐ Easter (10 to 14 April): daily 2–6; April, May & Sept: Sat, Sun & BH only 2–6; June to Aug: daily except Thur 2–6. **Events:** children's & family events during the season; tel. for details

£ £2.50, children £1.25; family ticket £6.25. Parties £2. Parties outside normal opening hours £3 per person. Parking 40m

☐ Shop open as house

♿ Access to all ground-floor rooms; close car-parking at rear of house and by costume museum; access to small sales point by arrangement with guiding staff; picnic area accessible; gravel paths in garden. WC. Sympathetic Hearing Scheme

❦ Herb garden

☕ Light refreshments in servants' hall, open as house. Picnic areas in garden and woodland

👶 Baby-changing facilities. Toy collection; children's costumes and activities. Play area

▥ Pre-booked school groups welcome. Study centre. Teachers' pack and pupil worksheets. Key Stages 1–4 tours available

🐕 In grounds, on lead

➡ (9: G5) 1ml from Moneymore on Moneymore–Coagh road, B18 [H866828]
Bus: Ulsterbus 110/20 Belfast–Cookstown (passing close NIR Antrim Stn), alight Moneymore village, ¾ml (tel. 01232 333000)

WELLBROOK BEETLING MILL 🎫 🚤 🛗 🚶 🎫 *Tyrone*

20 Wellbrook Road, Corkhill, Cookstown, Co. Tyrone BT80 9RY
Tel: 01648 751715/751735

Linen manufacture was of major importance in 18th-century Ireland, and beetling was the final stage in the production process. This water-powered hammer mill has its original machinery, still in working order, and is situated in an attractive glen through which there are many good walks

O Easter (10 to 14 April): daily 2–6; April, May, June & Sept: Sat, Sun & BH only 2–6; July & Aug: daily, except Tues 2–6

£ £1.80, children 90p; family ticket £4.50. Parties £1.30 per person. Pre-booked parties outside normal opening hours £2 per person. Parking. For information contact the Custodian

🛍 Shop open as Mill

👁 'Touch and Sound' tours can be provided by arrangement

🎒 Pre-booked school visits welcome, especially those involved in the Cross-Community Contact Scheme. Key Stage 2 tour available, based on technology & change in Victorian times

🐕 In grounds only, on leads

➔ (**9**: G5) 4ml W of Cookstown, ½ml off Cookstown–Omagh road (A505): from Cookstown turn right at Kildress Parish Church [H750792], or follow Orritor Road (A53) to avoid town centre *Bus:* Ulsterbus 90 from Cookstown, with connections from Belfast (passing close NIR Antrim Stn) (tel. 01648 766440)

Index by property name

Coast and countryside properties shown in italics

Index of properties by county
Coast and countryside properties shown in italics